Chemical Applications of Molecular Beam Scattering

Chemical Applications of Molecular Beam Scattering

M. A. D. FLUENDY *and* K. P. LAWLEY
Lecturers in Chemistry
University of Edinburgh

CHAPMAN AND HALL · LONDON

First published 1973
by Chapman and Hall Ltd
11 New Fetter Lane, London EC4P 4EE
© *1973 M. A. D. Fluendy and K. P. Lawley*

Typeset by Santype Limited (Coldtype Division),
Salisbury, Wiltshire
Printed in Great Britain by
Lowe and Brydone (Printers) Ltd., Thetford, Norfolk

SBN 412 11810 6

Distributed in the U.S.A.
by Halsted Press, a Division
of John Wiley & Sons, Inc., New York

Library of Congress Catalog Card Number 73-6262

Preface

The ideas and methodology developed by nuclear physicists have recently had an important influence in chemistry. The use of a cross-section rather than a rate constant to characterize collision processes is now widespread and interest is increasingly directed to the detailed dynamics of molecular encounters rather than the overall kinetic mechanism. This change in emphasis is reflected not only experimentally in new techniques but also in theoretical developments where the adaptation of scattering theory to chemically reactive collisions is an active field.

The stimulus for this change in approach has been a surprisingly small amount of data obtained by the molecular beam technique. Progress has been limited both by experimental difficulties and the relative novelty to chemists of many of the techniques required. Although important experimental improvements are in prospect, these practical difficulties, rather than any lack of scientific interest, are likely to limit the application of molecular scattering methods. Nevertheless, where applicable, they provide a uniquely detailed insight into intermolecular forces and chemical reaction.

Because of the importance of technical problems, we have thought it worthwhile to discuss experimental matters in some detail. Thus, Chapters 3, 4 and 5 deal with molecular beam sources, selectors and detectors respectively.

This book does not aim at anything like a comprehensive treatment of scattering; rather we have tried to provide an account of those ideas and results which will be of immediate use in interpreting the results of scattering experiments and which will illustrate the beam approach to chemical kinetics. Thus Chapters 2 and 6 are concerned with the classical and quantum theories of elastic scattering, while Chapter 9 indicates, very much in outline, the way in which these methods can be generalised to deal with more complex situations, such as energy transfer collisions. Finally in Chapters 7 and 8, the results of experimental work in elastic and reactive scattering, where the technique has made its greatest impact, are described.

In writing this book we have attempted to provide a link between the twin streams of chemical kinetics and collision physics and so demonstrate the latter's utility in the chemical field. The level throughout would be roughly described as 'graduate physical chemist' and should be readable by a beginning graduate student.

It is a pleasure to acknowledge the help of our colleague Dr Alastair Rae in reading the manuscript and making numerous helpful suggestions, also Dr Roger Grice for similarly helpful comments on Chapter 8. Finally we thank our research and undergraduate students for their lively and critical interest in the preparation of this manuscript.

Malcolm Fluendy
Kenneth Lawley

Edinburgh,
May 1972

Contents

CHAPTER ONE

Introduction

1.1 Molecular collisions in chemistry

Collisions are fundamental to chemistry. Thus, chemical and thermal equilibrium are maintained by collisions, while the rates of chemical change, mass and energy transfer are all controlled by the frequency and detailed dynamics of molecular collisions. Yet in spite of their central place in chemistry, it is only in the last twelve years that a really concerted beginning has been made in the direct study of inter-molecular dynamics. By comparison, in physics, the field of particle scattering has been of major importance since the days of Rutherford, particularly in the study of nuclear and elementary particles. The principal theme of this book is that the application of conceptually similar scattering methods to chemical problems gives an insight into intermolecular dynamics that could not be obtained in any other way.

A loose division between the interests of chemists and physicists in scattering can be made on energetic grounds. Most chemical processes such as bond rearrangement and ionization occur on impact with energies less than a few tens of electron volts. In distinction, the physics of fundamental particles extends through the GeV range. There has recently been a marked increase in interest in ion and electron scattering processes occurring between 1 and 100 eV and in this energy range the fields of chemistry and physics merge (J. B. Hasted, 1964; N. F. Mott and H. S. W. Massey 1965; H. S. W. Massey, 1971).

The objective of a large part of physical chemistry is the understanding of the macroscopic properties of matter in terms of the fundamental laws of

1

physics. Thus experiments are usually carried out on a bulk sample of matter which is in thermal equilibrium with its surroundings. The Boltzmann distribution of molecules among the available states is assumed not to be disturbed and if the measured property, for example reaction rate, is a function of the quantum state of the molecule, only an ensemble average value can be obtained. Full interpretation of such measurements involves a statistical theory of the state of the sample as well as of the quantum mechanics of the isolated processes, e.g., of binary collision leading to reaction.

By using molecular beam scattering techniques it is possible to select a single quantum state or range of states for measurement and to explore the dynamics of the molecular collision and the angular and energy dependence of the associated scattering. In this way direct molecular information can be obtained without recourse to rather inadequate theories relating molecular to non-equilibrium bulk properties. It will be worth outlining this technique now so that its application may be more clearly discussed.

1.2 The beam technique

Any molecular scattering experiment involves a molecular or atomic beam which is allowed to strike a target in such a way that the results of the beam-target collisions can be monitored. A molecular beam is a well collimated stream of molecules moving through a high vacuum while the target may consist of a small volume of gas, a solid surface or another molecular beam. The background pressure in the apparatus must be low enough so that molecular collisions with the beam are not so frequent as to destroy its collimation. The density of molecules in the beam or their velocity relative to each other must also be small enough to eliminate collisions between them and consequent broadening of the beam. Molecular collisions are now introduced in a controlled manner by inserting the target. For the moment we will consider the case of two crossed beams.

A typical cross-beam experiment is shown schematically in Fig. 1.1; in this example the detector is moved about a fixed scattering centre. The beams are generated by effusion or continuum expansion from two 'oven' sources and are directed at right angles to each other (orthogonality is not a necessary requirement, but simplifies analysis of the results). The beams are collimated by narrow knife-edge slits and may be velocity selected by mechanical or, in the case of paramagnetic species, magnetic devices so that only a narrow band of velocities is transmitted. These devices are described more fully in Chapter 4. The detector, the subject of Chapter 5, presents only a small

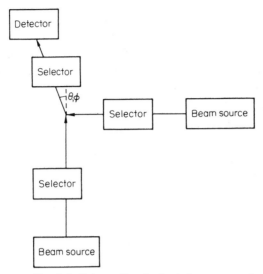

Fig. 1.1 Schematic of a basic beam experiment.
According to the aims of any particular
experiment, some or all of the quantum state or
velocity selectors may be omitted.

effective area to the scattering centre and usually functions as an ionization device converting the molecular flux to an electric current.

As the detector is moved around the scattering centre the intensity of scattered particles is measured as a function of deflection angle, defined by reference to one of the beams. The scattering caused by the target or cross beam is differentiated from that due to the background pressure by comparing signals with the cross-beam alternately on and off. The measurement at each angle takes from a few seconds to many minutes depending upon the strength of the signal. This basic measurement of intensity versus angle is then repeated over a wide range of collision velocities and internal states of the collision partners.

It is important even at this early stage in the discussion to form some idea of the intensities and magnitudes of signal that can be expected since the technique is always likely to be limited by these experimental constraints. For an *effusive source** we might typically expect to form a beam 10 mm tall, 0.05 mm wide at a distance of 1 m from the source with a flux there of 5×10^{16} mol s^{-1} m^{-2}. This intensity falls off as the square of the distance from the source. Thus a detector with an effective area of 1 mm^2 would

---

* As will be seen in Chapter 3 more intense beams can be generated by working under conditions of hydrodynamic flow.

collect 5×10^{10} mol s^{-1} and if it ionized the beam with unit efficiency would yield a current of about 10^{-8} A. Such currents are readily measurable and with an ionization efficiency of 10^{-4}, as for example in a mass spectrometer detector, the resulting currents are still adequate. Even the additional introduction of a velocity selector which may reduce the beam intensity to 1 per cent or less of its original intensity, equivalent to a current of 10^{-14} A, presents no great problems. There is thus no difficulty in detecting a single molecular beam, even using a detector that registers only one ion for 10^4 neutral molecules. Unfortunately the detection of a scattered beam is much more difficult.

Consider an experiment in which two beams intersect. The number of collisions occurring in their intersection region of volume V is:

$$Z_{AB} = \frac{F_A F_B}{v_A v_B} V v_{AB} \sigma \tag{1.1}$$

where F_A and F_B are the fluxes of the two beams in mol s^{-1} m^{-2}, v_A and v_B are their velocities and v_{AB} the relative velocity ($v_{AB} = (v_A^2 + v_B^2)^{1/2}$ for beams meeting at right angles). σ is the cross-section representing in terms of an effective area the probability of collisions removing molecules from the beam. This quantity will be defined more closely later; suffice it to say that for typical molecular systems σ is of the order 500 Å^2 for the sum of all processes that can remove molecules from the beam, i.e., σ is the *total* cross-section. For specific results of a collision, e.g., chemical reaction, the effective cross-section will be much smaller, varying downwards without limit.

For two 'standard beams' colliding at a distance of 100 mm from their respective sources in a collision volume of $10 \times 0.05^2 = 2.5 \times 10^{-2}$ mm^3 and with velocities of 5×10^3 m s^{-1}, i.e., in the thermal energy range:

$$Z_{AB} = \frac{5 \times 10^{18}}{5 \times 10^3} \times \frac{5 \times 10^{18}}{5 \times 10^3} \times 2.5 \times 10^{-2} \times 10^{-9} \times 7 \times 10^3 \times 5 \times 10^{-18}$$

$$\sim 9 \times 10^5 \text{ collisions s}^{-1}.$$

If the scattered molecules are evenly smeared out over all angles in the laboratory then the number of particles per second striking a detector subtending a solid angle θ_d to the scattering centre is:

$$N_{\text{detector}} = \frac{\theta_d}{4\pi} Z_{AB} \text{ s}^{-1}. \tag{1.2}$$

Thus a detector 5 mm tall and 0.2 mm wide located 100 mm from the scattering centre will receive about 7 particles per second — an ion current of 10^{-18} A even with unit ionization efficiency — a very low flux indeed that can only be measured by using particle counting methods and even then only if the noise or background is sufficiently small.

In practice the scattered material is not distributed evenly over 4π sr but is strongly peaked near the undeflected beam, i.e., small angles of deflection predominate. Scattering is more intense and so more easily measured in this region than our simple calculation would suggest, though correspondingly more difficult at wide angles.

It is also instructive to compare the number density in a 'standard beam' ($F/v \sim 10^{15}$ m^{-3} at 0.1 m from the beam source) with that due to the background gas or contamination in our apparatus. A typical 'good' laboratory vacuum of 10^{-7} Torr corresponds to 10^{15} mol m^{-3} so that the 'vacuum' is as dense as our primary beam and many times more so than the scattered material. As a consequence the number of particles scattered from the background molecules is much greater than that scattered from the target cross-beam, since the path length through the apparatus is many times the thickness of the target. It is clear then that scattering experiments present some considerable difficulties with respect to the intensity of the particle fluxes that must be detected, particularly since the background particle densities are so high.

Here is perhaps the reason that scattering methods are a relatively new development in the study of molecular collisions, since high pumping speeds permitting the attainment of pressure in the range 10^{-7} to 10^{-9} Torr have only recently become available.

1.3   The field of application for beam techniques

Beam methods in chemistry have so far been used to study intermolecular forces, bimolecular reactions and, by single beam techniques, some electric and magnetic properties of isolated molecules. A beginning has also been made in investigating internal energy transfer accompanying bimolecular collisions.

We first briefly compare the beam and conventional methods of measuring intermolecular forces, which has been one of the important fields of physical chemistry and chemical physics for several decades. Certain characteristic advantages and disadvantages of beam methods will emerge that recur wherever these techniques are used. Conventional and beam methods of measuring reaction cross-sections will then be outlined to illustrate the new approach of the beam method.

The measurement of the second virial coefficient can be taken as representative of conventional methods for determining intermolecular forces (Hirschfelder *et al.,* 1964). It is a bulk property, derived from the gas compressibility and is a function of temperature, $B(T)$. The relationship between $B(T)$ and the intermolecular potential $V(R)$ of spherical molecules is:

$$B(T) = 2\pi N \int_0^\infty (1 - \exp(-V(R)/kT)R^2 \, dR \qquad (1.3)$$

where N is Avogadro's number and k Boltzmann's constant. $B(T)$ is in general a smoothly varying function of T. It has not proved possible to obtain the functional form of $V(R)$ by an analysis of the temperature dependence of $B(T)$, the temperature range required for inversion of the data is so wide as to preclude experimental observations over the whole range (and in any case such inversions are unique only for monotonic potentials). If a particular functional form for $V(R)$ is assumed, with three or four adjustable parameters, then values for these parameters can be found which fit the observed values of B over a temperature range of perhaps $200°$. The experimental method requires careful attention to technique, is subject to systematic errors and the results are generally only reliable for nearly perfect (i.e. nonpolar) gases.

The molecular beam approach makes use of the fact that collision dynamics are determined by the intermolecular potential. In particular, the angle of deflection in a binary collision is a function of the relative kinetic energy, the relative angular momentum and $V(R)$. In a typical beam experiment designed to investigate the intermolecular potential between two dissimilar molecules A and B, a beam of A molecules whose velocity has been selected to lie in a narrow range about v_A is crossed with a beam of B molecules moving with the velocity v_B. The beam intensities will be sufficiently low so that any beam molecule passing through the collision zone undergoes either no collision or collides only once with a molecule from the other beam. A detector is then scanned round the scattering centre and the intensity of scattered particles (it is probably necessary here to distinguish between species A and B) is recorded as a function of deflection angle measured from the direction of the parent beam. Surprisingly complicated scattering patterns are obtained in this way. Part of the structure is due to the fact that intermolecular potentials are not monotonic functions, additional peaks are interference effects resulting from the wave-like nature of the colliding particles and further complications are introduced by the fact that measurements are made in a laboratory system of co-ordinates rather than in a frame moving with the centre of mass of a particle pair.

In addition to this angular pattern the attenuation of either beam as a result of scattering by the other can be measured. As in the scattering or absorption of light, the logarithm of the attenuation of the beam intensity $\ln(I_0/I)$, is proportional to a quantity σ having the dimension of area and designated the total cross-section for photon/particle or particle/particle scattering i.e.:

$$\ln(I_0^{(A)}/I^{(A)}) = n_B \sigma l \tag{1.4}$$

where n_B is the number density of target molecules in the collision region of length l. This relationship is based upon the conservation of particles.

If this attenuation measurement is repeated over a range of velocities of beam A, $n_B\sigma$ as a function of v_A will be obtained and if n_B is held constant, or measured, the velocity dependence of σ itself is found. We will show in Chapter 7 that σ is given by the following expression for a monotonic potential, $V = C_s R^{-s}$ (N. F. Mott and H. S. W. Massey, 1965):

$$\sigma(v) \simeq f_s \left(\frac{C_s}{\hbar v}\right)^{2/(s-1)} \tag{1.5}$$

where f_s = 8.083 for s = 6 Thus, even if n_B is not known, a plot of $\ln \sigma$ vs. $\ln v$ yields s directly while if n_B and hence σ is known absolutely C_s can be found. If the potential is not monotonic the above result holds only at very low and very high energies where s is given a value appropriate to long and short range parts of the potential respectively.

An effect common in beam work is found in the relative velocity distribution if the velocity of the beam molecules is not selected, and they simply effuse from an oven at temperature T. The velocity distribution in either beam is now v^3 Maxwellian, i.e., the probability of finding a molecule, mass m, with speed between v and $v + dv$ is:

$$P(v, T) \, dv = \frac{1}{2} (m/kT)^2 v^3 \exp(-mv^2/2kT) \, dv \tag{1.6}$$

Taking the two beam particles and the oven temperature to be identical and using the result:

$$v_{AB}^2 = v_A^2 + v_B^2$$

for the relative velocity, v_{AB}, of two beam particles (A) and (B) moving at right angles, one obtains:

$$P(v_{AB}; T) = \frac{1}{48} (m/kT)^4 v_{AB}^7 \exp(-mv_{AB}^2/2kT) \tag{1.7}$$

A considerable sharpening of the relative velocity distribution is evident. The total cross-section deduced from the beam attenuation is then:

$$\sigma(T) = \int_0^\infty \sigma(v_{AB}) P(v_{AB}, T) dv_{AB}. \tag{1.8}$$

Since we cannot be sure that the potential is effectively monotonic over the whole range of v_{AB} in the integration, a much more complicated expression than (1.5) for $\sigma(v)$ as a function of the intermolecular potential parameters must in general be used. The important point is that the unfolding of $\sigma(T)$ to give $\sigma(v)$ by Equation 1.8 is then almost as difficult as unfolding $B(T)$ to give $V(R)$ directly and illustrates the general rule that beam methods only achieve their full power when some velocity selection is used. It might seem from Equation 1.7 that a v^7 Maxwellian distribution is near enough a delta function for velocity selection to be unnecessary. However, it will emerge on closer examination of the problem that not only the magnitude but also the direction of the relative velocity must be closely defined if meaningful differential and total cross-sections are to be measured, and this is only poorly defined in unselected crossed thermal beams.

If part of the angular scattering pattern is observed, although the relationship between this pattern and the intermolecular potential is far more complicated than Equation 1.5, the structure in favourable cases is sufficiently detailed for an unambiguous assignment of three parameters in $V(R)$ to be made directly without recourse to statistical methods of fitting. It will emerge that, at any one energy, various features of the scattering pattern can often be associated with different parts of the potential.

We now turn to the second major application of beam techniques, the investigation of bimolecular reactions. Apart from a few special techniques the kinetics of chemical reactions have hitherto been investigated by mixing the reactants in a time, short compared with some time constant of the reaction, and sampling the mixture of appropriate intervals thereafter. It often requires considerable ingenuity to separate the effects of various competing reactions, but having done this the bi- and uni-molecular rate constants of each elementary reaction can be obtained. The temperature dependence of the bimolecular rate constant, $k_{AB}(T)$, gives the activation energy and pre-exponential factor. This is generally the limit of the information that can be extracted from bulk kinetic data.

Rate constants are directly useful in that with their aid the most probable path of a complicated many step reaction can be determined and interesting correlations made with other molecular properties. They are not, however, the most fundamental pieces of information about a reactive molecular encounter; more detailed questions can be asked such as, 'what is the probability of reaction when two reactant molecules collide with given relative angular momentum, kinetic energy and specified internal quantum states? Furthermore, how does this probability of reaction vary with the quantum states of the products and the angle through which they are scattered?' When such detailed questions are asked, either very fast spectroscopic methods of analysis have to be used, or the actual kinematics of reactive collisions investigated. In the former class are the methods of flash photolysis and the study of chemiluminescence but, important as these techniques are, neither provides a complete answer to the questions asked above, if only because the state of the reactants is not controlled. Difficult though these answers may be to obtain – and there are perhaps only two or three reactions for which nearly complete information is available – reaction probabilities between specified quantum states and into specified solid angles do provide the most detailed information possible about potential energy surfaces in reacting systems.

A somewhat idealized molecular beam experiment to investigate the reaction between species A and B would be along the following lines. Two beams, one of each kind of molecule, are prepared and allowed to intersect in a high vacuum. Ideally, both beams are velocity and state selected. A detector sensitive to the required product molecule C is then scanned round the point of intersection of the beams and in this rather painstaking way the intensity of scattered C molecules is mapped out. In the ultimate experiment the detector would be sensitive only to a particular quantum state of C. In order to interpret such data, it is useful to define the reaction cross-section for the process:

$$A(\nu_A) + B(\nu_B) \longrightarrow C(\nu_C) + D(\nu_D) \tag{1.9}$$

at a relative velocity v of the reactants; the ν_i stand collectively for the set of quantum numbers needed to specify the state of the species present. The definition is best given in practical terms at this point:

total number of C molecules emerging per second in state ν_C

$= \sum_{\nu_D} \sigma(\nu_A, \nu_B, \nu_C, \nu_D; v) \times$ number of A molecules in the scattering volume × mean density of B molecules in the scattering volume × relative molecular velocity.

The scattering volume is simply that volume defined by the intersection of the two beams, and the density of particles in a beam is the flux per unit velocity. It will be recognized that this definition parallels that of the gas kinetic cross-section in the elementary theory of hard sphere gases (R. D. Present, 1958); σ would then be the cross-section for collision. A very similar definition holds for the experimentally simpler case of a beam of A molecules passing through a static gas of B molecules. The reaction volume would then be the product of the beam cross-section area and the path length of the beam through the gas.

Returning to our hypothetical scattering experiment, the flux of C molecules integrated over all scattering angles yields $\sigma(v_A, v_B, v_C, v_D; v)$ after suitable normalization. The bimolecular rate constant is related to $\sigma(v)$ thus:

$$k(v_A, v_B, T) \propto \sum_{v_C, v_D} \int \sigma_{v_C v_D}^{v_A v_B}(v)\, v^3\, \exp\left(-\mu_{AB} v^2 / 2kT\right) dv \qquad (1.10)$$

$$k(T) \propto \sum_{v_A v_B} k(v_A, v_B, T) \exp\left(-[E v_A) + E(v_B)]/kT\right)$$

where it has been assumed that a Maxwellian distribution of velocities holds in the reacting mixture (μ_{AB} is the reduced mass of the pair A..B, see Section 2.1 and the partition functions in the Boltzmann weighting of the initial states have been omitted for simplicity). Once again the energy dependence of the quantity measured in the beam experiment is replaced by the temperature dependence of a property, $k(T)$, measured in thermal equilibrium with a heat bath. In deciding which is the more useful quantity, $k(T)$ or $\sigma(v)$, from the point of view of the theorist, it should be remembered that transition state theory and allied phase space theories give $k(T)$ directly, whereas purely quantum or classical theories that consider one collision at a time give $\sigma(v)$ and its angular dependence. Reaction cross-sections do have other advantages in that they obey microscopic reversibility which sometimes enables rather inaccessible cross-sections to be deduced.

It has already been hinted that the full dependence of cross-sections on the quantum states of reactants and products has so far eluded measurement and that some averaging, especially over initial rotational states, is almost always present. However, it is important not to lose sight of the most important advantages of the beam method which are that a single step in a reaction is isolated and that the rapid separation of the products after collision freezes the population of the final states. A unique feature of the beam method arising from this is that the angular distribution of products emerging from the collision can be measured. This information is a sensitive probe of the kinematics of the reaction. In fact, it will emerge that angular distributions are just as interesting as the energy dependence of reaction cross-sections.

Rate constants will not feature prominently in this book but before leaving them it is worth noting that although $k(T)$ can in principle be unfolded via Equation 1.10 to obtain $\sigma(v)$ if a sufficiently wide temperature range is available, it will in practice be almost impossible to achieve this range. The difficulties in extracting reaction probabilities as a function of the relative energy from $k(T)$ can be illustrated by the following simplified example. Suppose $\sigma(v)$ is a single step function of v, then suppressing the v_i,

$$\sigma(v) = 0, \qquad 0 < v < v^*$$
$$\sigma(v) = \sigma^*, \qquad v^* < v < \infty$$
(1.11)

$$(v^* = \sqrt{2E^*/\mu}, \text{ where } E^* \text{ is the activation energy})$$

then, $k(T)$ is readily found by integrating Equation 1.10 to be of the Arrhenius form when $kT \ll E^*$

$$k(T) \approx \sigma^* \left(\frac{\mu}{kT}\right)^{3/2} \left(\frac{2}{\pi}\right)^{1/2} \frac{2E^*}{\mu^2} kT \exp(-E^*/kT). \qquad (1.12)$$

Now suppose that the single step function Equation 1.11 is replaced by a double step function, σ^* increasing by a factor f at E_2^*, i.e. in addition:

$$\sigma(v) = f\sigma^*, \qquad v > \sqrt{2E_2^*/\mu}. \qquad (1.13)$$

Upon evaluating the integral in Equation 1.10 again, $k(T)$ is found to be:

$$k(T) \approx \sigma^* \left(\frac{\mu}{kT}\right)^{3/2} \left(\frac{2}{\pi}\right)^{1/2} \frac{2kT}{\mu^2} E_1^* \exp(-E_1^*/kT)$$
$$\times \left\{1 + \frac{E_2^*}{E_1^*} (f-1)\exp(-[E_2^* - E_1^*]/kT)\right\}. \qquad (1.14)$$

Unless measurements are carried out in the temperature range $kT \sim E_2^* - E_1^*$, it will be very difficult to detect the presence of the second step, and this condition would clearly be very difficult to fulfil if $E_2^* \approx E_1^*$, since it is also necessary to maintain the ratio E_1^*/kT to a value at which reaction with a measurable rate actually occurs. Using beam techniques, on the other hand, it is only necessary to ensure that the energy resolution is smaller than $E_2^* - E_1^*$ and that beam energies can be obtained to scan across both E_1^* and E_2^*.

Perhaps a second example from reaction kinetics is not out of place. Suppose it is required to differentiate between the following two hypothetical energy dependences of the reaction cross-section, the distinction having important theoretical implications:

$$\text{model (1)} \qquad \sigma(E) = \sigma^*$$

$$\text{model (2)} \qquad \sigma(E) = \sigma^* E^*/E \qquad\qquad (1.15)$$

the cross-section being zero for $E < E^*$ in both cases. The bimolecular rate constant can readily be calculated for the two cases as:

$$(1) \quad k_1 \propto \sigma^*(E^* + kT/2)(kT)^{-\frac{1}{2}} \exp\left(-E^*/kT\right)$$

$$(1.16)$$

$$(2) \quad k_2 \propto \sigma^* E^*(kT)^{-\frac{1}{2}} \exp\left(-E^*/kT\right)$$

This functional difference would be very difficult to detect unless the rate constant were measured over a wide range of temperature in the region $kT \gg E^*$. To use the beam method to distinguish between the cases in Equation (1.15) a smaller energy range is necessary. The only requirement is that the relative energy of the beam particles must be greater than the activation energy and one of the beams can remain thermally cold. The great advantage of the beam technique in this type of measurement lies in its ability to achieve a comparatively narrow distribution of velocities about the high velocity of interest. In contrast, in the bulk experiment, the population at high velocities can only be increased by raising the temperature and hence at the same time broadening the velocity distribution.

The use of molecular beam methods to measure the magnetic or electric dipole moment of molecules or atoms has already been mentioned. In these experiments, the molecules isolated in the beam interact with laboratory magnetic or electric fields which serve to focus particles with a selected effective dipole moment on to a detector. In this way extremely accurate determinations of the dipole moment associated with particular quantum states may be made. Thus these measurements compare with bulk values for the dipole moment in the same way as reactive cross-sections for specific quantum states compare with bulk rate constants.

It is again characteristic of beam methods that the formulae for the deflection of a molecule in an applied field, or for the focal length of a beam focusing device involve the molecular parameters and the speed of the molecule. In contrast, the interpretation of bulk properties such as dielectric polarization involves the temperature of the sample.

In this book we are primarily concerned with collision processes and although much of the technique is common to both fields we will not discuss beam spectroscopic measurements further. A number of excellent works may be referred to for further details (N. F. Ramsey, 1956; K. F. Smith, 1955).

CHAPTER TWO

The Classical Mechanics of Molecular Scattering

2.1 Classical mechanics of two-body collisions

As is well known, the transport and equilibrium properties of gases can be treated successfully by classical mechanics, quantum effects appearing only in the properties of individual molecules. The quantum corrections to bulk behaviour are normally important only for light gases at very low temperatures. In contrast, scattering experiments are a much more delicate tool for observing two-body interactions and we will see later that quantum mechanics plays an essential part in many scattering effects. Nevertheless, classical mechanics is capable of illuminating the outline of the subject and provides a vital conceptual frame in which to introduce the underlying ideas and language. The elementary theory will now be summarized and further details can be found in H. Goldstein, 1964; L. D. Landau and E. M. Lifschitz, 1960.

It was found in Section 1.2. that the primary information to come from a crossed beam scattering experiment, is the fraction of the incident beam flux, N/N_0, that results in scattering into a specified solid angle. If we take this solid angle to be the infinitesimal $d\omega$, we are interested in the relationship between $d(N/N_0)/d\omega$ and the intermolecular potential. In this chapter we shall consider the simplest possible situation: that in which the particles are structureless and interact by a central conservative force. No energy can then be exchanged between the relative motion of the particles and any internal modes; collisions of this type are called *elastic*. In distinction, *inelastic* collisions involve the transfer of energy from or to internal modes while in *reactive* collisions chemical bonds are made or broken. This present

14

restriction to elastic collisions is less severe than might at first seem, because such collisions normally predominate in a scattering experiment.

The force between structureless particles interacting by a central potential (in the absence of any external field) depends only on their distance apart; it does not depend on their absolute position in space. We thus replace the vector positions of the two particles R_A and R_B, defined with respect to a fixed origin in the laboratory, by their relative position vector $R_{AB} = R_{AC} - R_{BC}$ and by R_{cm} the position of the centre of mass of the two particles (Fig. 2.1). Since the potential energy of the system depends only on R_{AB} and not at all on R_{cm} the motion of the centre of mass is unaccelerated and does not contribute to the chemistry. Thus we need only consider the particles' relative motion, though as we shall see later the motion of the centre of mass may profoundly affect the appearance of scattering in the laboratory.

Working in these relative or centre of mass co-ordinates reduces the problem to that of a single particle of mass μ moving about a fixed centre of force. We may write the energy as

$$E = \frac{1}{2} \mu \dot{R}_{AB}^2 + \frac{L^2}{2\mu R_{AB}^2} + V(R_{AB}) \tag{2.1}$$

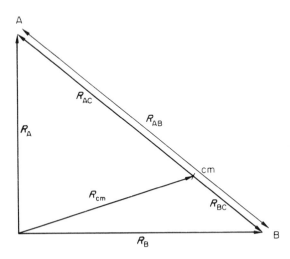

Fig. 2.1 Position vector diagram for two particles A and B colliding. The centre of mass position vector, R_{cm}, divides the relative position vector R_{AB} in the inverse ratio of the masses of A and B and the centre of mass is at cm.

and the orbital angular momentum as:

$$L = \mu R_{AB}^2 \dot{\chi} \qquad (2.2)$$

where μ is the reduced mass, $m_A m_B/(m_A + m_B)$, and χ is the angle between the relative velocity vector $\dot{R}_{AB}$ and an initial beam direction R_A or R_B.

Since there are no angle dependent terms in the potential, no couple can act on the system and the angular momentum in conserved. Thus the motion is confined to the plane defined by $\dot{R}_A$ and $\dot{R}_B$.

The radial velocity and hence $d\chi/dR_B$ follows from Equations 2.1 and 2.2:

$$\dot{R}_{AB} = \pm \left\{ \frac{2}{\mu} \left(E - \frac{L^2}{2\mu R_{AB}^2} - V(R_{AB}) \right) \right\}^{\frac{1}{2}} \qquad (2.3)$$

$$\frac{d\chi}{dR_{AB}} = \pm \frac{L}{\mu R_{AB}^2} \left\{ \frac{2}{\mu} \left(E - \frac{L^2}{2\mu R_{AB}^2} - V(R_{AB}) \right) \right\}^{-\frac{1}{2}} \qquad (2.4)$$

The sum of the true potential $V(R_{AB})$ and the centrifugal term $L^2/2\mu R_{AB}^2$ is known as the effective potential. Depending on the precise form of $V(R)$ there may be one or more classical turning points of the motion corresponding to the zeros of Equation 2.3 where the radial velocity is zero. If several turning points exist these will be separated by classically forbidden regions. Thus, classically, a pair of particles approaching from infinity can penetrate only as far as the outermost turning point (Figs. 2.2, 2.3).

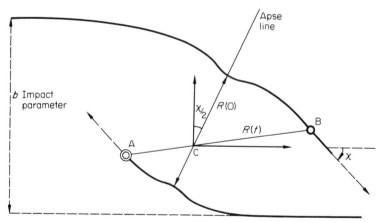

Fig. 2.2 The trajectories of two particles colliding under the influence of a central force, displayed with the centre of mass fixed at C. The angle of deflection is $\chi(b)$ and the distance of closest approach is $R(0)$. For the case illustrated, $m_A > m_B$.

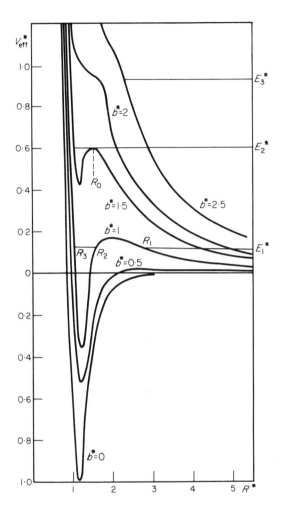

Fig. 2.3 A family of effective potential curves
for the Lennard-Jones potential Equation (2.12).
The reduced energy V_{eff}/ϵ is plotted against the
reduced separation R/σ and the results for a
range of reduced impact parameters b/σ are
shown. A particle incident with reduced energy
E_1^*, $b^* = 1$ will approach to a distance R_1^* and
the classically allowed region between R_2^* and
R_3^* will be inaccessible. At an incident energy
E_2^*, the two particles go into orbit with radius
R_0^* when the impact parameter is $1\cdot 5$. At E_3^* no
orbiting is possible at any impact parameter and
the distance of closest approach decreases
smoothly with b.

Equations 2.3 and 2.4 can be integrated to yield $R_{AB}(t)$ and $\chi(R_{AB})$. Before doing so we adopt the convention that the collision starts at $R_{AB} = \infty$, $t = -\infty$ and the turning point is reached at $t = 0$. $\dot{R}_{AB}$ is negative until the turning point $(R_c = R(0))$ and then positive, the two branches (the roots of Equations 2.3 or 2.4) joining smoothly at $t = 0$. We now change the representation of $\chi(t = \infty)$ to $\chi(b)$ in order to show the parametric dependence of the asymptotic angle of deflection on the impact parameter. The form of $\chi(b)$ can be seen in Fig. 2.5. The impact parameter b is defined as the perpendicular distance apart of the two asymptotic lines of approach and is related to the orbital angular momentum and the asymptotic velocity, $v = \sqrt{2E/\mu}$, by:

$$L = \mu v b \qquad (2.5)$$

On integrating Equation 2.4 we can obtain $\chi(\infty)$, the total deflection, as:

$$\chi(E, L) = \pi - 2 \int_{R_c}^{\infty} \frac{L\,dR}{R^2 \left[2\mu \left(E - V(R) - \frac{L^2}{2\mu R^2} \right) \right]^{\frac{1}{2}}} \qquad (2.6)$$

where the subscript AB on R_{AB} has been dropped and where a negative sign for $\chi(\infty)$ indicates an overall bending of the trajectory towards the target. The only result of these elastic encounters is thus to rotate $\mathbf{R}_{AB}$ and, as we shall see in Section 2.4, to transfer some kinetic energy between the two particles. Various qualitative conclusions and approximations will be extracted from Equation 2.6 but for most potentials the integration cannot be performed analytically. Tables of the deflection function, $\chi(b)$, will be found in J. O. Hirschfelder *et al.*, 1964 for the Lennard-Jones potential.

Although beams in the laboratory can be made extremely narrow, there will be no selection of impact parameters on a molecular scale. If we examine a large number of collisions we find that the impact parameters are randomly distributed over a plane normal to the relative velocity that is virtually infinite in extent compared with atomic dimensions. To compare our classical calculations with experiment we must therefore first calculate the deflection as a function of impact parameter, denoted by $\chi(b)$, and then weight each deflection or transition probability by the probability of finding that value of b for the impact parameter in our random distribution of collisions. From Fig. 2.4 bearing in mind that the trajectories are uniformly distributed across the incident plane on the left, the probability of a given collision occurring with an impact parameter between b and $b + db$ is proportional to the area of the first shaded ring, $2\pi b\,db$. The conservation of particles can be applied to

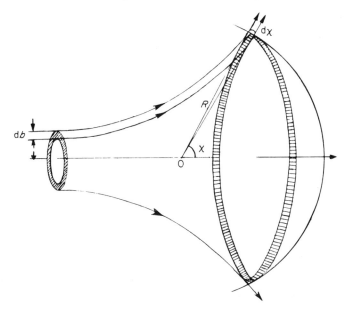

Fig. 2.4 Particles incident in the annular region between b and $b + db$ emerge through the shaded strip between an angle χ and $\chi + d\chi$. The target molecule is at O and the scattered flux is mapped over a large sphere radius R, centered at O.

the general collision with the aid of Fig. 2.4 to yield the result that all the particles which enter the collision zone with impact parameters between b and db must emerge into the solid angle $d\omega$ subtended by the shaded strip lying between χ and $\chi + d\chi$. The emerging particles are counted a distance R away from the scattering centre where R is sufficiently large for the intermolecular force to be negligible and the trajectories are again straight lines. The number of particles crossing the shaded strip at R per second is then:

$$dn = I_0 \times 2\pi b \mid db \mid \qquad (2.7)$$

where I_0 is the incident flux and we assume a unique relationship between χ and b. We define the differential cross-section $\sigma(\chi)$ for elastic scattering from a single target molecule as:

$$\sigma(\chi)d\omega = \frac{\text{number of molecules scattered into solid angle } d\omega \text{ per second}}{\text{incident flux}} \qquad (2.8)$$

$\sigma(\chi)$ has the dimensions of area and $\sigma(\chi)d\omega$ is the effective area presented by the target molecule for scattering through an angle between χ and $\chi + d\chi$. If the potential is independent of the azimuthal angle ϕ, molecules entering the collision with angles between ϕ and $\phi + d\phi$ leave with the same angle and so the flux is uniform around the 'exit' strip in Fig. 2.4 and we can proceed with considering the fate of the whole bundle of trajectories lying initially between b and $b + db$. Introducing the expression for the solid angle $d\omega$,

$$d\omega = 2\pi \sin \chi \mid d\chi \mid \tag{2.9}$$

and dn from Equation 2.7 into Equation 2.8 gives:

$$\sigma(\chi) = b/(\sin \chi \mid d\chi/db \mid). \tag{2.10}$$

Disregarding the possibility of divergence of this expression we can also define a total elastic cross-section by integrating $\sigma(\chi)$ over the surface of the macroscopic sphere traversed by the detector:

$$\sigma_{\text{total}} = \int_0^{2\pi} \int_0^{\pi} \sigma(\chi) \sin \chi d\chi d\phi = 2\pi \int_0^{\pi} \sigma(\chi) \sin \chi d\chi. \tag{2.11}$$

σ_{total} is now a measure of the probability of molecules being scattered from the beam, i.e., of its attenuation. Other more specialized cross-sections may be defined for particular processes; thus, for a change in quantum state of the system from ν_i to ν_j, the total cross section (referred, as always, to a single target molecule) is defined as:

$$\sigma_{\nu_i}^{\nu_j} = \frac{\text{number of collisions per second in which } \nu_i \rightarrow \nu_j}{\text{incident intensity in state i}}$$

We now look more closely at the elastic deflection function $\chi(b)$. Qualitatively, two very different cases can be distinguished according to whether the potential $V(R)$ is monotonic or whether it possesses extrema. The Coulomb potential is an important example of the former type, but intermolecular potential potentials generally exhibit one minimum. Intermolecular potentials are often parametrized in the Lennard-Jones (12:6) form:

$$V(R) = 4\epsilon \{(\sigma/R)^{12} - (\sigma/R)^6\} \tag{2.12}$$

where ϵ is the well depth and σ the position of the inner zero of the potential. Returning to the deflection function and noting that:

$$\int_b^\infty \frac{b\,dR}{R^2(1-b^2/R^2)^{1/2}} = \pi/2 \qquad (2.13)$$

we can see from Equation 2.6 that positive monotonic potentials (purely repulsive), for which $R_c > b$, lead to positive angles of deflection while purely attractive potentials (for which $R_c < b$) lead to negative angles of deflection. For potentials with both attractive and repulsive regions the angle of deflection changes from negative to positive as the impact parameter decreases. The minimum value of the angle of deflection is called the rainbow angle, although the optical analogy is not perfect. A typical family of deflection curves for a bipolar potential is shown in Fig. 2.5 for a range of incident energies. An important qualitative feature emerges from an inspection of these curves. As the collision energy E decreases the rainbow angle moves to larger impact parameters and at the same time becomes more negative until at critical energy E_c the deflection angle reaches $-\infty$, this behaviour persisting at all lower energies. Physically the two colliding particles have gone into orbit about their (moving) centre of gravity and a classically bound state has been formed. For a simple bipolar potential orbiting and the rainbow effect cannot occur at the same energy. The relation of these types of motion to the impact energy and impact parameter (or angular momentum) is shown in Fig. 2.6. In this figure the behaviour at each combination of reduced energy and angular momentum is plotted. Thus the leftmost 'line of zero deflection' is the locus of those values of L^* and E^* which result in a net zero deflection after collision.

To proceed further with the evaluation of the deflection integral, Equation 2.6, it is convenient to cast the intermolecular potential function into a dimensionless form. The reduction parameters required are a length and an energy. We take the energy parameter to be the well depth ϵ and measure distances in terms of the radial distance to the inner zero of the potential, σ. The expression for the Lennard-Jones potential then becomes:

$$V^*(R^*) = 4\{R^{*-12} - R^{*-6}\} \qquad (2.14)$$

where

$$R^* = R/\sigma$$

$$V^* = V/\epsilon$$

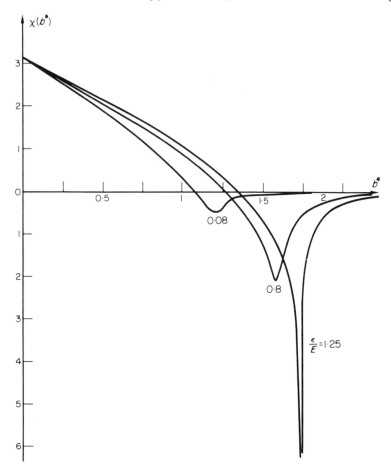

Fig. 2.5 The classical deflection function $\chi(b^*)$ vs. impact parameter b^* for a Lennard-Jones potential at various reduced well depths. The case $\epsilon/E = 1.25$ shows orbiting, the minima in the other cases are the rainbow angles.

and, below

$$E^* = E/\epsilon.$$

The deflection function expression is now:

$$\chi(b^*) = \pi - 2\int_{R_c^*}^{\infty} \frac{E^{*\frac{1}{2}}b^*\mathrm{d}R^*}{R^{*2}\left\{E^*\left(1 - \frac{b^{*2}}{R^{*2}}\right) - 4(R^{*-12} - R^{*-6})\right\}^{\frac{1}{2}}}. \qquad (2.15)$$

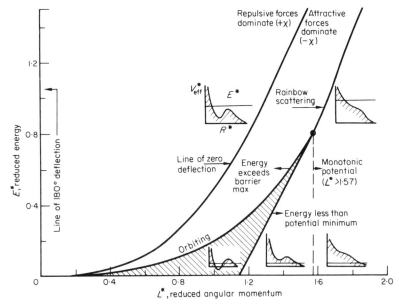

Fig. 2.6 Topology of classical scattering from a Lennard-Jones (12:6) potential. Tracing the deflection χ for a chosen value of E^* along the appropriate horizontal line; χ starts from the left with the value π at $L^* = 0$, and falls monotonically to zero at the line of zero deflection and is negative (net attraction) to the right of this line. χ approaches either $-\infty$ if the orbiting line is crossed or a finite minimum, the rainbow angle, if the rainbow line is crossed. Thereafter χ approaches zero as $L^* \to \infty$.

The changing form of V^*_{eff} is also conveyed pictorially on the diagram. In the shaded region there are three classical turning points.

(Reproduced from K. W. Ford and J. A. Wheeler, 1959).

The rainbow angle at a fixed energy with variable ϵ and σ depends only on ϵ as can be seen by the following argument; the rainbow angle is characterized by:

$$\partial\chi/\partial b^* = 0, \qquad \text{i.e.,} \qquad F(E^*, b^*_r) = 0. \qquad (2.16)$$

where $F(E^*, b^*_r)$ is a cumbersome expression of the reduced energy and impact parameter not needed explicitly. If, now, E^* is assigned a value, b^*_r can be found from Equation 2.16 and this value substituted into Equation 2.15 to give the rainbow angle without a knowledge of σ being necessary.

It emerges from a detailed consideration of Equations 2.15 and 2.16 that the reduced distance of closest approach associated with the rainbow angle is largely independent of the energy until close to the onset of orbiting.

Table 2.1

ϵ/E	χ_r (radians)	$-\chi_r.E/\epsilon$	R_c/σ
0.02	-4.089×10^{-2}	2.044	1.20
0.05	-1.026×10^{-1}	2.052	1.20
0.10	-2.066×10^{-1}	2.066	1.21
0.20	-4.202×10^{-1}	2.101	1.21
0.50	-1.140	2.281	1.22
0.80	-2.129	2.661	1.24
1.00	-3.237	3.237	1.25

This is exemplified in Table 2.1 where χ_r, ϵ/E and R_c^* are listed. The latter is almost constant for small ϵ^* at a value of $R_c^* \approx 1.2$, which corresponds to a turning point in the region of maximum negative slope of the potential, and stated in this form the result holds for other potential forms than the Lennard-Jones (12:6).

The conditions for orbiting are that the radial acceleration and radial velocity must simultaneously be zero, i.e., from Equation 2.3:

$$E^*(1 - b^{*2}/R_0^{*2}) - V^*(R_0^*) = 0$$

and

$$2E^*b^{*2}/R^{*3} - \left(\frac{\partial V^*}{\partial R^*}\right)_{R^*=R_0^*} = 0. \tag{2.17}$$

For the Lennard-Jones potential it can be shown that the maximum value of E^* for which orbiting can occur is 0.8. At impact energies above this value rainbow scattering will replace orbiting. From the conditions in Equation 2.17, the orbiting radius under the influence of a Lennard-Jones potential (12:6) is:

$$R_0^* = 1.308(1 - \sqrt{1 - 5E^*/4})^{-1/6}. \tag{2.18}$$

Inspection of Equation 2.18 indicates that R_0^* is only a very insensitive function of the reduced energy E^* and for energies not too close to zero is given by $R_0^* \approx 1.3$, which merges into the value 1.2 as the rainbow phenomenon replaces orbiting.

2.2   Classical scattering cross-sections

Having examined the behaviour of $\chi(b)$ for a typical bipolar potential, we must now consider its relation to the classical differential cross-section $\sigma(\chi)$.

The general form of this relation has already been given in Equation 2.10. It is important to note that although the deflection function $\chi(b)$ can have values ranging from $+\pi$ (direct back scattering) to $-\infty$ (orbiting), $\sigma(\chi)$ is only defined for the range $0 \to \pi$. A moment's thought will show that positive and negative deflection are indistinguishable in the laboratory since on the molecular scale it is impossible to tell whether the trajectory passed to the left or right of the target molecule. Both positive and negative deflections as well as those with $\chi > \pi$ are therefore mapped on to the range $0 \to \pi$ in the differential cross-section.†

From Equation 2.10 it is apparent that a singularity will occur in $\sigma(\chi)$ when $|d\chi/db| = 0$, i.e., at the extremum in the deflection function or rainbow angle. $\sigma(\chi)$ can also rise to infinity if $\sin \chi$ in the denominator of Equation 2.10 passes through zero while b is non-zero. Such a peak in the cross-section is called a forward or backward glory depending upon whether the deflection function is an even or odd multiple of π. The product $\sin \chi \sigma(\chi)$ when $\chi \to 0$, $n\pi$ does not exhibit this effect, but still diverges at the rainbow angle.

The rainbow phenomenon is frequently observed in molecular scattering and is of key importance in extracting an intermolecular potential from the observed scattering pattern. However, the finite energy spread in the beams and, less trivially, quantum effects, remove the divergence in $\sigma(\chi)$. Nevertheless, a pronounced maximum in the scattered intensity can often be observed with modest velocity selection.

The classical behaviour of $\sigma(\chi)$ near χ_r can be investigated in more detail by approximating the $\chi(b)$ curve near $b = b_r$ by a parabola having the same curvature at the minimum:

$$\chi(b) = \chi_r + q(b - b_r)^2 \tag{2.19}$$

so that:

$$\frac{d\chi}{db} = 2q^{1/2}(|\chi - \chi_r|)^{1/2}. \tag{2.20}$$

Then, the differential cross-section becomes:

$$\sigma(\chi) \cong b_r/(2\sin\chi \, q^{1/2} |\chi - \chi_r|^{1/2}), \tag{2.21}$$

---

† We shall see later that for indistinguishable particles this range falls to $0 \to \pi/2$.

and the signal received by a detector at χ_r subtending an angle 2Δ in the centre of mass system is:

$$I_\Delta(\chi_r) \propto \frac{b_r}{2q^{1/2}} \int_{-\Delta}^{\Delta} d\chi \, |\chi - \chi_r|^{-1/2} = 2b_r\Delta^{1/2}/q^{1/2} \qquad (2.22)$$

which is finite, although the normalized intensity, $I_\Delta \div$ (area of detector), tends to infinity as $\Delta \to 0$.

The glory phenomenon has proved more elusive. The forward glory would lead to scattering in the direction of the incident beam and would be detectable only at very narrow angles where the noise from the main beam makes measurement difficult. The effect has only been detected in measurements of the total cross-section. Backward glories are presumably rendered insignificant by the large value of $d\chi/db$ near $\chi = \pi$ making $\sigma(\chi)$ small (see Equation 2.10).

Inspection of the plots of $\chi(b)$ versus b (Figs. 2.5 and 2.7) shows that for a bipolar potential a given value of $|\chi|$ may result from collisions at three different impact parameters. If we retain our picture of the incident molecules being spread uniformly over a plane normal to the initial relative velocity three annular zones at b_1, b_2 and b_3 lead to scattering into the solid angle at χ. *Classically* the cross-section will be:

$$\sigma(\chi) = \sigma_1(\chi) + \sigma_2(\chi) + \sigma_3(\chi) \qquad (2.23)$$

each term on the right-hand side being given by Equation 2.10 with the appropriate value of b. In general, the contribution of the outermost branch of $\chi(b)$, corresponding to the largest value of the impact parameter, will be the major term because of the presence of the b factor in the numerator of Equation 2.10.

We now proceed to use some of the foregoing results to derive the limiting form of the classical differential cross-section at small angles. Mathematically, the method is to expand the expression for $\chi(b)$, Equation 2.6, in inverse powers of E^* and then, retaining only the leading term, to substitute the derivative for $|d\chi/db|$ in Equation 2.10. We will deal first with the large impact parameter contribution in Equation 2.23 and this will be the only contribution for a monotonic potential.

Taking a potential of the more general form:

$$V(R) = \sum_s C_s R^{-s} \qquad (2.24)$$

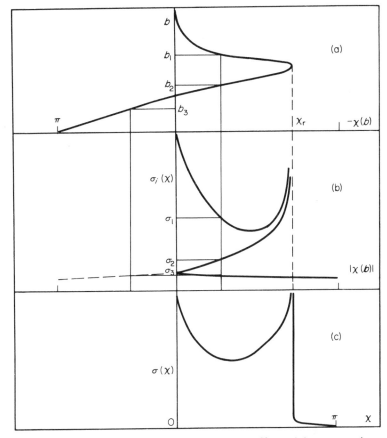

Fig. 2.7 The contributory branches of the differential cross-section.

   (i)   The deflection function $\chi(b)$ v b. χ_r is the rainbow angle.

   (ii)   The three contributions σ_i to the differential cross-section. The contribution to each σ_i comes from impact parameters around the corresponding b_i.

   (iii) The net differential cross-section as a function of the true polar angle of deflection, χ.

and substituting into Equation 2.4 gives a rather intractable integral which in the general case must be evaluated by numerical quadrature, for example, the Gauss-Mehler method or by the solution of the coupled differential equations, an approach which avoids the singularity at the turning point of Equation 2.6;

$$\dot{R} = -\left\{ \frac{2}{\mu} \left(E - \frac{L}{2\mu R^2} - V(R) \right) \right\}^{\frac{1}{2}} \qquad (2.25)$$

and

$$\dot{\chi} = L/\mu R^2 ,$$

for which several efficient digital computer programs exist. The expansion of χ in powers of the reduced potential parameters $C_s^* = C_s/E$ is not straight-forward and the result is quoted in Section 2.7. Here we confine ourselves to obtaining the first order approximation to χ by a physically more illuminating method involving Newton's second law explicitly in an approach that will also be found useful in the quantum treatment. The intermolecular force **F** is resolved into components parallel and perpendicular to the direction of relative motion and Newton's second law applied in the form of an action integral:

$$\Delta \mathbf{p} = \int_{-\infty}^{\infty} \mathbf{F} \, dt \qquad (2.26)$$

where $\Delta \mathbf{p} = \mathbf{p}_{\text{final}} - \mathbf{p}_{\text{initial}}$ is the vector change in relative momentum. If, as an approximation valid for small angles of deflection, we replace the trajectory by a straight line we can resolve $\Delta \mathbf{p}$ into two components:

$$\Delta p_z = \int_{-\infty}^{\infty} F_z \, dt$$

$$\Delta p_y = \int_{-\infty}^{\infty} F_y \, dt \qquad (2.27)$$

the motion being confined to the yz plane. The first integral vanishes $(F_z(-t) = -F_z(t))$ and the second yields:

$$\Delta p_y = 2b \left(\frac{\mu}{2E}\right)^{\frac{1}{2}} \int_b^{\infty} \left(\frac{dV}{dR}\right)(R^2 - b^2)^{-\frac{1}{2}} \, dR \qquad (2.28)$$

where the equations of the path:

$$v = dz/dt \quad \text{and} \quad z^2 = R^2 - b^2$$

have been used.

If the deflection angle is small:

$$\chi \simeq \Delta p_y/p_z \qquad (2.29)$$

and so:

$$\chi \simeq \frac{b}{E} \int_b^\infty \left(\frac{dV}{dR}\right) (R^2 - b^2)^{-\frac{1}{2}} \, dR \tag{2.30}$$

whence, for any of the terms in Equation 2.23:

$$\chi_s \simeq s C_s \, \pi^{\frac{1}{2}} \left[\frac{\Gamma((s + 1)/2)}{\Gamma\left(\frac{s}{2} + 1\right)}\right] \Big/ (2Eb^s). \tag{2.31}$$

It can also be seen from Equation 2.30 that the deflection angle χ in the small angle region is the sum of the contributions χ_s from each term in the potential.

We now complete the evaluation of the differential cross-section by combining Equations 2.10 and 2.30. In the limiting case where the dominant contribution to χ comes from only one term in the potential, the differential cross-section is given by:

$$\sigma_s(\chi) = \frac{1}{s}\left(s\pi^{\frac{1}{2}} \frac{\Gamma((s + 1)/2) \, C_s}{\Gamma\left(\frac{s}{2} + 1\right) E}\right)^{2/s} \chi^{-(2 + 2/s)} \tag{2.32}$$

Defining a reduced potential parameter C_s^*, with the aid of any convenient length parameter, d

$$C_s^* = C_s/(Ed^s)$$

Equation 2.32 can be put in the reduced form:

$$\sigma_s(\chi)^* = \frac{\sigma^{(s)}}{d^2} = \frac{1}{s}\left(s\pi^{\frac{1}{2}} \frac{\Gamma((s + 1)/2) \, C_s^*}{\left(\Gamma \frac{s}{2} + 1\right)}\right)^{2/s} \chi^{-(2 + 2/s)} \tag{2.33}$$

The contribution of the inner branches of the deflection function, if there were any, to the small angle cross-section would not be susceptible to simple approximation because the forces acting during the collision are not necessarily small, but a typical order of magnitude may be obtained from a rough value of $(d\chi/db)_{b\,=\,b_2}$ estimated from tables of angles of deflection for the Lennard-Jones potential. We suppose that three branches contribute to the scattering at some value of χ close to zero. Inspection of a typical deflection plot shows that as $\chi \to 0$ at b_0, the two inner branches (labelled (2) and (3) in Fig. 2.7) merge and that the deflection function in the region of b_2 and b_3 can be approximated by the linear term:

$$\chi = (b_0 - b)(d\chi/db)_{b=b_2,b_3}.$$

The contribution of these two inner branches to $\sigma(\chi)$ is thus:

$$\sigma(\chi) = \frac{b_2}{\sin \chi \left|\dfrac{d\chi}{db}\right|_{b=b_2}}$$

Both b_2 and $d\chi/db$ are relatively insensitive functions of energy (near $\chi = 0$) and one finds over the energy range $E/\epsilon = 1 - 10$:

$$\sigma_{\substack{\text{inner}\\ \text{branch}}}(\chi) \sim 0.4\,\chi^{-1}\,\sigma_{LJ}^2 \qquad (2.34)$$

where σ_{LJ} is the Lennard-Jones length parameter

To summarize, in a system in which a bipolar potential is operating, $\sigma(\chi)$ at angles appreciably less than the rainbow value (perhaps $\lesssim 0.1$ rad) is dominated by the outermost branch of the deflection function and hence the radial dependence of the longest range part of the deflection function can be found. At angles well beyond the rainbow and at reduced energies $E^* \gg 1$, the scattering becomes dominated by the shortest range part of the potential, but this region, even for 'normal' potentials, may well lie outside the range of thermal energy scattering.

It is not worthwhile identifying these regions more closely because small angle scattering is subject to important quantum effects which are discussed in Chapter 6. Nevertheless, Equation 2.32 retains a region of validity under low angular resolution even in a full quantum treatment.

Before leaving the subject of the differential cross-section, an important consequence of Equation 2.33 must be mentioned. We will suppose that Equation 2.33 gives the differential cross-section for all values of χ, not just in the small angle region — and for monotonic potentials for which there cannot be a rainbow region Equation 2.33 has qualitatively the right appearance of a rapid fall off in intensity at large angles. Integrating over χ

with Equation 2.33 substituted in Equation 2.11 gives the total cross-section

$$\sigma_{tot} = f(s) \int_0^\pi \chi^{-(1+2/s)} d\chi \qquad (2.35)$$

This integral is clearly divergent for all positive values of s and so we conclude that classical mechanics generally predicts infinite total cross-sections for potentials of infinite range. In fact, total cross-sections are finite and the experimental basis for this very important result is discussed in Chapter 7. The discrepancy is resolved by the wave mechanical treatment of scattering (Chapter 6), but the prediction of infinite cross-sections (whether total or differential) remains one of the more striking failures of classical mechanics. From an experimental point of view, the situation is less dramatic. Equation 2.35 predicts that if the attenuation, $(I_0 - I)/I_0$, of a beam by a cross beam or any sort of target is measured with a progressively narrower detector, a constant value is not achieved, but instead the attenuation tends to unity in some fashion with the detector width (assuming also that the beam width is kept narrower than the detector!) In practice, a limiting attenuation less than unity is readily observed with detectors of finite resolution.

We now introduce two further quantities which, like the angle of deflection, can serve to characterize a collision. These are the phase shift and the time delay. Both can be given a classical definition, but they achieve their full significance in the quantum theory of scattering. A particle moving through field free space has associated with it a wave motion of wavelength given by the de Broglie relationship:

$$\lambdabar = \hbar/mv = \hbar/\sqrt{2mE} = \frac{1}{k}. \qquad (2.36)$$

In the presence of a force field the wavelength depends on the position of the particle and a phase shift relative to an identical particle moving through a field-free region is introduced (see Fig. 2.8). It is only of interest to compare the motions of a particle along trajectories that have the same angular momentum and in regions sufficiently remote from the scattering centre for the phase shift to have become independent of position. We are thus led to a definition of the form:

$$\eta(b) = \lim_{R \to \infty} \left\{ \underbrace{\int_{R_c}^R \frac{dR}{\lambdabar}}_{\text{real path}} - \underbrace{\int_b^R \frac{dR}{\lambdabar}}_{\substack{\text{zero potential} \\ \text{path}}} \right\} \qquad (2.37)$$

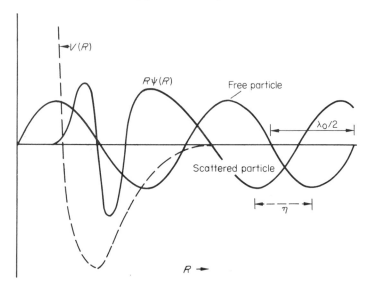

Fig. 2.8 The radial wave function $\psi(R)$ for a free particle and
a particle of positive total energy moving in the potential $V(R)$.

where, classically, the field-free path is a straight line trajectory that passes
within a distance b of the origin of the polar co-ordinate R and the
integration in both cases extends from the appropriate turning point to R. We
have defined the phase shift to apply to the radial motion and so the radial
velocity is inserted into the de Broglie relationship giving:

$$\eta(b) = k \left\{ \int_{R_c}^{\infty} \left(1 - \frac{V(R)}{E} - \frac{b^2}{R^2} \right)^{\frac{1}{2}} dR - \int_{b}^{\infty} \left(1 - \frac{b^2}{R^2} \right)^{\frac{1}{2}} dR \right\}. \qquad (2.38)$$

Because of the combined presence of the wave number and the classical
turning point this is called the semi-classical expression for the phase shift.
Differentiation of Equation 2.38 with respect to the angular momentum
quantum number $l = \mu v b / \hbar$ leads immediately to the result:

$$\frac{\partial \eta(l)}{\partial l} = - \int_{R_c}^{\infty} \frac{b \, dR}{R^2 \left(1 - \frac{V}{E} - \frac{b^2}{R^2} \right)^{\frac{1}{2}}} + \int_{b}^{\infty} \frac{b \, dR}{R^2 \left(1 - \frac{b^2}{R^2} \right)^{\frac{1}{2}}} = \frac{\chi}{2} \qquad (2.39)$$

(note that the lower limits of integration do not have to be differentiated
because the integrand is zero at the turning point).

Fig. 2.9 shows the relationship of phase shifts and deflection angles to the

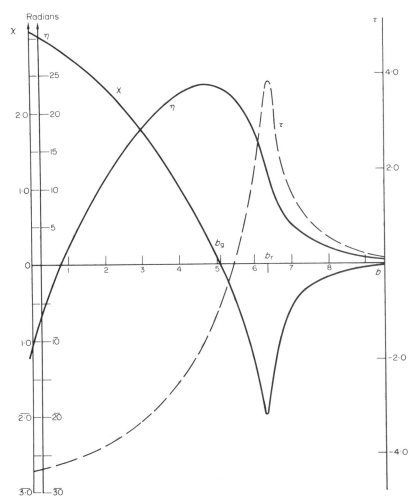

Fig. 2.9 The angle of deflection χ, phase shift η and time delay τ as a function of impact parameter for a Lennard-Jones potential with $\epsilon/E = 0.8$. The units of τ are 10^{-12} s and b is in Å.

impact parameters for a typical bipolar potential. Their mutual relationship exemplified in this figure will be of great importance throughout this book, and a great deal of the difficulty in analyzing scattering patterns comes from the fact that there is no simple relationship between $\chi(b)$ and $\eta(b)$ for a bipolar potential. Various perturbation approximations are available for the phase shift, but these will be discussed later when we return to consideration of the phase shift in the quantum treatment of scattering.

The time delay τ is defined in a similar way to the phase shift as the difference in time required for a particle to pass through a sphere of radius R about the scattering centre in the presence and absence of the force field. Again we compare only trajectories having the same angular momentum and let $R \rightarrow \infty$,

$$\tau(b) = 2 \lim_{R \rightarrow \infty} \left\{ \int_{R_c}^{R} \frac{dR}{v} - \int_{b}^{R} \frac{dR}{v} \right\}$$

$$= \frac{2}{v} \left\{ \int_{R_c}^{\infty} \left(1 - \frac{V(R)}{E} - \frac{b^2}{R^2} \right)^{-\frac{1}{2}} dR - \int_{b}^{\infty} \left(1 - \frac{b^2}{R^2} \right)^{-\frac{1}{2}} dR \right\} \quad (2.40)$$

It can readily be verified that:

$$\partial \eta(l, E)/\partial E = \tau/2\hbar. \quad (2.41)$$

Delay times may be positive or negative depending on whether attractive or repulsive forces dominate in the collision. For a normal intermolecular potential with values of the parameters that do not lead to orbiting, delay times $<10^{-12}$ s are predicted by Equation 2.40. From a computational point of view, the time derivative of $\eta(R)$ can be integrated simultaneously with Equation 2.3 and 2.4 (with time as the independent variable) to obtain complete information about a classical collision.

2.3 The Coulomb potential

Although $\chi(b)$ can be obtained analytically for a number of inverse power potentials (H. Goldstein, 1964) of these only the Coulomb potential is of importance in atomic or molecular systems. The effective potential in this case is (in e.s.u.)*

$$V_{\text{eff}} = Z_A Z_B e^2 / R + Eb^2 / R^2. \quad (2.42)$$

For like charges the potential is monotonically repulsive and for unlike charges the effective potential shows only one extremum in contrast to

* In S.I. Equation 2.42 becomes:

$$V_{\text{eff}} = (4\pi\epsilon_0)^{-1} Z_A Z_B e^2 / R + Eb^2 / R^2$$

where lengths are in metres, charges in coulombs, energy in joules and ϵ_0, the permittivity of free space, is 8.85415×10^{-12} C^2 N^{-1} m^{-2}. In this book e.s.u. are used throughout.

attractive potentials with a steeper R dependence than R^{-2} for which V_{eff} has both a maximum and a minimum. The deflection function, from Equation 2.6, is:

$$\chi(b) = \pi - 2b \int_{R_c}^{\infty} R^{-2} \left(1 - \frac{b^2}{R^2} - \frac{Z_A Z_B e^2}{ER^2}\right)^{-\frac{1}{2}} dR \qquad (2.43)$$

Changing to the dimensionless variable $u = b/R$ yields the standard form:

$$\chi(b) = \pi + 2 \int_{u_0}^{\infty} \frac{du}{\left(1 - u^2 - \frac{Z_A Z_B e^2}{be} u\right)^{\frac{1}{2}}} \qquad (2.44)$$

so that:

$$\chi = 2 \sin^{-1} \left\{1 + 4 \left(\frac{bE}{Z_A Z_B e^2}\right)^2\right\}^{-\frac{1}{2}} \qquad (2.45)$$

inverting and differentiating gives:

$$\frac{db}{d\chi} = \frac{Z_A Z_B e^2}{4E \sin^2(\chi/2)} . \qquad (2.46)$$

Thus from Equation 2.10:

$$\sigma(\chi) = \frac{1}{4} \left(\frac{Z_A Z_B e^2}{2E}\right)^2 \frac{1}{\sin^4(\chi/2)} , \qquad (2.47)$$

which is the Rutherford result originally derived for the scattering of α-particles by nuclei.

From Equation 2.46 it can be seen that no extremum in the deflection function exists so that in the Coulomb potential neither rainbow scattering nor orbiting can occur. The total cross is again infinite, while the phase shifts calculated from Equation 2.38 diverge logarithmically and only become finite for potentials falling off more rapidly than R^{-1}.

The potential between an ion and a dipole varies as R^{-2}, but contains a strongly angle dependent factor.

$$V = Ze\mu \cos\theta/R^2 \qquad (2.48)$$

where θ is the angle between $\mathbf{R}$ (the vector from the dipole to the ion) and the dipole axis. The dynamics of collisions involving non-central forces are intimately bound up with the transfer of energy between rotation and translation and none of the formulae for $\chi(b)$ in this chapter are applicable, although the impulse formulae Equation 2.26 can be adapted if the target is assumed stationary throughout the collision.

The long range potential between an ion and an isotropically polarizable molecule, with polarizability α, is:

$$V = -\frac{1}{2}\alpha Z^2 e^2 R^{-4} \tag{2.49}$$

the basis of the Langevin potential and of some models for ion-molecule reactions. Substituting this potential into the deflection function formula Equation 2.6 yields, after rearrangement, a standard elliptic integral of the first kind. The equation for the orbiting radius is readily found from Equation 2.17 to be:

$$R_0 = \left(\frac{\alpha Z^2 e^2}{2E}\right)^{1/4} \tag{2.50}$$

and the critical impact parameter for orbiting is $b_0 = \sqrt{2}R_0$.

We conclude this section by noting an important though approximate scaling rule of great use in the qualitative interpretation of scattering patterns. Inspection of Equation 2.31 shows that for small angle scattering $E\chi$ is a function only of the strength of the potential and the impact parameter. Thus, if we compare the scattering in a system at different energies but at angles that lead to the same value of $E\chi$, we can be sure that we are comparing events that occurred at the same impact parameter. Similarly, expansion of Equation 2.45 shows that $E\chi$ for Coulomb scattering with given values of Z_A and Z_B is a function only of b at small angles. A brief inspection of the deflection function expression Equation 2.15 shows that for the general potential, $E\chi$ is not solely a function of ϵ and b^*. However, the deflection can be developed as an expansion in the reduced potential parameters and the distance of closest approach. For the bipolar potential:

$$V = C_n R^{-n} + C_m R^{-m} \tag{2.51}$$

the form of the expansion is:

$$\chi = a_1 C_n/(ER_c^n) + b_1 C_m/(ER_c^m) + a_2 (Cn/ER_c^n)^2 + \ldots \tag{2.52}$$

If the linear term in E^{-1} is dominant, as it will be at high energies, a constant value of $E\chi$ implies a constant value of R_c. By comparing scattering at different energies but at a constant value of $E\chi$, we are examining trajectories with roughly the same value of the distance of closest approach. It is now customary in plotting scattering data to use $E\chi$ rather than χ as the abscissa and it is found that a variety of features in the differential cross-section, including some occurring on the dark side of the rainbow, are superimposable by this means. Amongst these is the rainbow itself which is characterized by a nearly constant value of R_c and in table 1 $E\chi_r$ is also listed and exhibits near constancy especially at $E^* > 2$. This property of $E\chi_r$ also enables tables of the deflection function to be extrapolated much more accurately by interpolating in $E^*\chi_r$ rather than χ_r itself.

2.4   The conversion from centre of mass to laboratory co-ordinates

So far, we have derived formulae for the angle of deflection of the inter-particle vector **R** and hence $\sigma(\chi)$ in terms of the intermolecular potential. We now seek a method of passing from $\sigma(\chi)$ to $\sigma(\theta)$ the differential cross-section in laboratory (lab) co-ordinates that would be measured in an actual experiment. With this transformation the path is then complete, in either direction, between the potential and the observed scattering pattern resulting from it. The transformation lab $\leftrightarrow$ cm is based on the triangle rule for the addition of vectors and deals only with quantities observed after the collision is over and so it holds for the transformation of both classical and quantum differential cross-sections. We recall that the angle of deflection, χ, in cm co-ordinates is the angle between the initial and final relative velocity vectors of the partners in a collision and that the angle of deflection θ in lab co-ordinates is the angle between the initial and final laboratory velocity vectors. It is then clear that central to the transformation is the 'Newton diagram' of the process, which is the vector diagram of the velocities of all the particles present before and after collision. A Newton diagram can be drawn for every type of molecular encounter, reactive or non-reactive and they are invaluable even at the preliminary stages of planning a beam experiment.

The simplest of all Newton diagrams (Fig. 2.10) results from the following process: a photon hits a molecule AB which then dissociates into two fragments A and B. In Fig. 2.10(a) the initial lab molecular velocity is v_{AB}, and those of the fragments v_A and v_B. The centre of mass initially coincides with that of the AB molecule and since the photon has a negligible momentum, the velocity of the centre of mass, v_{cm}, is equal to v_{AB}. After collision, the centre of mass continues with unchanged velocity and the two fragments emerge in opposite directions in the cm frame.

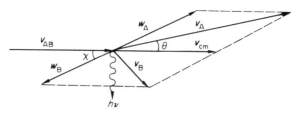

Fig. 2.10 (a) Velocity vector diagram for the process $AB + h\nu \rightarrow A + B$. The momentum of the photon is ignored. v_{AB} is the velocity of the molecule prior to dissociation in laboratory coordinates. w_A, w_B are the post-collision velocities of the fragments relative to the cm.

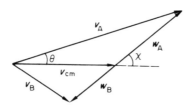

(b) The essential construction of (a) in condensed form, making up the Newton diagram. θ is the angle of scattering in the laboratory. v_{cm} now coincides with v_{AB}.

The direction in which the fragment A emerges is that of v_A, given by the vector addition of v_{cm} and w_A:

$$v_A = v_{cm} + w_A, \qquad v_B = v_{cm} + w_B \tag{2.53}$$

where

$$m_A w_A = m_B w_B \ .$$

The application of elementary geometry to Fig. 2.10 gives:

$$\cos \chi = -p \sin^2 \theta \pm \sqrt{p^2 \sin^4 \theta - p^2 \sin^2 \theta + \cos^2 \theta}$$

$$w_A = \sqrt{v_A^2 + v_{cm}^2 - 2 v_A v_{cm} \cos \theta} \tag{2.54}$$

where $p = v_{cm}/w_A$ the magnitude of w_A may be known in advance from the conservation of energy:

$$\frac{1}{2} m_A w_A^2 \left(1 + \frac{m_A}{m_B}\right) = h\nu - \Delta E \tag{2.55}$$

where ΔE is the energy required for the process $AB \rightarrow A + B$. The ideal beam experiment would measure the final laboratory velocity v_A in order to find ΔE and hence to identify the spectroscopic state of the products.

We next turn to two qualitative features of this scattering process that emerge from an inspection of Figs. 2.11 and 2.13. Firstly, if w_B is less than v_{cm}, then at any given angle of observation θ, A or B particles will emerge with two different velocities, v_f and v_s. That is, although two particles may emerge from a collision at the same lab angle, they have not necessarily undergone the same deflection in the cm system. The importance of this is that any theory of the scattering process will lead to a prediction of $\sigma(\chi)$ first, and the lab cross-section is then calculated from the sum of $\sigma(\chi_f)$ and $\sigma(\chi_s)$. If the fast and slow components of the scattered flux are not measured separately, there is no reliable way of deducing $\sigma(\chi_f)$ and $\sigma(\chi_s)$ separately although in practice χ_f is usually very different from χ_s and observations are conveniently restricted to angular regions in which $\sigma(\chi_f) \gg \sigma(\chi_s)$.

The second general use of the Newton diagram is in deducing the Jacobian for the transformation between lab and cm co-ordinates. Jacobians will be familiar to the reader in their purely mathematical role as the ratio of the infinitesimal volume in one co-ordinate system to the corresponding volume in another co-ordinate system of the same dimensionality:

$$dx_1 dx_2 \ldots dx_n = J\left(\frac{x_1 x_2 \ldots x_n}{\xi_1 \xi_2 \ldots \xi_n}\right) d\xi_1 d\xi_2 \ldots d\xi_n. \qquad (2.56)$$

Thus, in transforming from Cartesian to polar co-ordinates in ordinary

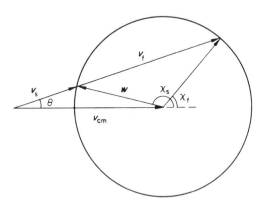

Fig. 2.11 The fast and slow collision products. Scattering of B at χ_f and χ_s in the cm system leads to particles emerging at the angle of observation θ with velocities v_f and v_s.

three-dimensional space we have:

$$dx \, dy \, dz = r^2 \sin \theta \, dr \, d\theta \, d\phi$$

so:

$$J \left(\frac{x, \, y, \, z}{r, \, \theta, \, \phi} \right) = r^2 \sin \theta.$$

In scattering problems the Jacobian of the cm to lab transformation has a simple physical significance. If we place a detector that subtends a solid angle $d\Omega$ at the scattering centre in lab co-ordinates, then from Fig. 2.12, all the particles that reach the detector must have emerged through the shaded area, i.e., into a solid angle $d\omega$ in the cm system, where:

$$\frac{d\Omega}{d\omega} = \frac{\sin \theta \, d\theta \, d\Phi}{\sin \chi \, d\chi \, d\phi} = \frac{(dA/v_A^2) \cos \alpha}{(dA/w_A^2)} \tag{2.57}$$

and so:

$$d\Omega = \cos \alpha \, (w_A/v_A)^2 \, d\omega$$

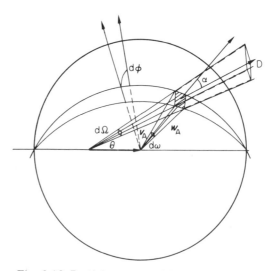

Fig. 2.12 Particles scattered into solid angle $d\omega$ in the cm system arrive in $d\Omega$ in the lab system. The detector D subtends an area dA (shaded) on the surface of the sphere on which the tip of w_A lies.

while from the definition of the differential cross-section:

$$\sigma(\omega)d\omega = \sigma(\Omega)d\Omega$$

so that

$$\sigma(\omega) = J\left(\frac{\cos\theta, \Phi}{\cos\chi, \phi}\right)\sigma(\Omega) \tag{2.58}$$

where

$$J\left(\frac{\cos\theta, \Phi}{\cos\chi, \phi}\right) = \cos\alpha \left(\frac{w_A}{v_A}\right)^2$$

$$= J\left(\frac{\cos\chi, \phi}{\cos\theta, \Phi}\right)^{-1} \tag{2.59}$$

The Jacobian for the fast and slow scattered particles at any angle of observation will be different and the observed differential cross-section measured without velocity analysis will be

$$\sigma(\theta, \Phi) = J_f\left(\frac{\cos\chi_f, \phi}{\cos\theta, \Phi}\right)\sigma(\chi_f) + J_s\left(\frac{\cos\chi_s, \phi}{\cos\theta, \Phi}\right)\sigma(\chi_s). \tag{2.60}$$

This result is quite general.

Returning to the photodissociation process, the polar direction is taken to be that of v_{AB} and clearly the azimuthal angles ϕ and Φ are identical. Application of the cosine rule to Fig. 2.10 yields the following result for the Jacobian $d\Omega/d\omega$ in terms of the observables θ and v_A:

$$J\left(\frac{\cos\theta, \Phi}{\cos\chi, \phi}\right) = \left[1 + \left(\frac{v_{AB}}{v_A}\right)^2 - 2\frac{v_{AB}}{v_A}\cos\theta\right]^{\frac{1}{2}}\left(1 - \frac{v_{AB}}{v_A}\cos\theta\right) \tag{2.61}$$

If v_A is not measured, but w_A is deduced from Equation 2.55 then we eliminate v_A from Equation 2.60 with the aid of:

$$\frac{v_A}{v_{AB}} = \cos\theta \pm \left[\cos^2\theta - 1 + \left(\frac{w_A}{v_{AB}}\right)^2\right]^{\frac{1}{2}} \tag{2.62}$$

The importance of the Jacobian can be illustrated by the edge effect,

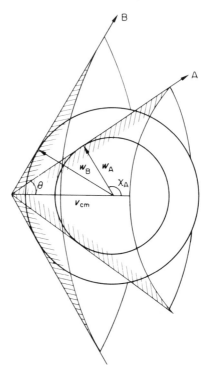

Fig. 2.13 The edge effect. Scattered A and B particles are restricted in the laboratory to emerge within cones generated by the rotation of w_A and w_B about v_{cm}.

which arises if w_A or w_B is less than v_{cm}. Reference to Fig. 2.13 shows that in this case the scattered intensity is zero at laboratory angles greater than $\theta_e = \sin^{-1} (w_A/v_{cm})$ and that, classically, the laboratory differential cross-section must rise to infinity at θ_e since here $\cos \alpha$ is zero. This conclusion is not altered by the application of wave mechanics since the trajectories at the edge are not coherent (they have emerged at slightly different values of χ). But, as in the discussion of the rainbow, the intensity at the edge measured by a real detector subtending an angle Δ remains finite. In Fig. 2.14 the effect of the operation of the Jacobian at the edge is illustrated for the case $w_A = v_{cm}/2$ in a reaction in which the products are scattered isotropically in the cm system, i.e., $\sigma(\chi) = \sigma_0$. The contributions of the slow and fast product molecules are shown separately, 90 per cent of the observed intensity coming from the fast component at low angles. The effect of scanning this scattering pattern with a detector of finite width ($\Delta = 0.01$ rad) is also shown.

A Newton diagram and Jacobian identical to those for the photodissociation process will apply to dissociation following the collision of an electron with a molecule if the momentum of the electron can be neglected in comparison with the molecule.

We now turn to the co-ordinate transformation for the elastic and reactive scattering of two particles for the important case in which the number of particles is conserved, i.e.

$$A + B \longrightarrow C + D$$

($A \equiv C, B \equiv D$ for elastic scattering).

Before the collision $\mathbf{R}_{cm}$ and $\mathbf{R}_{AB}$ are given by the vector diagram Fig. 2.1, whence, by differentiation with respect to time the velocity diagram is obtained (Fig. 2.15): after collision the particles C and D emerge with velocities $\mathbf{w}_C$, $\mathbf{w}_D$ relative to the centre of mass and hence the emergent laboratory velocities $\mathbf{v}_C$ or $\mathbf{v}_D$ can be obtained by vector addition of $\mathbf{w}_C$ or

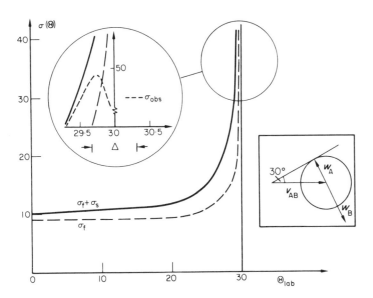

Fig. 2.14 The laboratory cross-section for scattering exhibiting the edge effect. σ_f and $\sigma_f + \sigma_s$ are shown, together with the effect of finite apparatus resolution Δ on the observed cross-section near the edge angle. Also shown is the Newton diagram.

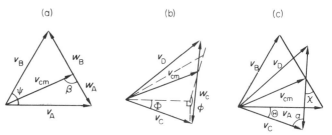

Fig. 2.15 The velocity vector diagrams before (a) and after (b) scattering and superimposed with v_{cm} in common (c). (a) lies in the plane of the paper; v_C, v_D and v_{cm} lie in a plane tilted with respect to (a).

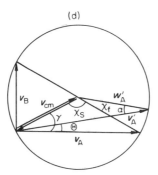

(d) The Newton diagram for the elastic scattering of two particles of equal mass.

w_D and v_{cm}. v_{cm} is thus common to both the pre- and post-collision velocity vector diagrams and the two v_{cm}'s can be superimposed by a simple translation to give Fig. 2.15(d), the Newton diagram.

From an experimental point of view, it is convenient to define angles of deflection with respect to one of the beam directions which can be measured and is independent of energy, rather than with respect to the direction of v_{cm}. The Jacobian for the general case has been given by F. A. Morse and R. B. Bernstein (1962) among others, and the derivation follows similar lines to the photodissociation case. The details of this transformation are given in appendix B. As in the photodissociation case if the final velocity of the product from a reactive collision is not measured there is considerable uncertainty as to the Jacobian for this transformation. Since, in general, the disposition of exothermicity between translational and internal modes of the products is not known this can lead to problems in interpretation. In principle measurements of the laboratory out of plane scattering can reduce this uncertainty but in practice experimental difficulties in providing out of plane motions are formidable.

2.5 The hard sphere potential

We will illustrate the foregoing results by deriving the differential cross-section expression in cm and lab co-ordinates for the hard sphere potential. It must be said at the outset that the hard sphere potential is never a good approximation for the small angle scattering of real molecules because of its finite range, but it has been used extensively in the kinetic theory of gases and is the limiting form of progressively steeper repulsive potentials. The potential is:

$$V = 0 \quad R \geqslant d$$

$$V = \infty \quad R < d$$

The mechanics of the collision are that, at the moment of impact, the component, w_n, of the relative velocity w_{AB} along the line of centres is reversed and the final vector, w', is obtained by adding $-w_n$ to the unchanged tangential component w_t of w_{AB} (Fig. 2.16) whence:

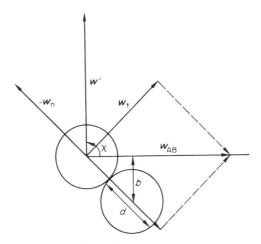

Fig. 2.16 The collision of two hard spheres in the cm system. The relative initial velocity is w_{AB}. After collision the component of $\overline{w}$ along the line of centres is reversed to give $-w_n$. The final relative velocity w' is then the sum of $-w_n$ and the unchanged tangential velocity w_t. χ is the deflection angle and the impact parameter is b.

$$\cos(\pi - \chi) = 1 - 2(b/d)^2 \tag{2.63}$$

Substituting in Equation 2.10 gives the differential cross-section,

$$\sigma(\chi) = \frac{1}{4}d^2 \tag{2.64}$$

which is independent of χ.

The Jacobian for transforming from cm to lab is:

$$J\left(\frac{\cos \chi, \phi}{\cos \theta, \Phi}\right) = \frac{v'_A}{w_A} \frac{2v'^2_A}{w^2_A + v^2_A - v^2_{cm}} \tag{2.65}$$

where the necessary relationships for measurement in the plane of the two beams are Fig. 2.15(d):

$$
\begin{aligned}
v'_A &= v_{cm} \cos(\gamma - \theta) + w_A \cos \alpha \\
\alpha &= \sin^{-1}[(v_{cm}/w_A)\sin(\gamma - \theta)] \\
\gamma &= \sin^{-1}[m_B v_B/(2(m_A + m_B)v_{cm})] \\
w_A &= (m_B/(m_A + m_B))/(v^2_A + v^2_B)^{1/2}
\end{aligned}
\tag{2.66}
$$

In the case $m_A = m_B$, $w_A = w_B$, the lab cross-section is found to be from Equations 2.65 and 2.66,

$$\sigma(\theta, \Phi = 0) = d^2 \left| \cos\left(\frac{\pi}{4} - \theta\right) \right| \tag{2.67}$$

and is plotted in Fig. 2.17. The zero intensity at $\theta = -\pi/4$ and $3\pi/4$ is due to the zero velocity of the molecules emerging in the laboratory at these angles. Defining a more symmetrical lab angle, $\beta = \pi/4 - \theta$, the reader can verify directly that:

$$2\pi \int_{-\pi/2}^{\pi/2} \sigma(\beta) \sin \beta \, d\beta = 2\pi \int_0^\pi \sigma(\chi) \sin \chi \, d\chi,$$

so that the total cross-section remains unchanged under the cm $\leftrightarrow$ lab transformation. Note that implicit in this verification is the knowledge that the differential cross-section in either co-ordinate system is independnet of the azimuthal angles associated with χ or β; whilst the former symmetry is quite general, the laboratory azimuthal symmetry is peculiar to this problem.

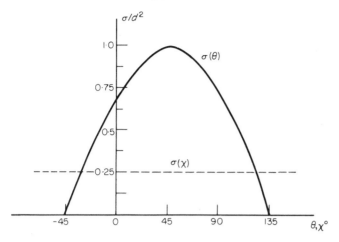

Fig. 2.17 The differential cross-section for the scattering of like hard spheres in lab (θ) and cm (χ) co-ordinates. The increase in intensity in the lab in the direction of motion of the centre of mass is apparent. Both the cross-sections are reduced by d^2, where d is the hard sphere diameter.

2.6 High energy collisions

Scattering phenomena investigated at energies large on the chemical scale ($\gtrsim 5$ eV) are generally performed with one beam thermal and the other at the required energy. The target or slow beam molecules can then be regarded as stationary before impact. The wider range of processes that are available with superthermal collisions compared with thermal energy bombardment is indicated in the following scheme:

$$A + B_2 \xrightarrow{\text{I}} A + B_2 \qquad \text{(elastic)}$$
$$\xrightarrow{\text{II}} A + B_2^* \qquad \text{(inelastic/internal excitation)}$$
$$\xrightarrow{\text{III}} AB + B \qquad \text{(reaction)}$$
$$\xrightarrow{\text{IV}} A + B + B \qquad \text{(dissociation)}$$
$$\xrightarrow{\text{V}} A + B_2^+ + e \qquad \text{(ionization into a variety of channels)}$$

The last two possibilities become more probable with increasing energy at the expense of reaction. At high energies the Newton diagram takes on a simplified form, and those for processes I, II, IV and V (if the momentum of the ejected electron is neglected) are summarized in Fig. 2.18.

If the lab velocity v_A and angle of scattering θ of the emergent A atoms is

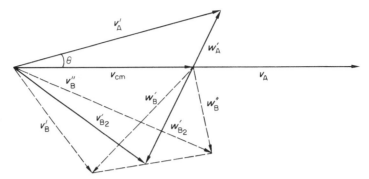

Fig. 2.18 Newton diagram for the collision of fast A with stationary B_2. Two possibilities are shown; (1) $A + B_2 \rightarrow A + B_2$ (full lines), characterized by $v'_A < v_A$ (2) $A + B_2 \rightarrow A + B + B$ (dotted lines) in which the two B particles emerge with different lab velocities v'_B and v''_B.

measured, then the energy transferred to internal motion, ΔE, (resulting in excitation, dissociation or ionization) is given by:

$$\frac{v'_A}{v_A} = \frac{m_A}{m_A + m_{B_2}} \left[\cos \theta \pm \left\{ \left(\frac{m_{B_2}}{m_A} \right)^2 \left(1 - \frac{\Delta E}{E_{cm}} \right) - \sin^2 \theta \right\}^{\frac{1}{2}} \right] \qquad (2.68)$$

where E_{cm} is the initial relative kinetic energy, $\frac{1}{2}\mu w_A^2$. It is important to measure the magnitude of v_A so that the predominant collision process at various angles of scattering can be inferred from ΔE.

2.7 Summary of useful formulae

The more important classical formulae connected with scattering are summarized here; they are numbered according to their position in the text.
The deflection function is defined by:

$$\chi(b) = \pi - 2 \int_{R_c}^{\infty} \frac{b \, dR}{R^2 (1 - V(R)/E - b^2/R^2)^{\frac{1}{2}}} \qquad (2.6)$$

and an approximation for small deflections is:

$$\chi(b) \approx \frac{b}{E} \int_b^{\infty} \frac{dV}{dR} (R^2 - b^2)^{-\frac{1}{2}} dR \qquad (2.30)$$

For the (12.6) L.J. potential a useful approximation is:

$$\chi(R_c) = -\frac{15}{16}\pi\frac{4\epsilon}{E}\left(\frac{\sigma}{R_c}\right)^6 + \frac{693}{512}\pi\frac{4\epsilon}{E}\left(\frac{\sigma}{R_c}\right)^{12} + 0\left[\frac{\epsilon}{E}\left(\frac{\sigma}{R_c}\right)^6\right]^2$$

which is good to ± 10 per cent for deflection less than, roughly, 0.3 rad. Another formula for the deflection function sometimes more convenient for approximation (F. T. Smith *et al.*, 1966), e.g., in deriving Equation 2.30, is:

$$\chi(b) = -b\int_{R_c}^{\infty}\left(\frac{R}{E}\frac{dV(R)}{dR}\right)\left(1-\frac{V(R)}{E}\right)^{-1}\left(1-\frac{V(R)}{E}-\frac{b^2}{R^2}\right)^{-\frac{1}{2}}\frac{dR}{R^2}.$$

The classical differential cross-section is:

$$\sigma_{cl}(\chi) = b\Big/\left\{\left|\frac{d\chi}{db}\right|\sin\chi\right\}.\tag{2.10}$$

For a potential of the form $V = C_s R^{-s}(s \geqslant 3)$:

$$\sigma_{cl}(\chi) = s^{-1}\left(s\pi^{\frac{1}{2}}\frac{\Gamma([s+1]/2)\,C_s}{\Gamma\left(\frac{s}{2}+1\right)E}\right)^{2/s}\chi^{-(2+2/s)}.\tag{2.32}$$

The semi-classical phase shift is given by:

$$\eta_{sc}(b) = k\left\{\int_{R_c}^{\infty}\left(1-\frac{V(R)}{E}-\frac{b^2}{R^2}\right)^{\frac{1}{2}}dR - \int_{b}^{\infty}\left(1-\frac{b^2}{R^2}\right)^{\frac{1}{2}}dR\right\}$$

$$\tag{2.38}$$

which satisfies the relationship:

$$\frac{2}{k}\frac{\partial\eta}{\partial b} = \chi(b).\tag{2.39}$$

An approximation for small phase shifts is:

$$\eta(b) \approx \frac{k}{E}\int_{b}^{\infty}\frac{dV}{dR}(R^2-b^2)^{\frac{1}{2}}dR.\tag{2.69}$$

The rainbow angle is given approximately by:

$$\chi_r \approx 2\epsilon/E$$

for a range of $(n, 6)$ potentials and is useful for $\epsilon/E < 0.4$ (see also Table 2.1).
Finally the relationship between the phase shift function and the differential
cross-section is:

$$\sigma_{sc}(\chi) = \left(2 \left| \frac{\partial^2 \eta}{\partial b^2} \right| \sin \chi \right) (kb)^{-1} \tag{2.70}$$

Appendix A The transformation between lab and cm co-ordinates for reactive scattering

For a reaction of the type $A + B = C + D$, useful relationships are (Morse and
Bernstein, 1962)

$$J_c \left(\frac{\cos \theta, \Phi}{\cos \chi, \phi} \right) = \left(\frac{w_c}{v_c} \right)^2 |\cos \alpha| \tag{2.A1}$$

$$\chi = \cos^{-1} \left\{ \frac{w_A^2 + w_C^2 - (v_A^2 + v_C^2) + 2v_A v_C \cos \theta \cos \Phi}{2w_A w_C} \right\} \tag{2.A2}$$

and

$$w_C = w_A \left\{ \frac{m_A m_D}{m_B m_C} \left(1 - \frac{\Delta E}{E_i} \right) \right\}^{1/2} \tag{2.A3}$$

where ΔE is the difference between the final (E_f) and initial (E_i) relative
kinetic energies, Fig. 2.19.
    To pass from cm to lab, use:

$$v_C = \{v_{cm}^2 + w_C^2 - 2v_{cm} w_C (\cos \chi \cos \beta - \sin \chi \sin \beta \cos \phi)\}^{1/2} \tag{2.A4}$$

where the quantities appearing on the right hand side are most conveniently
written in terms of the Cartesian components the of the particle velocities:

$$v_{cm} = (m_A v_{Ax} + m_B v_{Bx})^2 + m_B^2 v_{By}^2 {}^{1/2}/(m_A + m_B)^2 \tag{2.A5}$$

$$\cos \beta = \frac{v_{Cx}(v_{Ax} - v_{cmx}) - v_{Cy}^2}{v_A[(v_{Ax} - v_{Cx})^2 + v_{Cy}^2]} \tag{2.A6}$$

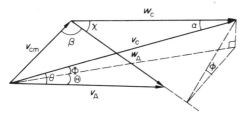

Fig. 2.19 Part of the Newton diagram for $A + B \rightarrow C + D$. Only the velocities of A and C are shown. Φ and θ are the polar angles of v_C with respect to v_A, so $\cos \theta = \cos \theta \cos \Phi$. ϕ is the azimuthal angle of w_C with respect to the plane containing v_A and w_A, with w_A as the polar direction.

$$\cos \alpha = \frac{v_{Cx}(v_{Cx} - v_{cm\,x}) + v_{Cy}(v_{Cy} - v_{cm\,y}) + v_{Cz}^2}{|v_C| [(v_{Cx} - v_{cm\,x})^2 + (v_{Cy} - v_{cm\,y})^2 + v_{Cz}^2]^{1/2}} \quad (2.A7)$$

and so forth, where the x/y plane is defined by the two incident beams. In transforming from lab to cm, ΔE will in general not be known. If the magnitude as well as the direction of v_C is measured, a possible recipe for effecting the transformation is:

(1) compute $\cos \alpha$ from Equation 2.A7
(2) compute w_C from

$$w_C = v_C \left[\cos \alpha \pm \sqrt{\frac{v_{cm}^2}{v_C^2} - \sin^2 \alpha} \; \right] \quad (2.A8)$$

(the sign is chosen by inspection of the Newton diagram). The cm angle of deflection is then obtained from 2.A2 and the Jacobian from 2.A1 with or without the cosine factor as appropriate.

In elastic scattering, the final lab velocity is usually not measured. A useful set of equations for in-plane scattering is then:

$$|w_A| = \sqrt{v_{cm\,y}^2 + (v_A - v_{cm\,x})^2} \quad (2.A9)$$

The presence of the $\cos \alpha$ factor in the Jacobian for *reactive* scattering has been the subject of some debate. If the product differential cross-section is measured with velocity analysis the Jacobian required is $J(\cos \theta, \Phi, v_C/\cos X, \phi, w_C)$ and this, after some rather heavy trigonometry is found to be simply $(w_C/v_C)^2$ (K. T. Gillen *et al.*, 1971 and references therein). The reader can more readily verify this for the simpler case of photodissociation with the aid of the relevant Newton diagram, Fig. 2.10. If the quantum state of the product is measured, then Equation A1 is the appropriate Jacobian.

$v_{Ax} = v_{cmx} + v_{cmy} \tan \theta$

$$\frac{\pm \sqrt{(v_{cmx} + v_{cmy} \tan \theta)^2 - (1 + \tan^2 \theta)(v_{cm}^2 - w_A^2)}}{1 + \tan^2 \theta} \qquad (2.A10)$$

where the positive sign gives the fast scattered component and the negative sign the slow component.

$$v_{Ax} = v_A x \tan \theta \qquad (2.A11)$$

The two cm scattering angles contributing at an angle of observation θ are:

$$\chi = \cos^{-1} \left\{ \frac{(v'_{Ax} - v_{cmx})(v_{Ax} - v_{cmx}) - (v'_{Ay} - v_{cmy})v_{cmy}}{w_A^2} \right\}$$

where the fast or slow value of v'_A is used as appropriate.

CHAPTER THREE

Molecular Beam Sources

3.1 General design considerations — signal/noise

Some hint of the experimental difficulties inherent to the scattering technique has already been given. Before proceeding to discuss in detail the particular aspects of generation, state selection and detection of molecular beams we propose to consider the experiment as a system. In this way the relative contributions of these parts to the overall performance can be better estimated.

In Fig. 3.1 we show a rather generalised experimental configuration incorporating two sources S_1, S_2, three filters F_1, F_2, F_3 and a detector D. In any real experiment it is unlikely that all the selectors shown would be a feasible proposition, nevertheless we include them here for completeness; it is then a simple matter to drop any unwanted terms from the results. We define the following quantities: I_1 and I_2, the beam fluxes of molecules with velocities v_1 and v_2 in molecules s^{-1} sr^{-1}, the transmission of the filters T_1, T_2 T_3 defined as the ratio of molecules (with specified velocities v_1, etc.) incident to that transmitted, the respective beam widths W_1, W_2, and height h define the scattering volume $W_2 W_2 h$. The distances l_1, l_2 and l_3 are from the sources and detector to the scattering centre. The laboratory differential cross-section is σ_j (E, θ) for in-plane scattering by the process labelled j e.g. elastic scattering at angle θ. The effective area of the detector is A_d and it has an efficiency of q counts per incident molecule of species i.

We further assume that the number density of background molecules of all types present in the apparatus is n_b cm^{-3} and that they have a mean velocity

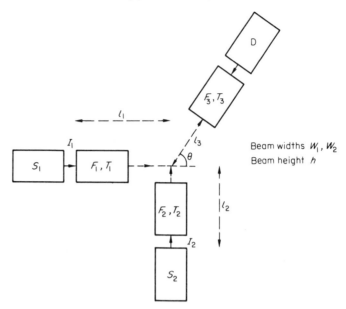

Fig. 3.1 Generalized scattering experiment.

v_b cm s^{-1}. The number density of the molecules to which the detector is sensitive is n_i cm^{-3} (also with mean velocity v_b).

The density of species 1 at the scattering centre is:

$$\frac{I_1 T_1}{l_1^2 v_1} \text{ cm}^{-3} \tag{3.1}$$

The number of collisions Z_{12} leading to scattering by process j into unit solid angle at θ in the laboratory is:

$$Z_{12} = \frac{I_1 T_1 I_2 T_2 W_1 W_2 h \sigma_j(E, \theta)(v_1 - v_2)}{v_1 v_2 l_1^2 l_2^2} \text{ s}^{-1} \tag{3.2}$$

where $E = \frac{1}{2}\mu(v_1 + v_2)^2$ = the impact energy and $W_1 W_2 h$ is the scattering volume. The number of counts recorded by the detector will be:

$$Z_{12} T_3 A_d q / l_3^2 \text{ s}^{-1}. \tag{3.3}$$

Thus the detected signal is:

$$S = \frac{I_1 T_1 I_2 T_2 W_1 W_2 h \sigma_j(E, \theta)(v_1 - v_2) T_3 A_d q}{v_1 v_2 l_1^2 l_2^2 l_3^2} \text{ s}^{-1}. \tag{3.4}$$

The feasibility of the experiment will depend upon the count rate S. Clearly if S becomes very small e.g. less than 0.001 counts s^{-1} the experiments will be exceptionally tedious and perhaps even impractical. However, before this stage is reached it is normally found that the noise count limits the sensitivity attainable. It is the signal to noise ratio which is crucial.

The noise counting rate is difficult to estimate, unlike Equation 3.4 for the signal for which all the parameters can be fairly well guessed. It arises from two principal sources:

(a) From the partial pressure of the species being detected inevitably present in the detector region and (b) from scattering of the beams by background gas.

For the first contribution the noise counting rate will be:

$$N_n = n_i \, q A_d v_b / 3 \quad s^{-1} \tag{3.5}$$

representing the flux of molecules on to the detector surface. The difficulty is in estimating n_i. Even a partial pressure of 10^{-16} torr corresponds to 3 atoms per cm^3 or at thermal energies some 10^5 collisions $cm^{-2} \, s^{-1}$ on the detector!

In the second contribution we are concerned with the densities of the target beam and the background gas (of all species). The count rate arising from this source will be:

$$N_n \simeq \frac{n_b T_1 I_1 W_1 W_2 h T_3 A_d q \sigma_b(\theta)}{l_1^2 l_3^2} \, s^{-1} \tag{3.6}$$

(We assume that the detector views only the scattering volume).

Noise from this source will be much more severe in the case of elastic scattering for which $\sigma_b(\theta)$, the differential cross-section for scattering from background gas into angle θ, will be of the same magnitude as the cross-section being studied.

In general it will be an objective of design to achieve a target gas density greater than 100 times that of the background i.e.

$$n_b \simeq 0.01 \, T_2 I_2 / v_2 l_2^2. \tag{3.7}$$

The noise count rate we have calculated represents the mean counting rate; as we shall discuss later in Chapter 5 it is the fluctuations in this rate that play the crucial part in an experiment. By making successive observations with one or other beam switched off we can estimate the signal plus noise and the noise alone, hence by subtraction estimating the signal with an uncertainty which depends upon the standard deviation of the noise. If we assume that all the noise processes contributing are 'white' (i.e. purely random) we can estimate their standard deviation as the square root of their mean.

The signal noise ratio is thus:

$$S/N = \text{Signal count rate}/(\text{noise count rate})^{\frac{1}{2}} \qquad (3.8)$$

or combining Equations 3.4, 3.5 and 3.6:

$$S/N = \left[\frac{I_1 T_1 I_2 T_2 W_1 W_2 h\sigma_j(E,\theta)(v_1 - v_2)(T_3 A_d q)^{\frac{1}{2}}}{v_1 v_2 l_1^2 l_2^2 l_3^2} \right]$$

$$\times \left[\frac{3}{n_i v_b} + \frac{l_1^2 l_3^2}{n_b T_1 I_1 W_1 W_2 h\sigma_b(\theta)} \right]^{\frac{1}{2}} \qquad (3.9)$$

This relation provides the kernel of the molecular scattering design problem. Note in particular that the signal/noise varies as the inverse squares of the distances in the apparatus, linearly with the beam intensities but only as the square root of the detection efficiency.

Unfortunately it is not sufficient simply to choose values for the dimensions so as to provide an adequate signal/noise ratio. Our choice is limited not only by practical considerations of machinability and strength of materials but more fundamentally by considerations of resolution. In any experiment we are concerned with measuring some parameter of the molecular behaviour rather than of the apparatus. This implies that the angular and energy resolutions of the apparatus must all be adequate to observe the effect of this parameter. In this chapter we shall not be concerned with the question of the resolution required to determine some specific molecular parameter, a topic reserved for discussion in Chapter 7. Rather, given a required resolution in the laboratory system, we will examine the resulting apparatus constraints.

3.2 Resolution

The resolution of velocity and state filters will be discussed later (in Chapter 4). Here we are concerned with the effect of apparatus dimensions on the measurement of the angular dependence of scattered intensity i.e. on total and differential cross-sections. We shall assume for the sake of simplicity that the velocities and states of our colliding particles are already completely defined. The extension of these arguments to cover beams with a distribution of velocities or states being straightforward though tedious. With this simplification the resolution of our apparatus will depend solely upon the geometric aperture of the detector and shapes and divergences of the beams.

Different techniques of beam generation (as discussed later in this chapter) will yield their own characteristic distribution of intensity with respect to angle in the forward direction. In general this distribution is too broad for direct application and a system of collimating orifices is used to further define the beam. Such a system consisting of a source of uniform brightness at O of width W_s and a collimation slit C of width W_c will yield a trapezoidal beam intensity distribution as shown in Fig. 2, of size

$$A = W_c + (W_c - W_s)\,a$$
$$B = W_c + (W_c + W_s)\,a$$
$$a = l_{cd}/l_{sc} \tag{3.10}$$

The dimensions are normally chosen with $W_c \gg W_s$ so as to yield a reasonably steep sided beam of the required width W_c. All the other dimensions being kept as small as is compatible with other apparatus constraints.

When measured by a detector with a finite angular width M the trapezoidal distribution will be broadened. The apparent profile as measured by the detector now being:

$$I(\theta)_{\text{apparent}} = \int_{-M/2}^{M/2} I(\theta + \theta')\,d\theta'. \tag{3.11}$$

It might be thought that this apparent width represented the resolution of the whole beam detector system. Unfortunately the beam height, which has not yet been explicitly considered, complicates this simple picture. The angular resolution of a system is normally described in terms of the 'Kusch' angle. That is the angle of deflection suffered by molecules in the beam at which the beam intensity registered by the detector, is reduced to 50% of that at zero degrees. The change in intensity with angle for tall beams can only be calculated if we allow for scattering occurring out of the plane defined by AC and O in Fig. 3.2 and 3.3. Here we see that molecules in each element ds in the beam are scattered both in and out of this plane. If the beam or target molecules producing this scattering are polarized (i.e. have aligned angular momenta) this scattering may depend on the polar angle ϕ as well as

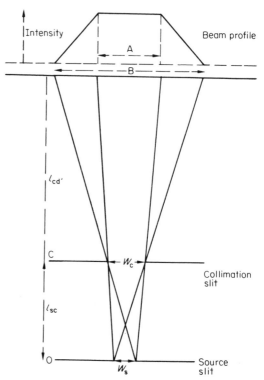

Fig. 3.2 Relation of source and collimation
apertures to the beam profile.

on θ. For the usual case of unpolarized beams, however, the scattering intensity is independent of the angle ϕ. The fall in intensity registered by a detector placed in line with the beam as the deflection of the beam particles increases can be calculated and is a useful function to describe the overall angular resolution of the experiment. When scattered through an angle θ at a random azimuthal angle, particles originally travelling in a small section of the beam will arrive in an annular area in the detector plane. Part of this flux may miss the detector, resulting in a decrease in the recorded intensity $I(\theta)$. By integrating over the area of the beam, the total change in intensity at the detector can be calculated as a function of θ and an efficiency function $\mathscr{I}(\theta)$ for detecting molecular deflections can be computed. For tall rectangular beams and detector, R. J. Cross and C. J. Malerich, (1970) have shown that if:

$$\mathscr{I}(\theta) = (I(0) - I(\theta))/I(0)$$

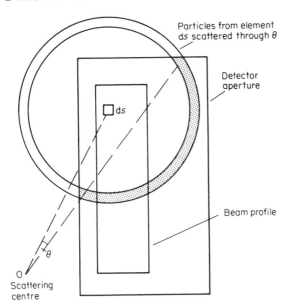

Fig. 3.3 Effect of out-of-plane scattering on resolution. Effective response for scattering through θ is obtained by integrating over all elements ds in the beam.

then:

$$\mathscr{I}(p) = 0, \quad p \leqslant 1 - \alpha$$

$$\mathscr{I}(p) = (\pi\alpha)^{-1} \{[p^2 - (1-\alpha)^2]^{\frac{1}{2}} - (1-\alpha)\cos^{-1}[(1-\alpha)/p]\},$$
$$(1-\alpha) \leqslant p \leqslant (1+\alpha)$$

$$\mathscr{I}(p) = (\pi\alpha)^{-1} \{[p^2 - (1-\alpha)^2]^{\frac{1}{2}} - [p^2 - (1+\alpha)^2] - (1-\alpha)$$
$$\times \cos^{-1}[(1-\alpha)/p] + (1+\alpha)\cos^{-1}[(1+\alpha)/p]\}, \quad (1+\alpha) < p \quad (3.12)$$

where $p = l_{ds}\theta/b$ and $\alpha = a/b$, l_{ds} being the detector-scattering centre distance, a the half width of the detector and b the beam half width. The Kusch angle, θ_K, of course corresponds to $\mathscr{I}(\theta) = 0.5$. Unfortunately we are still not out of the wood. As a simple example we will consider the single beam + gas target experiment to measure the total collision cross-section. Here we observe the attenuation of a beam passing through a collision chamber (or possibly a cross beam) containing a known pressure of the target.

The total cross section is $\sigma = 2\pi\int_0^\pi \sigma(\theta)\sin\theta d\theta$, where $\sigma(\theta)$ is the differential cross-section describing the angular dependence of the scattering.

We have already seen that the narrow angle contribution to this integral predominates.

In the laboratory the observed angular dependence for an apparatus with perfect resolution would be:

$$\sigma(\theta) = \int_0^{2\pi} \sigma(\theta, \Phi) d\Phi = \int J\left(\frac{\cos\theta, \Phi}{\cos\chi, \phi}\right) \sigma(\chi, \phi) d\phi$$

(since the random velocities of the target molecules makes the scattering symmetric about the main beam), where, as already discussed in Chapter 2 $J(\cos\theta, \Phi/\cos\chi, \phi)$ is the Jacobian describing the CM → LAB transformation.

If the total cross-section is to be measured to an accuracy ϵ then the apparatus efficiency function $\mathscr{I}(\theta)$ must be such that:

$$\epsilon = 2\pi \int_0^{\pi} \sigma_{lab}(\theta_{lab}) \sin(\theta_{lab}) \mathscr{I}(\theta_{lab}) d\theta_{lab} - 2\pi \int_0^{\pi} \sigma_{lab}(\theta_{lab}) \sin(\theta_{lab}) d\theta_{lab}$$

$$(3.13)$$

or more approximately the Kusch angle must be small compared to the angle η for which:

$$\epsilon \sim \int_0^{\eta} \sigma_{lab}(\theta_{lab}) \sin(\theta_{lab}) d\theta_{lab}.$$

For elastic scattering the CM value of η can be estimated rather approximately using the uncertainty relation as:

$$\eta_{CM} < \frac{\hbar}{\mu v}\left(\frac{\pi}{\sigma_{tot}}\right)^{\frac{1}{2}} \qquad (3.14)$$

where σ_{tot} is an approximate cross section for the potential and μ and v are the reduced mass and relative velocity of the collision partners. For molecular systems η will typically be less than a few minutes of arc at thermal speeds.

Since mechanical alignment considerations make slits with a width of less than 0.03 mm difficult to work with, this resolution requirement generally predicates a beam length of some 0.1 – 1 m, thus introducing a considerable intensity loss. It should also be noted from Equation 3.13 that the resolution required will be a function of the Jacobian. If this is unfavourable in the sense of compressing a large CM range of angle into a narrow laboratory one then the experimental resolution will be correspondingly worse. In general one tries to operate with this factor in one's favour by scattering and detecting the lighter of the two particles.

Further problems arise from the motion of the target gas in the scattering chamber. Firstly this random target motion with respect to the laboratory frame will broaden the relative velocity distribution and may if severe wash out any energy dependent structure in the total cross section. This topic and the appropriate correction factor are discussed in more detail in Chapter 7 also (K. Berkling et al., 1962). A second effect more relevant to this discussion arises from the spread of Jacobians arising from the target velocity distribution. Thus some collisions which for a stationary target would have fallen outside the detector will now be detected and will thus reduce the apparent total cross section. In some cases further corrections may be necessary to allow for the finite width of the target zone.

It will be easily appreciated that the apparatus resolution depends upon many factors including the nature of the beam and target materials and their temperature as well as the apparatus geometry. The Kusch criterion coupled with Equation 3.14 enables a first estimate of the required geometry to be made. However, for the accurate interpretation of measured attenuations in terms of total collision cross-sections very careful analysis of the whole range of factors contributing to the resolution is required.

In a cross beam experiment the resolution problem is yet more complex. Once again the experimental design must proceed via some approximate forward calculation using guessed potential parameters. The effect of various apparatus geometries can then be explored in a laborious but straightforward way using numerical integration techniques to produce an apparatus-averaged cross section in either the CM or LAB systems. In many cases it will be found that the particular purposes of an experiment do not require a very close approach to the apparatus with perfect resolution. Indeed at this stage some trade between resolution and signal/noise ratios as calculated by Equation 3.9 is almost inevitable.

3.3 Vacuum considerations

The most important component in any molecular beam experiment is quite simply the vacuum in which the beams are formed and their collisions studied. As a consequence the development of beam experiments has been closely linked to improvements in vacuum technology. It is not the purpose of this book to discuss vacuum technique; however, a few specialised topics arising in beam experiments are worth considering.

In any beam experiment there are three major requirements of the vacuum technique.

(i) To provide mean free paths very long in comparison with beam path lengths, thus avoiding significant attenuation and broadening of the beams.
(ii) To maintain the density of background material at a much lower figure than the density in the collision target or cross beam.
(iii) To minimise background densities in the beam detector chamber, particularly of species that are indistinguishable by the detector from the beam species.

The mean free path requirement is not normally difficult to achieve. The mean free path for a molecule with total cross section σ_{tot} is:

$$\lambda_f \sim (4\sqrt{2}\ \sigma_{tot}n)^{-1}. \tag{3.15}$$

Thus for a typical molecular cross section on adequate λ_f may be achieved with pressures of the order $10^{-5} - 10^{-6}$ torr. An exception to this rule may arise in the case of very slow atoms or molecules when the cross section may become very large indeed compared to that obtaining at normal thermal velocities.

The background density requirement is more severe. As we will see later in this chapter a typical effusive source may yield a flux of 10^{13} molecules sr^{-1} s^{-1}. For thermal velocities this corresponds to a static pressure of $< 10^{-7}$ torr in a target zone 1 m from the source. Considering the much larger path though the background pressure in the chamber as compared to the target zone itself we can see that ideally we should need to achieve pressures below 10^{-9} torr if background scattering is to be reduced to 10% of that for the target. In practice by keeping all beam paths as short as possible and by ensuring that the detector 'sees' only a narrow volume around the scattering centre this limit can be relaxed. A pressure of $10^{-7} - 10^{-8}$ torr in this region is quite commonly accepted at present.

The final requirement for low background densities in the detector region is very severe, particularly in the case of universal detectors such as mass spectrometers. This problem is discussed in more detail in the chapter dealing with detectors and its magnitude can be appreciated from the static partial pressure equivalent to a flux of 1 molecule s^{-1} cm^{-2} at thermal speeds, namely $\sim 10^{-21}$ torr. In vacuum terms we shall normally be reduced to simply doing as well as possible in this region, perhaps 10^{-10} torr total pressure.

In the design of systems to provide the required environment the beam fluxes themselves provide the major gas load, other contributions from wall and component outgassing being small in comparison. In this situation, differential pumping, in which the system is divided into a series of separately pumped chambers communicating only by narrow orifices through which the beam passes, offers important advantages. In Fig. 3.4a and 3.4b a 'nozzle source' with an aperture $\sim 5 \times 10^{-3}$ cm^2 and a driving pressure of 10^3 torr provides the beam, typically of intensity 10^{19} molecules sr^{-1} s^{-1} in the forward beam direction.

The gas load will obviously depend upon the temperature and molecular weight of the gas in the source.

The number passing through orifice $\approx$

$$\left(\frac{\text{Area of orifice x molecular velocity x n. density}}{4} \right) \text{ s}^{-1} \quad (3.16)$$

For the conditions given here the gas load will be ~ 20 cm^3 at N.T.P. To achieve a pressure of 10^{-8} torr in this chamber (requirement ii) a pumping speed of $\sim 10^9$ litres s^{-1} is needed — a speed that could be achieved by a

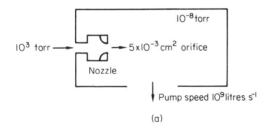

(a)

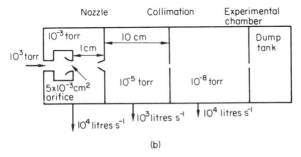

(b)

Fig. 3.4(a) and (b) showing the advantages of differential pumping in reducing the pump speed required to obtain the desired ultimate pressure in the experimental chamber.

pump with a completely effective area (in the sense that all molecules that cross it are pumped) of > 100 square metres!

In a system employing differential pumping the speed requirements are very much reduced. The total gas load is balanced between several chambers the maximum possible amount being pumped at the higher pressures. In this arrangement the source operates in a separate chamber (Fig. 3(b) since the beam path in this chamber is short (~ 1 cm) the comparatively high pressure of 10^{-3} torr will suffice. The pumping speed required in this chamber is now only $\sim 10^4$ litres s^{-1}. The second collimating chamber serves as a buffer between this chamber and the experimental one. The pumping load in this chamber based on the beam intensity and the entrance aperture to it is:

Beam Intensity x solid angle of entrance
$$= 10^{17} \text{ molecules s}^{-1} \sim 2 \times 10^{-2} \text{ cm}^3 \text{ s}^{-1} \text{ at N.T.P.} \quad (3.17)$$

so that a pumping speed of 1,000 litres s^{-1} would maintain a pressure of 10^{-5} torr. In the final experimental chamber the gas load will consist of all the gas scattered from the beam (say 10% of the beam flux) plus that which enters from the buffer chamber via its exit aperture. Thus for the dimensions in the figure a pumping speed of 10^4 litres s^{-1} is required, a speed readily obtained at these pressures by cryo panels or titanium getter pumps.

The great savings in pump speeds and hence in cost by the use of this staged pumping is very clear. These pumping speeds are obtainable by a combination of diffusion and liquid nitrogen cooled cryo-traps. For the higher vacuum chambers where the actual N.T.P. gas load is small, Ti getter pumps, preferably working on a liquid nitrogen cooled substrate provide great pumping speeds at relatively low cost for most chemical species, Table 3.1. This type of pump has now made the attainment of pressures of the order $10^{-8} - 10^{-9}$ torr a simple operation not requiring baking or other elaborate techniques necessary when only the slower ion pumps were available (which are now only required to handle the inert gases).

The major difficulty in constructing vacuum systems of the staged type, particularly for cross beam experiments, lies in the geometry, the requirements of short path lengths to the scattering centre and detector conflicting directly with the need for differential pumping stages and the actual size of the pumping equipment required to handle the gas load. When these problems are combined with the need to vary the detector angle, possibly both in and out of the plane, and to preserve some flexibility in the insertion of velocity filters etc. then considerable ingenuity is required to realise an effective system.

Table 3.1 Ti getter pump speeds litres s^{-1} cm^{-2}

Ti film temperature	Gas					
	H_2	N_2	O_2	CO_2	CO	H_2O
300 K	20	15	11	30	66	20
77 K	40	40		60	70	90

3.4 Beam sources — thermal energy

In Section 3.1 of this chapter we have shown how the overall signal/noise ratio depends upon the various apparatus parameters. In practice once having decided on the resolution required in an experiment our only remaining variables will be the beam intensities and detector sensitivity. Although in principle shrinking the distances which the beam must traverse is possible, machining and alignment considerations make it difficult to use beams less than a few tens of microns wide. The angular resolution required then dictates the minimum beam distances possible. Since the signal/noise ratio depends linearly upon the beam intensities but only as the square root of the detector sensitivity, the beam intensity available is usually the key factor in determining the feasibility of an experiment.

In recent years a wide range of techniques have been used to produce molecular beams. These methods have been discussed in a number of general reviews (H. Pauly and J. P. Toennies, 1965, 1968; N. F. Ramsey, 1956) as well as some more specialised reports (J. B. Fenn and J. Deckers, 1968; J. B. Anderson, et al., 1968). In general these techniques may be grouped into two main classes. Those covering the approximately thermal collision energy range extending at most up to 1 eV (3000 K hydrogen) and those operating at energies above this limit and thus not available from an equilibrium source. We shall see later that the intermediate region of beam energy, say from 1 to 20 eV, is an especially difficult one in which to work. The production of very slow beams is similarly difficult.

A further class of sources is designed to produce beams of free radicals, metastable species, dissociated atoms etc. These sources are normally adapted versions of the more usual types using electron or photon fluxes to produce the required excitation. In all these devices their efficiency as sources will depend most importantly on the following factors.

(i) The forward intensity in molecules sr^{-1} s^{-1} along the beam axis. Clearly the greater this intensity the better.

(ii) The ratio of forward intensity to the total gas load. In other words the directivity of the beam as it emerges from the source. A beam having most of its intensity in the useful forward direction will be more economic in its pumping requirements for a given beam intensity.

(iii) The range of velocities which the source will produce. Ideally we should like to vary the beam energy smoothly and continuously over a wide range from a few milli electron volts to several thousand eV. In practice sources are much less versatile.

(iv) The velocity dispersion in the beam Δv(*width at half height*)/v. If the beam energy is readily variable then a very narrow spread in the velocities of the molecules emerging from the source is desirable. Alternatively a suitable velocity selector can be used with a source producing a range of velocities so as to obtain the benefit of both a wide energy range and a narrow dispersion in velocity (though at some cost in intensity).

(v) The atomic and molecular state of the particles in the beam. In some cases we may wish to produce beams of dissociated atoms or other excited species. We shall almost always require to operate with beams in a well characterized internal state.

(vi) The stability of the source both as regards short term changes in intensity or in alignment and in the longer term due to corrosion etc.

Most thermal energy beam sources utilise a flow system in which the beam material flows as a vapour from an oven into a chamber of lower pressure. Here collimation and differential pumping stages are used to produce a final well defined beam in the experimental or collision chamber. This type of system can operate under two different regimes – *molecular effusion* or *'hydrodynamic flow'*. In the molecular flow condition the molecules move through the slit and beam without undergoing collisions. Their motion is thus mutually independent. Under these conditions the 'Knudsen number' K_n where

$$K_n = \frac{\text{Mean free path in source}}{\text{smallest dimension of orifice e.g. slit width}}$$

is greater than 1. For the reverse condition $K_n < 1$ hydrodynamic or bulk flow occurs through the orifice and for some distance down stream. Collisions are frequent and a degree of energy transfer from the internal modes of the molecules to beam translational energy occurs.

(i) Effusive sources $K_n > 1$

Historically the earliest (L. Dunoyer, 1911) and still the best characterized, in that the beam properties can be fairly accurately predicted, is the effusion source or 'oven'. This consists of a small chamber containing the beam material as a vapour at a pressure of a few torr. The beam leaves the chamber via a narrow slit ~0.02 mm across and perhaps 10 mm tall. The gas pressure in the source is adjusted so as to produce molecular effusion rather than bulk flow through the slit. This condition is fulfilled by making the mean free path in the source greater than the slit width ($K_n > 1$). The slit height is not critical in this respect.

Under these conditions simple kinetic theory considerations predict that the number of molecules, N, leaving the source per second is:

$$N = \frac{1}{4} n \bar{v} A_s \quad \text{for } n \ll 1/W\sigma \tag{3.18}$$

where A_s is the area of the slit, n is the number density and $\bar{v}$ the mean velocity of the molecules in the source. The slit width is W and the molecular cross section σ.

Since the flux is equal into every solid angle element the angular distribution of the molecules emerging from the slit follows a cosine law. The flux at θ from the forward direction and at a distance r is:

$$I(\theta, r) = \frac{1}{4} n \bar{v} A_s \cos \theta / \pi r^2. \tag{3.19}$$

In terms of source pressure p, temperature and molecular weight:

$$I(\theta, r) = 1.11 \times 10^{20} A_s p \cos \theta / r^2 \, (MT)^{\frac{1}{2}} \, \text{mol mm}^{-2} \text{s}^{-1}, \tag{3.20}$$

or:

$$I(\theta, r) = 1.11 \times 10^{20} A_s p \cos \theta / (MT)^{\frac{1}{2}} \text{mol sr}^{-1} \text{s}^{-1}. \tag{3.21}$$

At a distance of 1 m from the source the intensity for any gas will be of the order 5×10^{10} mol mm^{-2} s^{-1}. Thus for a typical detector with an angular resolution of 0.1° a flux of $10^{10} - 10^{11}$ molecules per second will fall on the detector.

The cosine law flux distribution from an effusive source, Fig. 3.5 is very

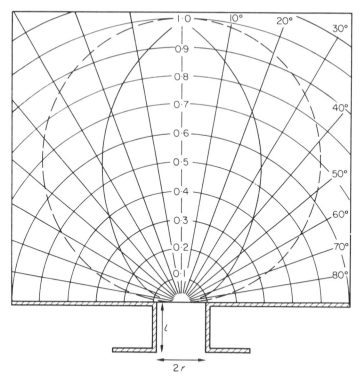

Fig. 3.5 Cosine distribution of flux from an effusion source (dashed line). The solid curve shows the distribution for a short canal (length = diameter). Reproduced from N. F. Ramsey, 1956.

broad and considerable collimation is required to produce a well defined beam. The directivity in respect of our standard beam (0.1°), that is the ratio of useful molecules in the beam to the total number emitted from the source is only $\sim 10^{-10}$. Simple effusion sources are thus relatively uneconomic in their pumping requirements.

The velocity distribution in the emergent beam is readily calculable. Since the slit is narrow compared to the dimensions of the source the gas inside is in thermal equilibrium with a Maxwellian velocity distribution:

$$N(v)dv = C\frac{v^2}{\alpha^3} \exp(-v^2/\alpha^2)dv \qquad (3.22)$$

where α is the most probable velocity $(2RT/M)^{\frac{1}{2}}$ and C is a constant.
The number of these molecules which escape per second depends upon their

velocity. The distribution of velocity in the beam is therefore:

$$vN(v) \text{ i.e.}$$

$$I(v)dv = C\left(\frac{v}{\alpha}\right)^3 \exp(-v^2/\alpha^2)\frac{dv}{\alpha}. \tag{3.23}$$

For many purposes this distribution is too wide to yield the required energy resolution and some form of velocity selection might then be used. The velocity distribution calculated is found to hold well in experiments except at the lowest velocities in the tail of the distribution. Here slightly lower intensities than predicted are observed, probably due to collisions scattering out the slow molecules from the beam.

The energy range over which useful beam intensities can be obtained is about a factor of 5 centred on kT for the source temperature. The maximum energy available even with high temperature operation of the source thus lies in the region below 1 eV.

Since the source operates at thermal equilibrium and very few collisions occur in the beam itself the effusion technique produces an equilibrium mixture of internal states and molecular species. This can be an important advantage. We shall see later that many of the other types of beam source are much less well defined in this respect. Furthermore by heating the source the internal distribution can be changed in a controlled fashion.

The effusion source is very simple in construction. For condensable materials such as alkali metals, single or double chamber ovens may be used in which the source both contains the charge of beam material and maintains thermally the required operating vapour pressure. The second chamber can then be used to vary the vapour temperature without altering the vapour pressure, in this way varying the velocity distribution in the emergent beam.

The heaters for effusion sources of this general type are normally made from Nichrome or tantalum wire. They are arranged so as to raise the orifice or slit temperature somewhat above that of the bulk of the oven; thus preventing condensation and blockage of the slits. Other problems arise from corrosion, particularly around the defining slits. Monel is the usual material for these ovens but for some very corrosive species such as the halogens it may be necessary to construct the source from graphite or to use gold slits.

Some materials, e.g. NaOH, are especially prone to bumping or 'spritzing' in the ovens producing unstable intensities in the beam. This difficulty may be minimized by careful control of the temperature when initially heating the charge and by the use of baffles inside the source itself.

Some typical designs of effusion source are shown in Fig. 3.6

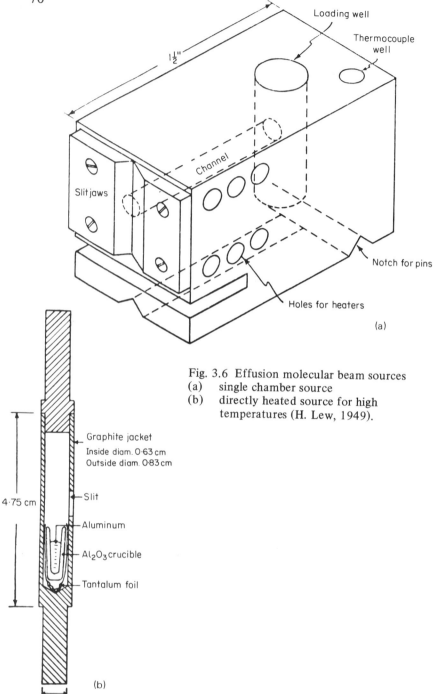

Fig. 3.6 Effusion molecular beam sources
(a)   single chamber source
(b)   directly heated source for high
      temperatures (H. Lew, 1949).

In practice these sources are usually operated at somewhat higher pressures than those yielding strictly effusive flow. The intensities obtained are then somewhat higher and rather more material is concentrated in the forward direction.

A much greater improvement in directivity while still maintaining the effusion condition can be achieved by the use of long canals or arrays of such canals in place of the thin defining slits at the orifice of these sources. For a single long canal the directivity is improved by a factor $3l/8r$. The critical distance for the mean free path now being the canal length l rather than the aperture radius r. This longer mean free path and the consequent lower operating pressure in the source means that the forward intensity in the beam is less than that from a thin slit. The advantage lies in the greater directivity, the gas load for a given intensity falling by the factor $3l/8r$.

Much more useful are arrays of such canals. In particular glass plates containing multiple parallel capillary tubes with radii down to 3μ and an overall transparency of 75 percent can be obtained commercially. For a given total gas load a higher forward flux can be obtained from these arrays than from a thin slit (provided that the mean free path in the source is comparable to the tube length).

The improvement in forward intensity compared to that produced by a thin slit orifice operated at the *same pressure* has been calculated by J. A. Giordmaine and T. C. Wang (1960) to be:

$$\frac{I(0) \text{ array}}{I(0) \text{ thin orifice}} = \frac{0.32}{\pi^{1/4}} \left(\frac{\bar{v}}{N}\right)^{1/2} \frac{1}{d} (A\tau m)^{1/4} \qquad (3.24)$$

where A is the total source area, τ is the transparency of the array, m the number of holes in the array, N the total flow rate in molecules s^{-1}, d the collision diameter and $\bar{v}$ the mean velocity of the molecules in the source. The half intensity width of the array and the thin orifice beams are approximately in the inverse ratio of their forward intensities as given by Equation 3.24 above. The actual experimental performance of these arrays is a little worse than that predicted, presumably due to collisions between molecules emerging from different channels (J. C. Johnson, et al., 1966).

As the pressure inside any of these array sources is raised, the effective channel length decreases until eventually the array behaves like a thin orifice of equal effective area. This behaviour is nicely illustrated in Fig. 3.7. The maximum forward intensity obtainable from these arrays is thus no better than from an orifice. The improvement in directivity obtained, however, is considerable, Fig. 3.8.

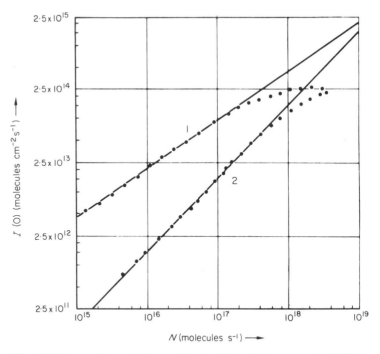

Fig. 3.7 Comparison of forward intensities at 1m versus total flow (i.e. gas load) for a channel array (1) and an orifice source (2). Reproduced from H. Pauly and J. P. Toennies, 1965.

The most important application of these devices is in the cross or target beam source where a relatively extended target region is permissible and the minimum gas load is desirable. Glass arrays are now available in quite large sheets ~5 cm and in a variety of geometries. Some workers have recently described shaped arrays in which the channels are not parallel but are angled so as to bring the beam material to a fairly well defined focus. Clearly collisions within the converging beam must limit the densities achievable and it is not yet clear how useful this technique will prove.

The velocity distribution from an array source has been reported to be slightly deficient in slow velocities as compared to the effusive v^3 distribution.

(ii) Hydrodynamic flow sources, $K_n < 1$

The hydrodynamic source is gaining very rapidly in importance, since intensities up to 10^3 greater than those from effusive orifices can be obtained. There seems little doubt that in cases where the intensity limits experimental performance hydrodynamic sources will be the normal choice.

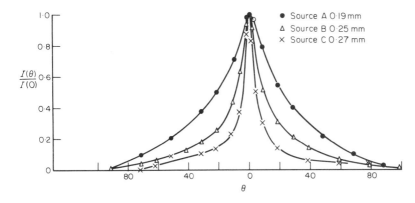

Source	Tube length cm	Effective radius of single tube cm	No. of tubes	Overall source diameter cm	Approximate shape of tube cross section
A	0.66	1.65×10^{-2}	224	0.51	Hexagonal
B	0.31	2.35×10^{-3}	1.28×10^{1}	1.3	Circular
C	0.95	2.69×10^{-3}	1.80×10^{4}	1.1	Triangular

Fig. 3.8 Ratio of intensity at θ to forward intensity for several sources and pressures. (Reproduced from J. A. Giordmaine and T. C. Wang, 1960).

This type of source originated with a suggestion by A. Kantrowitz and J. Grey, 1951, that the Maxwellian gas inside an effusive source be replaced by a supersonic jet of gas already moving in the beam direction. An arrangement to exploit this idea is shown schematically in Fig. 3.9. The beam material emerges through a nozzle from a chamber in which the pressure is of the order $10^{2} - 10^{3}$ torr. The flow is hydrodynamic through this nozzle and a large jet of gas expands into the nozzle chamber. This jet strikes a truncated hollow cone known as the skimmer. In this way a sample of the rapidly translating gas is obtained and the remaining gas in the jet deflected away for pumping. In the region of the skimmer the flow changes from continuum to molecular, i.e. the collision rate drops very sharply. The post skimmer chambers serve to collimate the beam and to provide the differential pumping necessary. (See Section 3.3).

Since the operation of this source includes the transition from continuum to molecular flow the actual conditions present in these gas jets has been of considerable interest (J. B. Anderson et al., 1965, 1966; E. L. Knuth, 1964). Although much progress has been made in their understanding a complete

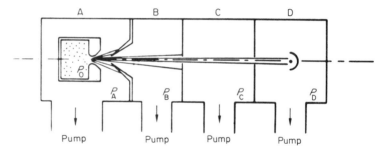

Fig. 3.9 Schematic of a nozzle beam source. A, B, C, and D are the nozzle, collimation, experimental and detection chambers respectively. The separate differential pumping stages are a crucial feature.

theory is still not available. However, from a users viewpoint a simple theory combined with some pragmatism in design and operation is usually adequate.

The simple theory of the action of nozzle beams is based upon the assumption that the expansion is isentropic. The increase in forward velocity of the beam then comes from a reduction in the local enthalpy of the gas. The lowering in temperature, from T_i to T_f, accompanying the expansion is given by:

$$T_f/T_i = \left[1 + \frac{\gamma - 1}{2} M^2\right]^{-1} \tag{3.25}$$

where $\gamma = C_p/C_v$ and M is the Mach number in the collision free zone downstream from the jet. The Mach number is defined as:

$$M = V/C \tag{3.26}$$

where V is the bulk velocity and C the local velocity of sound. Typically $M \sim 10$ and so with $\gamma = 5/3$, T_f/T_i may approach 3×10^{-2}, a very considerable degree of cooling. In a beam of molecules having internal energy, some of the energy for the increase in forward translational energy can come from vibration and rotation and it is hard to predict in practice whether relaxation among all the degrees of freedom is complete (this would be reflected in the value of γ used above). The marked lowering of the relative as opposed to the bulk kinetic energy of the beam molecules can result in dimerisation or clustering in certain cases, there being enough collisions to stabilise thesynew species (R. J. Gordon et al., 1970).

The increase in forward velocity after expansion can be calculated in the ideal case to be:

$$v_f/v_i \simeq M \left(\frac{\gamma}{3} \frac{T_f}{T_i} \right)^{1/2}. \tag{3.27}$$

Again taking a Mach number of 10, but with a beam of diatomic molecules in which rotational relaxation is complete ($\gamma = 7/5$), we find that the increase in translational energy compared to an effusive source of the same temperature is twofold. From the decrease in the internal temperature of the beam we can also calculate the width of the velocity distribution after expansion:—

$$\frac{\Delta v}{v} \sim \left(\frac{2}{\gamma} \right)^{1/2} \Big/ M. \tag{3.28}$$

Finally the actual forward intensity of a nozzle beam $I(o, v)$ as a function of velocity can also be calculated from simple kinetic theory. If n_0 and α_0 are the number density and velocity in the source, A_s the area of the skimmer and M is the Mach number at the skimmer. Then Anderson and Fenn have shown that:

$$I(o, v) = \frac{n_0 A_s}{\pi^{3/2}} \left(\frac{v}{\alpha_0} \right)^3 \left[1 + \frac{\gamma^{-1}}{2} M^2 \right]^{3/2 - (1/\gamma - 1)}$$

$$\cdot \exp\left\{ -\left(\frac{v}{\alpha_0} \left[1 + \frac{\gamma - 1}{2} M^2 \right]^{1/2} - \frac{\gamma^{1/2} M}{\sqrt{2}} \right)^2 \right\}. \tag{3.29}$$

In comparison with an effusive source the ratio of forward intensities at the most probable velocity is approximately

$$\frac{I_{\text{nozzle}}(v)}{I_{\text{effusion}}(v_{\text{most prob.}})} = \frac{n_{0 \text{ nozzle}}}{n_{0 \text{ effusion}}} f(M, \gamma) \tag{3.30}$$

For Mach number >5 (the interesting range) $f(M, \gamma) \simeq 9$ for monatomic gas and $80/M^2$ for diatomics. The improved intensity provided by a nozzle source thus originates very largely in the greater source densities that can be used. The vital advantage lies in the removal of the effusion constraint on the mean free path in the source.

The elementary calculations presented so far have all been in terms of the Mach number. The actual development of this ratio as the expansion proceeds has been calculated by P. L. Owen and C. K. Thornhill, (1948). With the important proviso that the expansion was free and without shock waves their calculation yielded the prediction illustrated in Fig. 3.10. Here the Mach number in a free jet is shown as a function of the ratio of distance

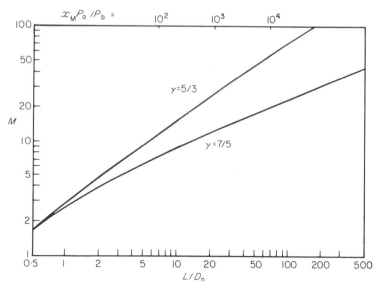

Fig. 3.10 Calculated values of Mach number at distance L downstream from nozzle of diameter D_n. Location of Mach disc x_M for various pressure ratios is shown on top. Reproduced from H. Pauly and J. P. Toennies, 1968.

downstream from nozzle to the nozzle diameter. Thus naively by selecting a suitable skimmer nozzle distance we might expect to produce a beam of any desired Mach number and hence be able to predict the other characteristics of the beam. Unfortunately while it is true that the nozzle skimmer distance is of prime importance a number of other factors, complicate the picture. Firstly J. B. Fenn and J. Deckers, 1963, have found that in contrast to the Owen-Thornhill calculations in which Mach number increased monotonically a definite maximum or Terminal Mach number is reached. Here the collision rate becomes so low that free molecular flow occurs and no further expansion takes place. They find the Terminal Mach number M_T to be given by:

$$M_T \simeq 1.2 \left(\frac{\lambda_0}{D_n} \right)^{-0.4} \tag{3.31}$$

where λ_0 is the mean free path in the source and D_n is the nozzle throat diameter.

A second complication arises from the presence of shock waves in the expanding jet. From Schlieren photographs these shocks are known to have

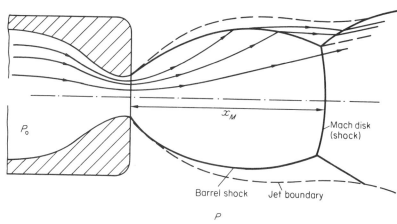

P_o

x_M

Mach disk (shock)

Barrel shock Jet boundary

P

Fig. 3.11 Flow lines and shock fronts in an expanding gas jet. Reproduced from H. Pauly and J. P. Toennies, 1968.

broadly the configuration shown in Fig. 3.11. Particularly important is the shock front perpendicular to the flow direction known as the Mach disc. This shock is believed to originate in collisions of the beam molecules with the background gas. Its position varies roughly as [nozzle pressure/background pressure] $^{1/2}$ and its location is shown in Fig. 3.10.

Forward of the Mach disc the expansion is approximately free and the ideal Owen-Thornhill calculations are reasonably valid. Aft of the disc recompression of the gas occurs and the beam is attenuated. In practice many workers have found an optimum nozzle − skimmer distance to exist. At short distances nozzle-skimmer interference appears while at large distances the Mach disc degrades the beam.

Fenn and Deckers have found experimentally that the intensity actually observed compared to that predicted by calculations is decreased approximately in the ratio Knudsen No. at skimmer $\div M$. In practical operation the nozzle skimmer distance is adjusted to yield the optimum beam flux. Under these conditions the mean free path at the skimmer is several times the skimmer aperture and the exact shape of the nozzle and skimmer are relatively unimportant (K. Bier and O. Hagenna, 1963).

The relative performance of the nozzle and effusion sources have been compared by H. Pauly and J. P. Toennies, 1968, Fig. 3.12. It is clear that nozzle sources offer very much higher beam intensities and are much more economical in terms of forward intensity per given gas load than is the effusion source. However, the useful energy range is still rather limited. The

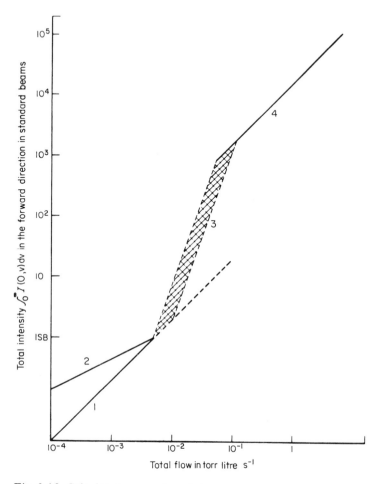

Fig. 3.12 Calculated comparison between
(1) Slit effusion source
(2) Multi channel effusion source
(3) Nozzle source (transition region)
(4) Nozzle source (hydrodynamic flow) $M = 10$
Aperture area same for all sources. Reproduced from H. Pauly and
J. P. Toennies, 1968.

beam energy available being roughly:

$$E = \int_0^{T_{nozzle}} C_p dT \qquad (3.32)$$

i.e. a few tenths of an eV at normal operating temperatures.

(iii) Constructional details

In a nozzle source the major design consideration will be the provision of sufficient pumping speed to handle the large gas flows produced by this type of source. As already discussed (Section 3.3) this will inevitably involve several stages of differential pumping. Much of the design effort will be expended in securing a compact design, minimising the beam path length but at the same time providing sufficient pumping speed along the beam. If the beam materials are condensible the pumping requirement is considerably eased since cryogenic pumping can be used. Other considerations will be the operating temperature of the nozzle and any corrosion problems.

A typical nozzle source (J. G. Skofronik, 1967) developed for beam experiments is shown in Fig. 3.13. The nozzle, skimmer and collimator were accurately machined from brass and precisely aligned in an aluminium mount. The nozzle is arranged to slide in this mount so that the nozzle skimmer distance can be varied during operation. The external angle of the skimmer was 86° and its internal angle 70°. The nozzle chamber was pumped by a 40 cm oil diffusion pump and the collimation chamber by a 10 cm one. The operating pressures were 200 torr stagnation pressure in the nozzle, 5×10^{-5} torr in the skimmer chamber and 10^{-6} torr in the collimator. With this system the observed intensity shows a maximum as the skimmer nozzle distance is varied. For N_2, H_2 and He beams intensities of 4×10^{18}, 3×10^{19} and 1.5×10^{19} molecules sr^{-1} s^{-1} were achieved.

A rather simpler design for alkali metals has been described by E. Hundhausen and H. Pauly, 1965. In essentials their source is simply an effusive oven fitted with a narrow convergent divergent slit. It is operated at much higher pressures than appropriate for an effusion source and is provided with sufficient pumping in the form of cryo panels to handle the vapour load. In another series of experiments using an inhomogenous magnetic field to separate the paramagnetic K atoms from K_2 it was shown that the dimer concentration was not markedly different from that obtaining at equilibrium in the nozzle chamber provided that the expansion was not taken beyond Mach 10. At higher expansions the fraction of dimers rose rapidly (D. Morgenstern and D. Beck, 1967).

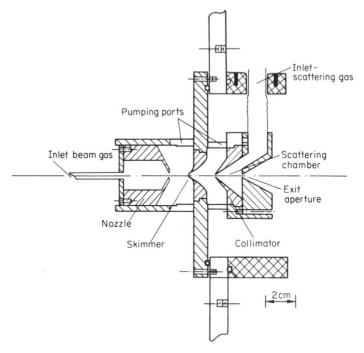

Fig. 3.13 Nozzle source for non-condensibles (J. G. Skofronik, 1967). The figure also shows the scattering chamber used with this source.

A design using liquid He pumps is shown in Figs. 3.14 and 3.15. Intensities for Argon of 4×10^{18} molecules sr^{-1} s^{-1} were obtained.

Nozzle sources have also been used to produce beams of dissociated atoms by combining the nozzle source with an R.F. discharge. In Fig. 3.16 a source developed to produce O atoms is shown. Here the nozzle chamber incorporates an R.F. loop so that a discharge may be maintained in the range 15—70 torr. The gas feed to the nozzle was a mixture of 95 percent He and 5 percent O_2. With this gas mixture the O_2 is approximately 30 percent dissociated by the discharge.

Since the helium is present in large excess the bulk flow velocity through the nozzle and into the skimmer is governed by the helium. The oxygen atoms and molecules ride with the jet as passengers at almost the same bulk speed as the predominant helium. The heavier O and O_2 are thus accelerated into the beam with velocities equal to the helium atoms, corresponding at their heavier mass, to energies much above thermal. For the system described an O atom flux of 10^{17} atoms sr^{-1} s^{-1} with translational energies up to 0.33 eV was obtained.

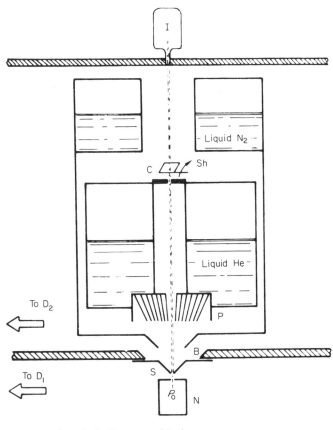

I   = Ionization gauge detector
Sh = Shutter
C   = Collimator
P   = Cryopump
B   = Shield opening
S   = Skimmer
N   = Nozzle
D_1 = 10 000 $l\,s^{-1}$ booster diffusion pump
D_2 = 10 $l\,s^{-1}$ diffusion pump

Fig. 3.14 Nozzle source using liquid He cryopumps (G. Scoles and F. Torello, 1967).

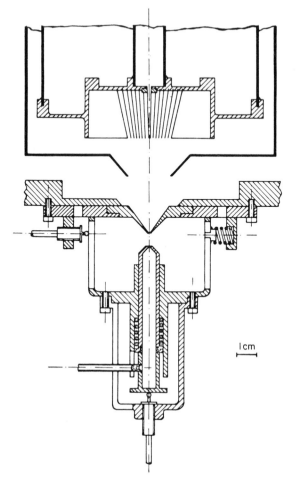

Fig. 3.15 Scale plan of nozzle source shown in Fig. 14 (G. Scoles and F. Torello, 1967).

3.5   Beam sources – superthermal energy

A wide range of techniques has been used to produce beams with energies above those obtainable thermally. The lower end of this energy range 1–20 eV has proved the most difficult one in which to work. This is particularly disappointing since this region is the most interesting of all to chemists embracing as it does the dissociation energies of all chemical bonds and the activation energies for most chemical reactions. In this region nozzle sources have been pressed into service either by running them at elevated

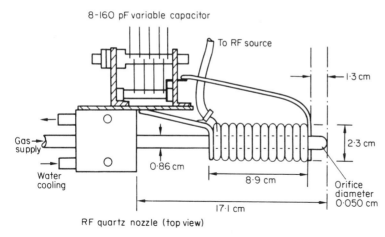

8-160 pF variable capacitor

To RF source

1·3 cm

2·3 cm

Gas supply

Water cooling

0·86 cm

8·9 cm

Orifice diameter 0·050 cm

17·1 cm

RF quartz nozzle (top view)

Fig. 3.16 Nozzle source with R.F. discharge to produce O atoms in mixed O_2/He 95% gas (D. R. Miller and D. F. Patch, 1969).

temperatures or by using the 'seeded beam' technique mentioned in the previous section. Recently a sputtering technique has also been used in which a solid target of the beam material is bombarded by high energy ions and the sputtered material collimated and velocity selected to form a beam.

In the energy range above 20 eV the charge exchange source is paramount. Here the beam material is first ionized and focused into a well defined and reasonably monoenergetic ion beam. This ion beam is then neutralized, usually by running it through a thin gas target of the beam material itself so that resonant charge exchange occurs. This technique is extremely convenient but limited in intensity at low beam energies by space charge effects.

(i) Nozzle sources for energies above 1 eV

The seeded beam method of aerodynamic acceleration can be applied to any heavy species. In this method a small percentage, e.g. 1–5 percent of the heavy beam molecule is mixed with a light inert carrier gas, usually helium, and expanded through a nozzle. The bulk flow rate is determined by the helium mass, the beam molecules riding along at this velocity. The final beam produced by skimming and collimation in the usual way thus consists of low energy helium atoms plus the high energy beam species. The technique is especially useful since it can be applied to fragile molecules that would not withstand acceleration by more violent means such as high temperatures. The energy, E, available with this method assuming that the heavy particles are accelerated to the same velocity as the light carrier gas, is:

$$E = \frac{M_{beam}}{M_{carrier}} \int_0^{T_{nozzle}} C_p dT \qquad (3.33)$$

where M_{beam} and $M_{carrier}$ are the molecular weights of the beam and carrier molecules.

In practice some degree of 'slip' occurs between the velocities of the two species. For small mole fractions the slip is quite small. This technique has been applied to a wide range of species, Fig. 3.17. Intensities are typically 10^{16} molecules sr^{-1} s^{-1}. For experiments in which the presence of the carrier gas in the beam is no disadvantage this technique is likely to be most valuable.

Another approach to producing fast beams from nozzle sources has used a plasma jet technique (R. W. Kessler and B. Koglin, 1966). Here the nozzle is arranged so that an arc can be burnt in the nozzle itself, thus raising the effective stagnation temperature to several thousand degrees. A device of this type, Fig. 3.18 has produced Ar beams of 3 eV energy and an intensity of the order 10^{19} atoms sr^{-1} s^{-1}. The further combination of this type of very high temperature source with the seeded beam method could lead to even higher energies, e.g. 20 eV for Ar in Ar/He mixtures.

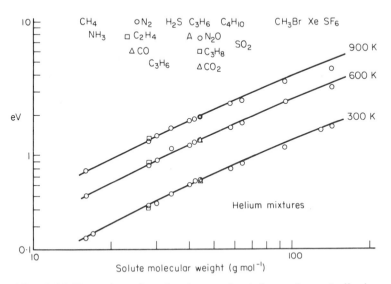

Fig. 3.17 Examples of molecules accelerated aerodynamically in Helium mixtures. (Reproduced from N. Abuaf, 1966). Molecular species are shown above their respective data points.

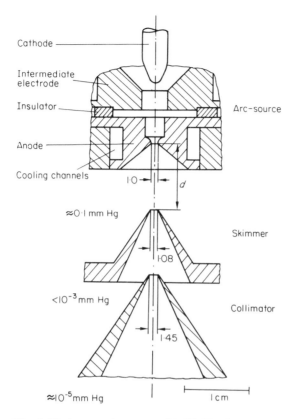

Cathode

Intermediate
electrode

Insulator

Anode

Cooling channels

Arc-source

≈ 0.1 mm Hg

Skimmer

$< 10^{-3}$ mm Hg

Collimator

$\approx 10^{-5}$ mm Hg

1 cm

Fig. 3.18 Arc nozzle source (R. W. Kessler and B. Koglin, 1966).

Heating the gas in the nozzle chamber by a shock source can yield even higher intensities (G. T. Skinner, 1966). A system for beam production using this technique is shown in Fig. 3.19. Very high intensities of the order 10^{21} molecules sr^{-1} s^{-1} at 2 eV can be obtained. Unfortunately the source is of necessity intermittent providing a beam pulse of only a few miliseconds duration and of poor duty factor. Correspondingly the pumping requirements are modest since the experiment is complete before the base gas pressure has risen. A disadvantage is the rather ill characterized nature of the particles in the beam, e.g. metastables may be present.

(ii) Sputtering sources

The sputtering of a solid target by energetic ion beams has been developed by the Amsterdam group to yield a very useful beam (J. Politiek et al., 1968). The device is shown in Fig. 3.20. The distribution of velocities in the ejected

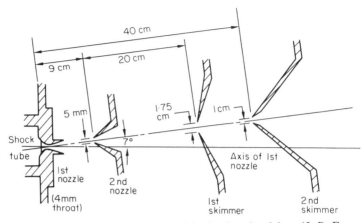

Fig. 3.19 Nozzle beam source with shock tube driver (J. B. Fenn, 1968).

atoms is relatively broad ranging from 0.2–45 eV for K, so that a velocity selector is essential. The intensity distribution for a K beam (though the device is not limited to alkalies) is shown in Fig. 3.21. Intensities appear to be $\sim 10^{13}$ atoms sr^{-1} s^{-1}, rather low.

(iii) Charge exchange beam sources

Sources of this type depend upon the fact that the cross-section for the resonant charge transfer process, i.e.

$$\text{fast} \rightarrow \qquad\qquad \text{fast} \rightarrow$$
$$X^+ + \quad X \rightarrow X \quad + \ X^+$$

is very much larger than the momentum transfer cross-section. If a well focused ion beam with a narrow energy distribution is passed through a thin gas target of the parent species charge transfer occurs with high probability. Furthermore the neutral species so provided retain most of their original directivity and energy distribution. The unexchanged ions can finally be swept out of the beam by a deflection field to leave the fast neutral beam. The technique is illustrated schematically in Fig. 3.22.

This ion technique is extremely convenient since while still ionized the beam may be mass analysed, deflected, modulated, etc., in a straightforward manner. The major drawback is that only relatively low intensities can be obtained, particularly at the lower beam energies, i.e. $\lesssim$20 eV.

This difficulty is a fundamental one due to the mutual repulsion or space

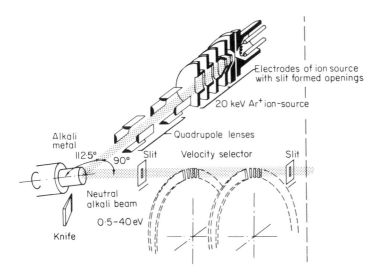

Fig. 3.20 Sputtering source for neutral beams (J. Politiek et al, 1968).

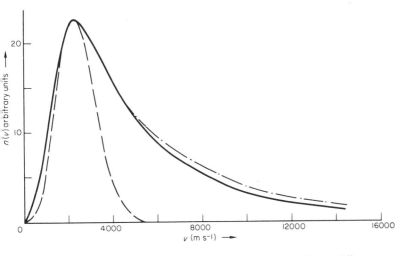

Fig. 3.21 Velocity distribution from a sputtering source. Dotted line − − − is flux calculated for an effusion source at same temperature. The other two lines represent measurements with a single and multi bounce surface ionizing detector. (J. Politiek et al., 1968).

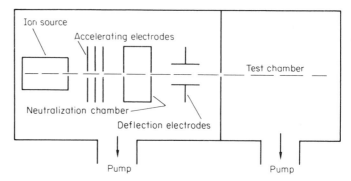

Fig. 3.22 Schematic arrangement of a charge neutralization beam source.

charge effects which limit the density that can be obtained in an ion beam. Very careful work indeed is needed to produce ion beams with energies below 5–10 eV.

The maximum ion current that can be focussed into a beam of divergence γ with energy V eV is:

$$I_{max} = 4.67 \, \pi\epsilon_0 \left(\frac{e}{2M}\right)^{1/2} \times V^{3/2} \tan^2 \gamma \qquad (3.34)$$

where e is the electronic charge and M the mass of the ion.

Beam fluxes after neutralization are necessarily less than this. In practice neutral fluxes of the order 10^{12} atoms sr^{-1} s^{-1} at 5 eV rising to 10^{16} at 100 eV have been obtained. At the lower energies this is many orders of magnitude less than that obtainable by seeded nozzle beam methods.

The actual production of these ions may be via electron bombardment as in the Nier source or by plasma discharges as in the duoplasmatron source. Alternatively some use has been made of surface ionization techniques since these may yield more monochromatic ion beams. The detailed design of these sources and their attendant lens and mass focussing systems has been discussed widely by other authors and is a major field in itself. We confine ourselves here to referring readers to these other texts (J. B. Hasted, 1964; J. R. Pierce, 1954).

A particularly simple and attractive surface ionising device described by R. K. B. Helbing and E. W. Rothe, 1968, is shown in Fig.3.23. The ionization, acceleration and neutralization all take place in a single chamber filled with alkali metal vapour, resulting in a particularly simple design. The ions are formed by ionization on a tungsten wire and are then accelerated by a potential towards a mesh screen. Some of the accelerated ions are then

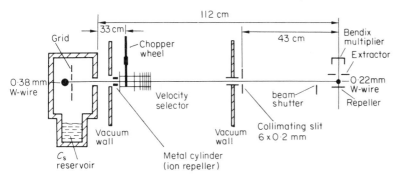

Fig. 3.23 Fast neutral alkali source. Exit slit on source box is 1.6 x 6 mm, a baffle (not shown) is installed above the Cs reservoir to prevent splashing on the electrodes (R. K. B. Helbing and E. W. Rothe, 1968).

neutralized by collision with the neutral alkali vapour and exit via the slits. The velocity distribution produced by this source was narrower than the resolution of the selector (6 percent) used to investigate it. This source seems particularly attractive at the lowest beam energies ~6 eV.

A more conventional exchange source is shown in Fig. 3.24 (B. S. Duchart, 1971). Here ionization of alkali metals is brought about by surface ionization on a porous tungsten disc, the alkali diffusing through from a chamber to the rear. The disc is heated to 1500°C by a radiation heater so that ionization is more than 90 percent complete for potassium. The resulting ions are extracted at a few hundred volts, accelerated in a second lens stage, steered by a series of X, Y deflection plates (which may also be used to pulse the

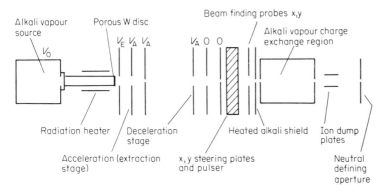

Fig. 3.24 Charge neutralization neutral beam source using surface ionization (B. S. Duchart, 1971)

beam for time of flight measurements) and finally enters the charge exchang chamber. This chamber is filled with alkali metal vapour by caref temperature regulation of a reservoir contained in the same chamber.

This system produced a neutral flux of $\sim 10^{14}$ atoms sr^{-1} s^{-1} at 100 eV The energy spead in the neutral beam as measured by time of flight method was ~ 0.1 eV.

3.6   Sources for Excited Species

The production of beams of excited species is an important requirement sinc the scattering technique is uniquely suitable for studying the collisio properties of such short lived species. The production of translationally ho atoms has already been discussed, here we consider species with interna excitation. The lifetimes of these species in the absence of collisions may b $> 10^{-3}$ s for some metastable atoms down to 10^{-8} s for species with a optically allowed electronic transition to the ground state. Depending upo the species required the state may either be generated specifically or selecte from a much larger mixed population (e.g. from a thermal equilibriur distribution). The selection devices are described in Chapter 4.

In general these techniques are simply a combination of the methods use to produce excitation in bulk experiments with the beam productio methods already described. The most important are thermal, electron impact optical pumping and chemical reaction.

(i) Thermal dissociation sources

This is perhaps the simplest technique and is suitable for exciting states wit an energy comparable to kT for the oven or arc source used. It is thus suitabl for producing most dissociated atomic species (except N) and the groun state fine structure levels of B, Al, Ga, In, Tl, Cl, Br, etc. The major proble with these sources are corrosion and in the dimensional instabilities which ca occur at high operating temperatures.

A typical design for a dissociated atom source is shown in Fig. 3.25 (M. A D. Fluendy et al., 1967). It consists of a hollow cylinder of tungsten (o graphite if for use with halogens) fed with gas at one end and heate electrically by a current ~ 600A. A slit of width 25μ is machined in its sid through which the atoms emerge. Two water cooled copper or nickel clamp provide electrical connections and secure the cylinder, which it clampe tightly at one end. At the other end expansion can occur between spring loade jaws. With this source, intensities for H atoms of $\sim 10^{18}$ atoms sr^{-1} s^{-1} wer obtained. A similar device with a graphite tube has been used for Br and

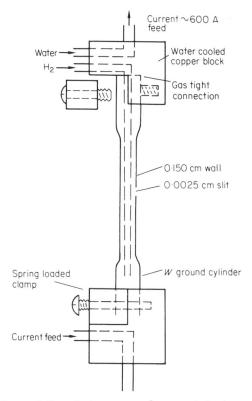

Fig. 3.25 Thermal dissociation source for atomic hydrogen. The tungsten tube is heated by a 600A a.c. supply coupled via the water cooling pipes. The tungsten tube is free to expand longitudinally between the lower spring loaded copper jaws. The whole copper block and tube assumbly is mounted rigidly on a carriage adjustable from outside the vacuum (M. A. D. Fluendy et al., 1967).

atoms (Y. T. Lee et al., 1969). Iodine can also be dissociated in a monel oven if gold slits are used (M. A. D. Fluendy et al., 1970).

Arc nozzle sources have also been used to produce atom beams of high intensity. If problems of stability and corrosion can be overcome this is likely to be an important technique.

(ii) Electron bombardment sources

This technique is a useful one for states with a lifetime of 10^{-3} s or longer, i.e. metastable states. The first and most famous example is its use in the Lamb-Retherford experiment. Here an atomic H beam produced by thermal

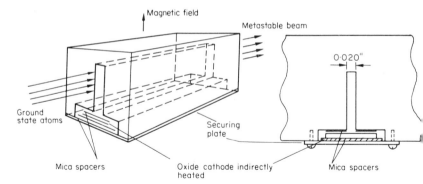

Fig. 3.26 Electron bombardment metastable source. A standard oxide cathode is used spaced ~0.008 cm from the stainless (nonmagnetic) steel anode by a mica sheet.

dissociation in a tungsten oven was crossed by an electron beam of controlled energy to excite the metastable state $H(2^2 S)$.

A more recent source designed to produce metastables for scattering work is shown in Fig. 3.26. A standard oxide cathode provides a source of electrons which are accelerated into the slit in the anode through which a beam of Hg atoms in the ground state is passing. The electrons are collimated by a magnetic field. A typical excitation curve is shown in Fig. 3.27, peaks due to the $6^3 P_{0,2}$ and $^3 D$ states can be seen.

The use of an electron source with a reasonably narrow energy spread thus permits the selective generation of these species. Intensities of the order 10^{10} atoms sr^{-1} s^{-1} were obtained (E. C. Darwall, 1972).

The extension of the electron excitation method to molecular species such as metastable CO and N_2 also appears possible (R. S. Freund and W. Klemperer, 1967; R. Clampitt and R. S. Newton, 1969). Another possibility is the use of certain negative ion resonances which decay to specific vibrational states.

(iii) Discharge sources

R.F. and microwave discharges have been used for the production of dissociated atoms either in an inert gas carrier (Figure 3.16) or as a pure beam. The mechanism is presumably again electron bombardment dissociation. A microwave source for atomic chlorine is shown in Fig. 3.28 (L. Davis et al. 1949). The source was mounted inside a microwave resonant cavity and fed with 50 watts of power; between 30 and 60% dissociation was achieved. An

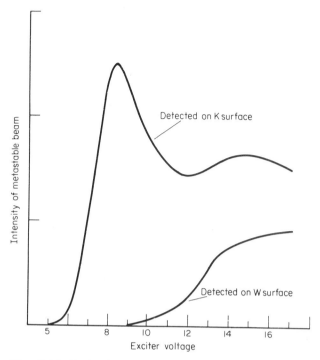

Fig. 3.27 Excitation curves observed for Hg using an electron bombardment source for metastable production (E. C. Darwall, 1972).

alternative source (D. S. Horne, 1969) is shown in Fig. 3.29 and uses an r.f. generator capacitively coupled to a quartz tube. Coating the inside of the tube according to the recipe of Ogryzlo (E. A. Ogryzlo, 1961) raised the Cl_2 dissociation from 36% at 0.8 torr to >90% at 0.5 torr. A disadvantage with these non equilibrium non specific excitation sources is the possible presence of metastable states in the beam.

(iv) Optical pumping

A technique similar to that described for electrons but using a photon flux as the exciting agent may be applied. The usefulness of this method depends very much upon the conjunction of a suitable absorption line and an intense light source. Even at saturation no more than 50% of the beam will be in the excited state. Depending upon the lifetime of the excited state the excitation may be applied either at the beam source or at the actual collision zone. If

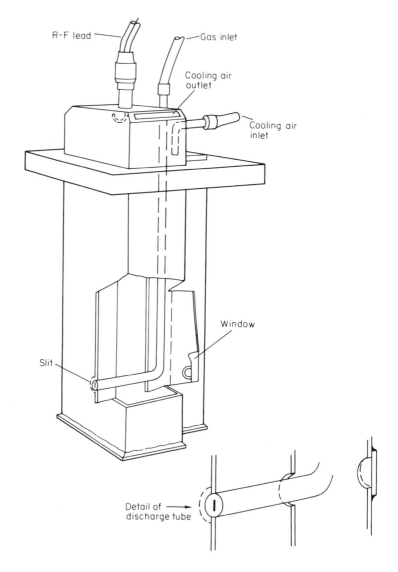

Fig. 3.28 Microwave discharge source for Cl atoms (L. Davis et al., 1949)

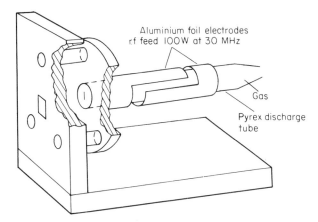

Fig. 3.29 r.f. discharge source for atomic chlorine (D.
S. Horne, 1969).

applied at the collision zone states with lifetimes as short as 10^{-8} s will
undergo collisions.

Microwave pumping of a vibration rotation line has also been used in
conjunction with selecting fields to produce beams in a specified vibration-
rotation state (T. G. Waech and R. B. Bernstein, 1968) and Chapter 4.

CHAPTER FOUR

Energy and State Selection

In a thermal beam source a wide range of rotational and translational states are populated. This population, with some modification if there is hydrodynamic flow at the orifice, will persist in the emerging beam. The ideal beam experiment requires complete selection of the quantum states of both collision partners, but we will find that this ideal is only partially achieved. Translational energy selection, through velocity selection, is always possible. Spin, rotational and even vibrational states can be selected but these cases are not yet numerous, comprising perhaps a dozen atoms and molecules.

State selection and focusing are often achieved simultaneously. If a molecule passing through the selecting device executes simple harmonic motion in its lateral movement then the possibility exists for focusing and the focal length will, in general, depend on the quantum state of the molecule. In designing a scattering experiment incorporating some state selection, the loss in intensity that results from using only a small fraction of the parent beams might seem to be crippling. In general, if more than one property is being selected in a beam (e.g. velocity + orientation) or if both beams are being selected (e.g. for velocity) then one of the selectors must have a focusing capability to recoup intensity.

The performance of these devices is ultimately limited by the constraint provided by the Liouville equation in that the density in phase space of the parent beam cannot be increased. Selectors may therefore isolate small volumes from this population, may accelerate them to other regions of phase space or distort them in other ways. They can never increase the density of molecules within a specified range of state parameters so that sources with a low characteristic temperature are desirable.

In some cases it is possible to alter the population of quantum states by optical pumping. The limit to the population change comes when the temperature (electronic, rotational etc., as appropriate) of the sample reaches that of the source of radiation. The effect of such population changes in a beam on scattering from the beam depends upon the lifetime of the excited state and is an interesting but, as yet, little used tool and will not be discussed further here (R. E. Drullinger and R. N. Zare, 1969).

4.1   Velocity selection

Almost every scattering phenomenon is velocity or energy dependent. In Chapter 2 it was found that the classical differential and total cross-sections for scattering under the influence of any potential, other than the hard sphere, were velocity dependent. In Chapter 6 it will be shown that the new effects that arise when quantum mechanics is applied to scattering, which may be generally classed as interference effects, are also velocity dependent. Furthermore, it is commonly found in chemical kinetics that reaction rates are an exponential function of temperature and this implies that the reaction cross section is energy dependent. Finally, it has been seen that the apparatus resolution depends upon the beam velocities, as does the Jacobian for transforming between laboratory and centre of mass co-ordinates.

Much information will thus be lost, together with one of the unique capabilities of beam experiments, unless scattering patterns are measured as a function of the relative velocity of the beam particles. Velocity filters select molecules whose velocity falls within a segment of the parent velocity distribution and we define the velocity resolution as the width Δv of this truncated distribution at half intensity divided by the median velocity transmitted. An important question in the design of the beam experiment is the amount of velocity resolution that is required and the amount that is practicable, having regard to the available beam intensity.

The usual requirement in the total cross-section experiment is that sufficient velocity resolution be available to identify the quantum 'glory' oscillations in the cross-section. The origin of these interference effects is discussed in detail in Chapters 6 and 7; suffice it at this point that these undulations are located at velocities v_n such that:

$$v_n \sim \epsilon\sigma/\hbar N \tag{4.1}$$

where ϵ, σ are the potential parameters and $N = 1, 2, 3$ indicates the first, second, third etc., oscillations in the cross section (counting from high velocity downwards). Thus to resolve these oscillations up to M, we need a resolution:

$$\frac{\Delta v}{v} \ll \frac{v_M - v_{M-1}}{v_M} \sim \frac{1}{M-1} \tag{4.2}$$

and generally $M \lesssim 5$.

As already seen in Chapter 2 the gross features of $\sigma(\theta)$ versus θ plots at different energies are superimposed to a good approximation by plotting $\sigma(\theta)$ against $E\theta$. The resulting spread in $\sigma(\theta)$ due to simultaneous uncertainties in v and θ is then:

$$\frac{\Delta \sigma(\theta)}{\sigma(\theta)} \propto 2\frac{\Delta v}{v} + \frac{\Delta \theta}{\theta} . \tag{4.3}$$

Thus if the angular resolution $\Delta\theta/\theta$ required to resolve a given feature in the differential cross-section is known the velocity resolution $\Delta v/v$, required will be approximately half this. The question of angular resolution has already been discussed in Chapter 3 and will be considered further in Chapter 7.

The price paid in intensity for this level of resolution depends upon the velocity distribution in the parent beam. For a v^3 Maxwellian distribution, the fraction of molecules with velocities within $\pm \Delta v/2$ of the most probable velocity v^* is

$$f_{\Delta v} \approx 1.00 \Delta v/v^* \tag{4.4}$$

Velocity resolution 1–10 per cent is commonly aimed at.

In an orthogonal crossed beam experiment, the relative velocity v_r is given by

$$v_r = \sqrt{v_A^2 + v_B^2} \tag{4.5}$$

and if $v_A \gg v_B$, $\Delta v_r/v_r \approx \Delta v_A/v_A$ and the faster beam only is velocity selected. If the unselected beam has a v^3 Maxwellian distribution, the full width at half intensity $\Delta v_B/v_B^*$ is ≈ 0.95. Substituting this into the expression for the overall spread in the relative velocity:

$$\Delta v_r/v_r \approx \Delta v_A/v_A \left(\frac{v_A}{v_r}\right)^2 + \Delta v_B/v_B \left(\frac{v_B}{v_r}\right)^2 \tag{4.6}$$

sets a lower limit on $\Delta v_r/v_r$ of $\approx (v_B/v_r)^2$, though it must not be forgotten that the spread in cross beam velocity also introduces a spread in the direction as well as the magnitude of v_r.

Velocity selection of neutral particles is usually performed mechanically by passing the beam through a series of phased choppers so that only those molecules moving in a narrow velocity band arrive at each chopper as it opens and so are transmitted (Fig. 4.1). The actual form of the device varies but is typically a series of thin slotted discs locked together and rotating about an axis parallel to the beam direction. The principle is an old one (J. A. Eldridge 1927), has been improved in the last two decades (R. C. Miller, and P. Kusch, 1955; H. U. Hostettler and R. B. Bernstein, 1960; J. Wykes, 1969) and the size has progressively decreased, the slots now being cut by photo-etching. Occasionally space can be saved by adopting a slightly different geometry (L. T. Cowley et al., 1970; A. E. Grosser et al., 1963; S. O. Colgate and T. C. Imeson, 1955) in which the beam passes across the surface of toothed concentric cups, Fig. 4.2.

For discs of negligible thickness, design is simple with the aid of a diagram of the type shown in Fig. 4.3. The motion of a molecule is displayed relative to the discs as stationary so that a tangential component v_c is added to the forward molecular velocity v_m, where v_c is the peripheral speed of rotation of the discs. The trajectory of the molecule then makes an angle α with the axis of the rotor, where

$$\tan \alpha = v_c/v_m$$

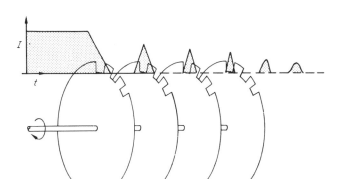

Fig. 4.1 A multi-disc velocity selector. Some of the particles in each pulse arrive at the next disc in time to pass through a slot.

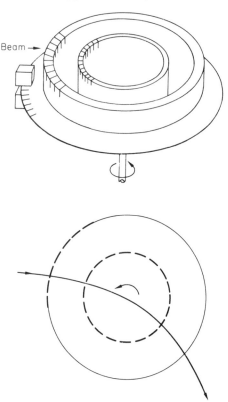

Fig. 4.2 Alternative design of velocity selector using only the motor
bearings.

Molecules will be transmitted when:

$$\tan \alpha = \Delta/L$$

where Δ is the offset of the exit slit from the entrance slit (see Fig. 4.3) and L
is the distance between first and last discs. The median velocity transmitted is

$$v_m = 2\pi R\omega L/\Delta = v_c L/\Delta \tag{4.7}$$

where $2\pi R\omega$ is the peripheral speed of the selector disc, v_c. Typical speeds of
rotation are $10,000 - 20,000$ r.p.m., leading to values for $v_c \sim 5 - 10 \times 10^3$ cm
s^{-1} for discs $\sim$5 cm radius — approaching molecular velocities and strength of
materials limitations.

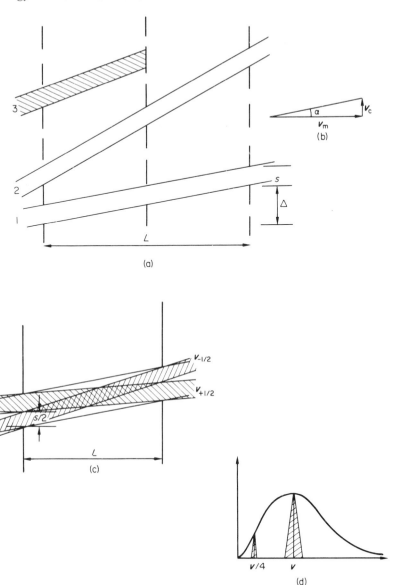

Fig. 4.3 The design of a slotted disc selector. (a) Molecules with the design velocity (1) are transmitted, but so are those (2) with ¼ of this speed. Those moving with ½ the design speed are stopped on the face of the second disc. The offset of each disc is determined from the vector diagram (see Equation 4.7), (b). The half width of the velocity bands transmitted is calculated from (c) in which only half those molecules with speeds $v_{\pm \frac{1}{2}}$ (shaded) are transmitted. (d) is the resulting velocity distribution (shaded), in which the outer envelope is the parent distribution.

The resolution of a mechanical selector of the parallel disc type is determined solely by the slit width S and the separation L. If the velocity distribution in the incident beam is effectively constant over a range of velocities transmitted (as would be the case for a high resolution selector working at the most probable speed in a Maxwellian distribution) the velocity distribution of the transmitted particles is triangular. The velocities at half intensity of this distribution, $v_{\pm \frac{1}{2}}$, are found from the condition that molecules travelling with these speeds are only transmitted if they enter the first slit before it is half open for $v_{-\frac{1}{2}}$ or when it is between half and fully closed for $v_{\frac{1}{2}}$. From Fig. 4.3(c),

$$\tan \alpha_{\pm \frac{1}{2}} = (\Delta \pm S/2)/L$$

so the velocity resolution for a particular band (full width at half height) when $v_c \ll v_m$ is:

$$\mathfrak{R}_{\frac{1}{2}} = \frac{\Delta v}{v_m} \simeq S/\Delta \qquad (4.8)$$

Thus once the working velocity and resolution required have been decided substitution into Equations 4.7 and 4.8 will yield simple relations for the selection of rotation speed, selector length and slit width.

It is usually desirable to keep the selector length as short as possible to minimise $1/L^2$ losses in intensity. The design then reduces to determining the maximum tip speed that can be produced and the smallest slit width practicable. A typical set of dimensions is:

Speed of rotation ω	10 000 rpm
Radius of disc R	5 cm
peak transmitted speed v_m	5×10^4 cm/s.
Slit width S	1 mm
Length L	10 cm
Overall offset $\Sigma \Delta_i$	1 cm
Resolution $\mathfrak{R}_{\frac{1}{2}}$	$\pm 5\%$

Mechanical velocity selectors become rapidly less useful at molecular speeds above 10^5 cm s^{-1}. From Equation 4.7 it is seen that as v_m increases, either (i) ω must increase in proportion or (ii) L must increase in proportion or (iii) Δ must decrease in proportion to v_m. If solution (i) is adopted, an upper limit is set by the mechanical strength of the discs; (ii) results in increasing loss of intensity ($\alpha\ 1/L^2$); (iii) has the disadvantage that in order to maintain the same resolution with increasing v_m, the slit width S must be decreased in proportion to Δ (from Equation 4.8). If slits are to be made narrower than $\sim 0.002''$ machining and especially alignment problems arise. With $S = 0.002''$, and $\omega = 10\,000$ rpm $L = 10$ cm, the maximum speed transmitted with a resolution of 5 per cent is 10^5 cm s^{-1} and this perhaps can be doubled by changing some of the other design parameters. At higher velocities time of flight or methods depending upon magnetic deflection of the beam are more useful.

The overall transmission of the slotted disc selector can be defined for a *parallel incident beam* as

$$T = \left(\frac{nS}{2\pi R}\right) \mathcal{R}_{\frac{1}{2}} \tag{4.9}$$

so for $\mathcal{R}_{\frac{1}{2}} = 10$ per cent, $T \sim 5$ per cent when the tooth: slit width ratio is 1:1.

A two disc selector has the disadvantage of transmitting sidebands, that is, molecules whose speeds are certain rational fractions of the design speed v_m. How this arises can be seen from Fig. 4.3. In the design shown the exit channel for the design speed is indexed as $n + 1$, where the entrance slit is the nth. Inspection of the figure shows that, with only two discs, slower molecules can exit through slots $n + 2$, $n + 3$, etc., if they have speeds $v_m/2$, $v_m/3$ etc., and molecules having speeds $> 2v_m$ (for equal tooth and slit widths) are transmitted through slit n. The fast molecules and those having $v = v_m/2$ are eliminated by inserting a third disc as shown; a fourth disc eliminates yet more sidebands and with five discs the elimination is virtually complete.

If the original beam is generated by flow through relatively long channels, there is a deficiency of slow molecules in the beam, and complete elimination of the slowest sidebands is not a pressing problem. A selector with fewer, thicker discs might be appropriate here, unless designed for very high speeds when a low moment of inertia is essential.

In an actual experiment, the incident beam is not parallel and the discs may have a thickness comparable to the slit width. Under these conditions, the transmission is best calculated by a computer sampling of trajectories through the device.

These selectors are normally driven by synchronous hysteresis motors, ball bearings of the dry self-lubricating type being used throughout the selector and motor. Careful attention to the dynamic balance of the rotor as well as accurate alignment of the discs is required. It is usually essential to provide water cooling for the bearings and drive motor. Further constructional details may be found in (J. L. Kinsey, 1966). In a crossed beam experiment, the full analysis requires that the velocity of the product as well as that of the incident particles be measured. Unless many inelastic channels are open, the velocity analyser need not have good sideband suppression and merely serves to pinpoint a particular process. In an experiment designed (K. T. Gillen et al., 1969) to find the correlation between the angle of inelastic scattering and the degree of internal excitation of the KI from the reaction $K + I_2$, a four disc selector was chosen for the incident K beam ($\mathcal{R}_{1/2} = 14.4$ per cent), the I_2 beam was unselected and a six disc selector was placed in front of the detector ($\mathcal{R}_{1/2} = 4.7$ per cent). A relatively coarse primary beam selector was appropriate because under the experimental conditions the velocity of the cross beam molecules was roughly one quarter that of the potassium.

4.2　Time of flight methods (T.O.F.)

There are at least two situations in which mechanical velocity selection is unsuitable. The first is when one of the beams is of unavoidably low intensity, e.g. a beam of metastable atoms. To insert a mechanical velocity selector would reduce the density of molecules at the scattering centre at least tenfold, in addition to the loss arising from the transmission factor, simply because of the increased source/scattering centre distance. This might well make the time taken to accumulate a statistically significant signal, impracticably long. Time of flight methods help here by simply not taking up any space – a single disc or deflecting plate is sufficient to chop a beam. Secondly, at energies above a few eV the length/speed of a mechanical velocity selector becomes inconveniently high, but T.O.F. techniques have an almost unlimited energy range.

The essence of the T.O.F. method is to chop one of the incident beams into a sequence of short pulses and to gate the detector in synchronism but with a measured phase and hence time lag. By scanning a range of time delays, a time of arrival spectrum (T.O.A.) of the scattered particles is built up. In its crudest form, the technique becomes identical with phase sensitive detection (see Chapter 5) in which relatively low chopping frequencies are used and the phase is not varied.

One of the earliest applications of the technique in beam work was that of S. N. Foner, 1966, who produced a chopped free radical beam of $\sim 50\mu$ sec. pulse width and gated a mass spectrometer detector over 20μ sec. periods. By this means, molecules reaching the detector directly were distinguished from those bouncing from the walls.

T.O.F. methods have been applied to pulsed supersonic beams, (energy $\sim 1\,\text{eV}$), in particular to the determination of the velocity distribution of molecules scattered from solid surfaces, e.g. (P. B. Scott, 1965), and to the determination of the velocity distribution in nozzle beams themselves (W. E. Amend, 1968). This technique is only possible if a detector of sufficiently fast response time is available (see Chapter 5) and will be most valuable in systems where rapid gating of the beam is also possible. Thus, beams of metastable species excited by electron bombardment may be gated for periods $\sim 10^{-8}$ s by pulsing the electron beam and an Auger detector for these species has a comparable response time. The technique is particularly fruitful in ion-molecule scattering where the highest energy resolution can be achieved (J. Schottler and J. P. Toennies, 1968).

There are not many general formulae that can be used in planning time of flight experiments. The key to the design is the calculation of the spreading of the initial pulse by the time it reaches the detector. This, in turn, determines the pulse repetition rate if undue overlapping of the pulses is to be avoided. The potentialities of the method can be illustrated by the process

$$K + I_2 \longrightarrow KI^\dagger + I, \quad \Delta E \sim 1.9\,\text{eV}$$

investigated between 5 eV and 100 eV. The purpose of the experiment is to map the angular distribution of the product KI and to measure its velocity in order to deduce its internal energy. We would like to measure the translational energy to ± 10 per cent and hence the velocity must be known to ± 5 per cent. The KI, whatever its internal state, is considerably delayed with respect to the elastically scattered K because of conservation of momentum requirements and so is easily distinguished by crude T.O.F. analysis.

The optimum set of values has to be found for the following parameters:

(1) The initial pulse width at source τ_s.
(2) The path length from source to scattering centre, L_s and from scattering centre to detector, L_d.
(3) The gate time for the detector, τ_d.
(4) The repetition rate, τ_R, which determines the duty cycle.

In deciding τ_s, the key factors are the extent of spreading of the pulse at the scattering centre and of the product pulse at the detector, due in both cases to the velocity distribution of the molecules leaving the source which would typically have a temperature of $1100°C - 1200°C$. The order of magnitude of this spreading can be found by following the motion of a pulse that begins as a delta function in time. If the velocity distribution within this pulse is initially v_i^2 Maxwellian (appropriate for ions emitted from a surface), electrostatic acceleration imparts a new velocity v_f to each molecule which is related to the initial velocity by:

$$\tfrac{1}{2}mv_f^2 = \tfrac{1}{2}mv_i^2 + eV_0 \qquad (4.10)$$

where V_0 is the accelerating voltage. Substituting this into the original velocity distribution and re-arranging to give the number of molecules between v_f and $v_f + dv_f$, then introducing the time of arrival through $v_f = L/t$, we find the distribution of arrival times is given by:

$$n(t) \approx n^* \left(\frac{u}{u^*}\right)^{1/2} e^{1/2} \, e^{-u/2u^*} \qquad (4.11)$$

where $\begin{cases} u = \dfrac{L}{t} - v_0, \quad v_0^2 = 2eV_0/m \\[3mm] u^* = \dfrac{L}{t^*} - v_0 \approx kT/2mv_0 \end{cases}$

and n^* is the peak arrival rate, $n(t^*)$, at t^*. The full width at half maximum (FWHM), i.e. $n(t_{1/2}) = n^*/2$, is found to be

$$\Delta\tau_\delta \approx 1.8 \frac{L}{v_0^3} \frac{kT}{m} \qquad (4\text{-}12)$$

If the original pulse has a FWHM equal to $\Delta\tau_s$, this has increased on arrival at the detector to a value given by

$$\Delta\tau \approx \Delta\tau_s + \Delta\tau_\delta \qquad (4.13)$$

for a δ-function pulse of potassium accelerated to 100 eV ($v_0 \approx 2 \times 10^6$ cm s^{-1}, $v_i^* \approx 8 \times 10^4$ cm s^{-1}) $\Delta\tau$ is approximately 5×10^{-8} s at 60 cm from the source; under these conditions initial pulse widths, τ_s, less than 10^{-7} s are unnecessary. The upper limit to τ_s, and hence the duty cycle, is determined by the velocity resolution required as we will see below.

More generally, if the initial pulse is not a Δ-function, the distribution in time of the intensity at time t is given by

$$I(L; t) = \int G(t') I_\delta (L; t - t') \, dt, \qquad (4.14)$$

where $G(t)$ is the initial distribution in time. The spread in arrival of the product KI pulse can be calculated from Equations 4.12 or 4.14 (with $L = L_d$) if the new mean pulse velocity, v'. is known from the exothermicity. This contribution to the spreading can be added to the value of $\Delta\tau$ in Equation 4.13 if the latter is small.

Finally, the effect of the gate width of the detector, τ_d, on the apparent shape of the pulse must be computed. With an electron bombardment detector or gated counter, the detector function is essentially rectangular with a width typically $\sim 1\mu$ s in the present example. More generally, the measured pulse shape is given by

$$I_{obs}(L; t) = \int_{t'-\tau_d/2}^{t'+\tau_d/2} I(L; t - t') S(t') \, dt', \tag{4.15}$$

where $S(t)$ is the detector function, the open time being between the limits of integration.

Returning to our model calculations, the parent potassium pulse has now reached the cross beam where it generated a pulse of KI which then travels to the detector, spreading as it does so. We can form a picture of both the elastically and reactively scattered particles by integrating Equations 4.11 and 4.15 numerically. The results at 1 eV are displayed in Fig. 4.4, calculated with the assumption of an initial δ-function pulse and that all the exothermicity goes into relative motion. Using momentum and energy conservation conditions, the reaction exothermicity, ΔE, can be calculated from the time of arrival of the K and KI pulses, τ_K and τ_{KI}. For small angle scattering of the product the result is:

$$\Delta E = \frac{(L_s + L_d)^2}{2\tau_K^2} \left[\frac{m_{KI}M}{m_I} \left(\frac{L_d/L_s}{(1 + L_d/L_s)\tau_{KI}/\tau_K - 1} + \frac{m_K}{M} \right)^2 - \frac{m_K m_L}{M} \right] \tag{4.16}$$

where M is the total mass of the two molecules. The experimental uncertainty in ΔE can then be estimated from the uncertainty in the times of arrival of the pulses, $\Delta\tau_K$ and $\Delta\tau_{KI}$. The duty cycle can be decided from the criterion adopted for the resolvability of adjacent pulses. If a 50 per cent valley: peak ratio is demanded, then in the 1 eV example it is seen from Fig. 4.4 that the minimum delay time between K pulses is approximately 140 microseconds. The initial K pulse width (τ_s) can be made as long as 5 microseconds without sacrificing too much energy resolution so the duty cycle is 5 : 140, a rather poor figure. At 100 eV a duty cycle equivalent to an overall transmission of 30 per cent can be achieved. In contrast to mechanical

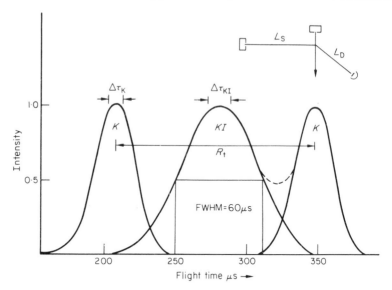

Fig. 4.4 TOA spectrum for K/I_2 scattering.

selectors transmitting a single velocity, the T.O.F. method, in conjunction with a multi-channel scaler at the detector, can record the whole velocity spectrum of the product at once and the technique therefore makes more effective use of the signal despite the lower transmission at lower energies.

Time of flight techniques may also be used in the measurement of total cross-sections (J. F. Wilson and G. D. Lempert, 1970). The T.O.A. spectrum of main beam pulses is measured with and without a target gas and the resulting distortion of the pulses through the velocity dependence of the beam attenuation can be interpreted in terms of the velocity dependence of the total cross-section. In the field of ion-molecule scattering, the vibrational energy transfer in the system

$$\text{Li}^+ (10 - 50 \text{ eV}) + \text{H}_2 (n = 0) \longrightarrow \text{Ii}^+ + \text{H}_2 (n = 0, 1, 2)$$

has been partially resolved (J. Schottler and J. P. Toennies, 1968) with a detector gate width (in the form of a multi-channel scaler) of 300 nanoseconds. This experiment is only made possible by starting with a nearly monoenergetic ion beam formed by magnetic velocity analysis. The interpretation of the results and an improved signal to noise factor comes from the knowledge that the energy loss must be in discrete vibrational quanta (see also below).

More efficient use still can be made of the available flux by using a cross correlation technique originally evolved for electrical wave filter analysis. In this, the delta function response, $I_\delta(L; t - t')$ in Equation 4.14 is obtained as the cross correlation ϕ_{GI} between a random modulation of the parent beam and the consequent detector response, i.e.

$$\phi_{GI}(\tau) = \int G(t - \tau) I(L; t) dt \qquad (4.17)$$

Multiplying Equation 4.14 by the parent pulse time distribution $G(t - \tau)$ and taking the time average (in theory over an infinite time interval) yields:

$$\int I(L, t) G(t - \tau) dt = \int G(t - \tau) \int G(t') I_\delta(L; t - t') dt' dt$$

but, making use of the random nature of $G(t)$,

$$\int G(t - \tau) G(t - t') dt = \delta(t' - \tau)$$

so

$$\phi_{GI}(\tau) = \int \delta(t' - \tau) I_\delta(L, t') dt' = I_\delta(L, \tau) \qquad (4.18)$$

and the measured correlation is identical with the delta function response of the apparatus. Inelastic collisions result in a further spreading of the arrival pulse in addition to that due to the spread of velocities present in the parent beam. The first step in analysis is then to cross correlate the signal with the initial random word pulse as in Equation 4.17 to obtain the scattered signal in response to a delta function in time at the source. A particular process resulting in an energy loss ΔE will give rise to a pulse at the detector whose shape $I_{\Delta E_n}(t)$ can be predicted by arguments similar to those leading to Equation 4.14 from a knowledge of the shape of the elastically scattered pulse. A fitting is then carried out in which $\phi_{GI}(t)$ is analysed in terms of a linear combination of the $I_{\Delta E_n}(t)$, the unknowns ΔE_n and C_n being found by a least squares procedure

$$\phi_{GI}(t) = \Sigma \, C_n I_{\Delta E_n}(t).$$

The chief advantage of the random word modulation lies in the greater spectral density that can be achieved in comparison with any approach to delta function modulation. Since the probability of the beam being on is equal to it being off, the spectral density or transmission is 50 per cent.

Furthermore, since the resolution depends only on the bandwidth of the noise modulation, this high transmission can be obtained without any loss of resolution inherent in the delta function approach.

The application of these techniques in an atomic scattering experiment is described by C. A. Visser et al., 1970. In this experiment the random modulation was pulse coded, the beam being either fully on or off for random periods thus avoiding problems of non-linearity that could arise with amplitude modulation.

The great advantage of all time of flight techniques lies in the ease with which the resolution and hence the transmission may be varied during the course of an experiment without recourse to moving parts inside the vacuum chamber.

4.3   Magnetic state selection

Unlike ions, neutral species are comparatively difficult to deflect by external fields. The 'handle' by which such a field interacts with the molecule is either its electric or magnetic moment and the deflection in an inhomogeneous field is then a function of the field gradient, the molecular moment and kinetic energy together with the distance traversed through the field. By choosing a field gradient of the right radial dependence and having axial symmetry, a bundle of paraxial molecular trajectories can be brought to a focus and the focal length is a function of the parameters just listed. The device can be regarded either as a velocity selector, a rotational state selector or a molecular orientation selector according to the requirements of the experiment. Rather than pursue a unified treatment, we begin by distinguishing the three important types of behaviour, according to whether the particle is an atom possessing a magnetic moment, a linear molecule with an electric dipole moment or a symmetric top.

We deal first with the focusing of atoms that have a permanent magnetic moment, μ. The energy of such an atom in a magnetic field B is

$$W_{m_J} = -\mu . B = m_J g \mu_B |B|, \qquad (4.20)$$

where m_J is the component of the total angular momentum in the direction of the field and μ_B the Bohr magneton. The force acting on the atom is

$$F_r = -m_J g \mu_B \, \partial B / \partial r. \qquad (4.21)$$

In order for the atom to execute transverse simple harmonic motion in the field, the magnitude of B must be quadratic in the displacement r and this is achieved with a hexapole field, Fig. 4.5. In the magnetic case, the field can be generated by permanent magnets or electromagnetically. In the latter case, if a current i is passed through a hexagonal array of conductors, each a distance R from the axis, the field is given by

$$B = \frac{3ir^2}{10\pi R^3} = B_0(r/R)^2 . \tag{4.22}$$

The direction of B picks out the direction of quantisation and the force acting on an atom distance r from the centre is $F = -2m_J g\mu_B B_0 r/R^2$ and this force is everywhere radial. The focal length is then readily found to be

$$f = \pi v R \sqrt{M/(2m_J g\mu_B B_0)} \tag{4.23}$$

where B_0 is the field strength at the pole tips in gauss and the atom is of mass M. A hexapole array of conducting loops gives rather too weak a field for ordinary applications (although B_0 is precisely calculable in this configuration), but an array of permanent magnets can easily produce 0.5 T at the pole tips, giving a focal length of roughly 12 cm for potassium at thermal speeds with a pole gap of 0.5 cm. The detailed design and use of a hexapole spin filter has most recently been described by H. M. Brash et al., 1969. Only

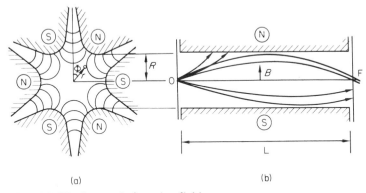

(a)   (b)

Fig. 4.5 The hexapole focusing field.
(a)   End on view showing arrangement of pole tips and lines of force.
(b)   Longitudinal view. The entrance slit is at O and the exit slit at F. Trajectories corresponding to two different velocities are shown, one of which is brought to a focus at the exit slit F. A third pair of trajectories is shown for atoms with moments parallel to the field, which leads to de-focusing.

atoms with $m_J > 0$ are focused, but a wide range of velocities come to a focus beyond the exit from the field. If the device is to be used as a velocity selector, entrance and exit slits must be positioned to reject all molecules except those whose focal plane lies at the exit slit.

The key quantity in hexapole lens design is a 'phase angle', ϕ

$$\phi = \frac{L}{R} \left(\frac{2 m_J g \mu_B B_0}{M} \right)^{\frac{1}{2}} \frac{1}{v} \qquad (4.24)$$

where L is the length of the magnetic field and R the radius of the circle on which the pole tips lie. Then, if a point source is located at distance 'a' from the entrance aperture, the image will be formed at distance 'b' beyond the end of the field where 'd' and 'b' are related by Fig. 4.6.

$$\phi_n = \arctan (L/a\phi_n) + \arctan (L/b\phi_n) + n\pi \qquad (4.25)$$

$$(n = 0, 1, \ldots)$$

a, b and L are generally dictated by other experimental requirements, e.g. resolution and so the value of the field strength B_0 for the required velocity v_0 is found from Equation 4.24 with ϕ assigned from Equation 4.25. 'Harmonics' will still be passed by the filter that arise from values of n in Equation 4.25 other than the chosen one (generally zero). However, the ratio v_n/v_0 will not be a rational one and so the addition of a simple two disc mechanical velocity selector will eliminate these velocity sidebands. The resolution of the filter regarded as a velocity selector is a function of the ratio of the radius W of the exit aperture to R, as well as of $A = a/L$ and $B = b/L$;

$$\frac{\Delta v}{v_0} = \frac{2\sqrt{2} \, \dfrac{W}{R} \, (A + B)(A^2 + 1/\phi_0^2)^{\frac{1}{2}}}{\phi_0 \sin \phi_0 \, \{ A^2 B^2 \phi_0^2 + A^2 + B^2 + AB(A + B) + (A + B + 1)/\phi_0^2 \}} \qquad (4.26)$$

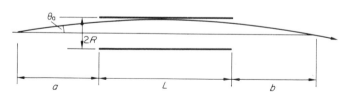

Fig. 4.6 The critical dimensions of the general hexapole filter. The magnetic field occupies a length L, the source is a distance a in front of the entrance and the focal plane is a distance b beyond the end of the field.

Tall beams, with slit rather than circular geometry can also be focused, but the velocity resolution will be poorer.

A typical hexapole lens, discussed in (H. M. Brash et al., 1969) had the following values of the parameters.

$$
\begin{array}{rcl}
L & = & 0.12 \text{ m} \\
L/R & = & 48 \\
A = a/L & = & 1.8 \\
B = b/L & = & 4.0 \\
W & = & 0.1 \text{ mm} \\
v & = & 390 \text{ m s}^{-1} \\
B_0 & = & 0.118 \text{ T (permanent magnet)} \\
\Delta v/v_0 & = & 11\% \text{ (FWHM)}
\end{array}
$$

Fields up to 2 T may be obtained with an electromagnet allowing $L \approx 0.03$ m to maintain the same value of ϕ. The gain in intensity as a result of the focusing action may be calculated from the angle of acceptance θ_a of the device for those particles that are brought to a focus. Referring to Fig. 4.6 and assuming that the effect of the central stop is negligible, θ_a is given by

$$\theta_a = R/L \, (A^2 + 1/\phi^2)^{-\frac{1}{2}}. \tag{4.27}$$

The number of particles N_f passing through the focus is thus:

$$N_f = \frac{1}{4} \, F_n F_{\Delta v} I_0 \theta_a^2 \tag{4.28}$$

where I_0 is the number of particles per second per steradian emerging from the source, F_n is the fraction of molecules in the selected band of quantum states and $F_{\Delta v}$ is the fraction in the transmitted velocity range. For mechanical selection, if the scattering volume subtends an angle θ_a' at the source, the corresponding expression for the number of particles passing through the scattering volume is $\frac{1}{4} F_{\Delta v} T I_0 \theta_a'^2$, where T is the mechanical transmission factor. In general, $\theta_a/\theta_a' \sim 2 - 10$ and a gain in scattered signal of at least an order of magnitude can be expected.

It is worth remembering that although many atomic states possess unpaired electrons, not all are suitable for magnetic focusing. Firstly, for the atom which has zero nuclear moment only those states with $m_J > 0$ can be focused and since the focal length depends upon $v/m_J^{\frac{1}{2}}$, sidebands will appear in the transmitted beam due to different combinations of m_J and v if $J > \frac{1}{2}$.

Secondly, if the nuclear spin is non-zero, the effective magnetic moment of the atom is, for weak field coupling:

$$\mu_{\text{eff}} = \left[\frac{\mu_J}{J} \left\{ \frac{F(F+1) + J(J+1) - I(I+1)}{2F(F+1)} \right\} \right.$$

$$\left. + \frac{\mu_I}{I} \left\{ \frac{F(F+1) + I(I+1) - J(J+1)}{2F(F+1)} \right\} \right] m_F \quad (4.29)$$

where $F(= I + J)$ is the total angular momentum, m_F its projection quantum number and $\mu_I = g_I \mu_N I$ where g_I is the nuclear g factor and μ_N the nuclear magneton. Since $\mu_N \approx \mu_e/2000$, the dominant contribution to μ_{eff} comes from the first term in Equation 4.29, but the range of m_F values renders a weak field magnet useless as a velocity selector. In the strong field case (in which the nuclear and electronic angular momenta are decoupled) the effective moment is given by:

$$\mu_{\text{eff}} = \mu_J \frac{m_J}{J} + \mu_I \frac{m_I}{I} \quad (4.30)$$

The field strength needed to achieve this depends upon the isotope and for the alkali metals working values might be in (in MHz)

K	Na	Rb	Cs	
450	1800	3000	9000	most abundant isotope
250		7000		less abundant isotope

Hexapole filters are very convenient for potassium and are just possible for Na and Rb. In the case of Cs, however, it is necessary to use a Stern Gerlach magnetic with yields more intense fields (I. I. Rabi, et al., 1934) but which is only a partially focusing device (see below). The states $m_J = 3/2$ and $1/2$ of gallium ($J = 3/2$) have also been selected with a hexapole lens (K. Berkling et al., 1962). Although this atom has a relatively large nuclear moment, the coupling of **I** and **J** is small because the unpaired electron is not in an s-orbital and hence has zero density at the nucleus. Halogen atoms and some of the metastable inert gas atoms might prove good candidates for magnetic focusing.

   If the experiment requires that both μ_{eff} and $-\mu_{\text{eff}}$ can be selected, then the older type of deflection field with two-wire geometry is used (N. F.

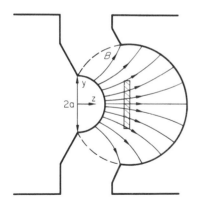

Fig. 4.7 A modern beam deflecting magnet, based on the two wire field. The magnetic field lines are shown and a tall beam (shaded) in roughly the position shown will experience a nearly constant field gradient over its height for values of y $\leqslant$ a. (N. F. Ramsey, 1956).

Ramsey, 1956). The inhomogeneous field is produced between two pole faces shaped such that $\partial B/\partial z \propto z$ and both B and $\partial B/\partial z$ remain nearly uniform over the height of the beam, Fig. 4.7. Since the restoring force in the z direction is again proportional to z,, there is focusing in this direction but not in the y direction. Particles with effective moment μ_{eff} suffer a deflection δ in traversing a field length L where:

$$\delta = L^2 \mu_{eff} \partial B/\partial z \ (2Mv^2)^{-1} \tag{4.31}$$

and by placing the exit slit appropriately, states with positive or negative moments can be selected. This is put to practical use in spin exchange experiments (D. E. Pritchard et al., 1970) and the device has also been used as a velocity selector for H atoms (M. A. D. Fluendy, 1965) but the lack of whole field focusing is a disadvantage here.

4.4 Electrostatic state selection

The electrostatic analogue of the 1st order Zeeman effect, by which magnetic sub-states are separated in a magnetic field, is the 1st order Stark effect exhibited by symmetric top molecules. The discussion of this effect exactly parallels that of spin focusing, except for two factors. Firstly, there are no complications due to the nuclear dipole moments which are zero in the electrostatic case. Secondly, the rotational state of a symmetric top molecule is specified by three quantum numbers $j,$ m and K. The non-vanishing component of the permanent dipole moment μ in the direction of the applied field $\mathbf{E}$ (which defines the axis of quantization) is given by:

$$\mu_E = \mu \langle \cos \theta \rangle = \mu m K / [j(j + 1)] \tag{4.32}$$

where θ is the angle of precession of the figure axis around the direction of the applied field. The induced energy is linearly dependent on E:

$$W^{(1)}_{jmK} = -\mu \cdot E = -\mu E mK/j(j + 1)$$

and the force is

$$F = \mu \, \text{grad} \mid E \mid mK/j(j + 1) \tag{4.33}$$

Thus, if both m and K are non-zero and either of them is negative, the mean dipole component is antiparallel to the field and focusing can be achieved if grad $\mid E \mid$ is positive. If either m or K is zero then the molecule behaves as a linear one and the energy dependence on the field is quadratic (see below).

Focusing will be obtained with an electrostatic hexapole array, for which the potential is given by

$$V = V_0 \left(\frac{r}{R}\right)^3 \cos 3\Phi \tag{4.34}$$

where R is the radius of the electrode tips from the axis Φ the azimuthal angle defined in Fig. 4.5 and V_0 the electrode potential. Then,

$$\mid E \mid = 3V_0 r^2/R^3 \tag{4.35}$$

The focal length is then readily found for the state (j, m, K)

$$f_{jmK} = \pi v \left\{ \frac{R^3}{6V_0} \left[\frac{M}{\mu} \frac{j(j + 1)}{mK} \right] \right\}^{\frac{1}{2}} \tag{4.36}$$

For a representative molecule having $\mu = 1.5D$, $M = 5 \times 10^{-23}$ g and moving at a speed of 3×10^2 m s^{-1}, a focal length of at least 0.15 m for an applied potential (V_0) of 2 KV is calculated. Although very polar $(\mu \geqslant 2D)$ symmetric top molecules are rare, convenient focal lengths can be obtained for some compounds of the type CYX_3 or for ammonia. For the rather heavy molecule CH_3I, a focal length of ~1 m has been attained.

With three quantum numbers as well as the velocity determining the focal length, the electrostatic hexapole analyser is better regarded as selecting molecules with a given value of $<\cos \theta>$ rather than in a particular rotational state. In this mode of operation a mechanical velocity selector is inserted between the exit of the hexapole array and the scattering centre, so that the range of values of $<\cos \theta>$ transmitted is considerably narrowed.

The method has been used particularly by Bernstein and his co-workers (R. J. Beuhler and R. B. Bernstein, 1969) for CH_3I and CHI_3 and by P. R. Brooks et al. (1969) for a wider group of CX_3Y molecules. The degree of the selection of $<\cos \theta>$ is largely determined by the resolution of the velocity selector. Thus, the geometrical arrangement of slits and stops essentially selects a range of values of ϕ, defined analogously to the magnetic case (Equation 4.24) as

$$\phi = \frac{L}{Rv} \left(\frac{2\mu \langle \cos \theta \rangle V_0}{MR} \right)^{\frac{1}{2}},$$ (4.37)

so

$$\left| \frac{\Delta \langle \cos \theta \rangle}{\langle \cos \theta \rangle} \right| \simeq 2 \left\{ \left| \frac{\Delta \phi}{\phi} \right| + \left| \frac{\Delta v}{v} \right| \right\},$$ (4.38)

and if $\Delta \phi / \phi$ is typically 10 per cent, the resolution in $<\cos \theta>$ will be 30 per cent with a good velocity selector.

The presence of the velocity selector with its poor transmission and spatial demands, together with the fact that such a small volume of the phase space of the molecules is being selected means that intensities will be small, perhaps $10^5 - 10^6$ particles arriving per second at the focus. Whether the molecules are oblate or prolate tops there is a statistical deficiency of those with values of $<\cos \theta>$ close to unity and the most probable value of $<\cos \theta>$ is in both cases zero, a non focusable orientation. With the angular resolution quoted above, the fraction of molecules having the required orientation will be ≤10 per cent. The beam intensity (for $<\cos \theta> \sim 1/2$) at the exit of a combined hexapole/mechanical selector might be $10^{-1} - 10^{-2}$ times that at the exit of a conventional mechanical selector, still sufficient for total cross section work.

Linear molecules possessing a permanent dipole moment exhibit a quadratic Stark effect in the presence of an electric field E and for a non-polarizable linear molecule the second order perturbation energy, $W_{jm}^{(2)}$ is given by

$$W_{jm}^{(2)} = \frac{\frac{1}{2}(\mu E)^2}{\hbar^2 / 2I} \left\{ \frac{j(j+1) - 3m^2}{j(j+1)(2j-1)(2j+3)} \right\}$$ (4.39)

so the radial restoring force becomes

$$F_r = - \frac{\mu^2 E \partial E / \partial r}{\hbar^2 / 2I} \mathscr{F}(j, m)$$

where

$$\mathscr{F}(j, m) = [j(j + 1) - 3m^2] / [j(j + 1)(2j - 1)(2j + 3)] \qquad (4.40)$$

If E can be made to vary in a linear fashion with r, the motion in the field is simple harmonic if both $\partial E/\partial r$ and the quantum number factor in Equation 4.40, $\mathscr{F}(j, m)$, are positive. For a quadrupole array of conductors the potential is given by

$$V = V_0(r/R)^2 \cos 2\Phi \qquad (4.41)$$

(where R is the distance of an electrode tip from the axis) and so the magnitude of the field at (r, Φ) is

$$| E | = 2V_0 r/R^2 \qquad (4.42)$$

which has the required r dependence.

The focal length (for the case a = b = 0, Fig. 4.6) is given by

$$f = \frac{\pi \hbar v R^2}{\mu V_0} \sqrt{\frac{M}{8I\mathscr{F}(j, m)}} \qquad (4.43)$$

where M is the molecular mass. All rotational states for which $\mathscr{F}(j, m) > 0$ can be focused (note that for $j = 0$, $\mathscr{F}(j, m) = -1/3$ and so this state cannot be focused). As with the hexapole field, there will in general be several combinations of v, j and m that lead to the same focal length and a velocity selector is always incorporated to narrow the range of j and m.

The question of what is being selected in classical terms is perhaps less clear than in the hexapole case. If the source temperature is high enough for the molecular rotation to be treated classically and very low values of j are not being selected, the mean dipole moment in the direction of the field is

$$\mu_E = \frac{\mu^2 E}{4W_{rot}} (3 \cos^2 \alpha - 1) \qquad (4.44)$$

where α is the angle between $\mathbf{J}$ and $\mathbf{E}$ and W_{rot} is the rotational energy appropriate to the source temperature. For a molecule with $\mu \sim 5D$ and with $E \sim 10^6$ volts m^{-1}, $\mu_E/\mu \leqslant 10^{-3}$ at thermal energies and so there is little net alignment of the dipole and even this asymmetry virtually disappears when the molecule leaves the quadrupole and enters the region of weaker uniform

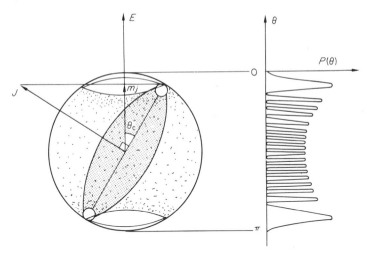

Fig. 4.8 The classical representation of the quantum motion of a linear dipolar molecule in a weak field E. A region near the poles, defined by the cone of semi-angle θ_c is forbidden to the classical motion. The quantum mechanical probability distribution of the axis orientation is shown on the right for the case $j \sim 20$, $m_j \sim 10$. As j increases, the quantum motion is more sharply centered at $\pm\theta_c$, where $\sin\theta_c = m_j/j$.

field. In this latter region the classical motion for fixed values of j and m is displayed in Fig. 4.8. In the absence of an applied field, the rotation is confined to a plane; when a field is applied, precession of $\mathbf{J}$ about $\mathbf{E}$ begins. Writing

$$\cos\theta_c = \sqrt{1 - m^2/(j(j+1))} \tag{4.45}$$

where θ_c is the minimum angle between the dipole axis and $\mathbf{E}$, it can be said that motion of a monoenergetic beam through a quadrupole lens selects the range of values of $\cos\theta_c$ and W_{rot} that together satisfy Equation 4.43 for the chosen value of the focal length. θ_c is found to range from $0°$ to roughly $35°$ (Equation 4.45) with $m^2 = 1/3j(j+1)$) for states which can be focused and each value of θ_c is weighted by the population of the corresponding rotational state in the beam. That is, a limited range of (j, m) states is selected and these have the molecular axis pointing more in a polar than an equatorial direction with respect to the axis of quantisation. Unlike the symmetric top case, this will not lead to marked anisotropy in the chemical cross-section for a reaction in which one end of the molecule is preferentially attacked.

However, anisotropy terms of even symmetry in the intermolecular potential can be investigated by altering the focusing conditions.

The device is most useful when designed to transmit only the lowest rotational states, $(1, 0)$ or $(2, 0)$, for then $\mathscr{F}(j, m)$ is a rapidly varying function of j and m and with mechanical velocity selection different rotational states are readily resolved. For the state $(1, 0)$ the focal length is given by:

$$f_{10} = 7.854 \, \frac{vR^2}{\mu V_0 r_{AB}} \, \frac{m_A + m_B}{(m_A m_B)^{\frac{1}{2}}} \times 10^5 \text{ m} \tag{4.46}$$

where v is in m s^{-1}, R is in m, μ is in Debyes, V_0 is in volts and r_{AB}, the bond length, is in Angstroms. The focal length is clearly shortest for slow (heavy) molecules with large dipole moments. Thus J. P. Toennies (1965) has focused the $(1, 0)$; $(2, 0)$ and $(3, 0)$ states of TlF and used them to investigate rotational transitions in a crossed beam experiment Fig. 4.9. For this particularly favourable molecule $(\mu = 4.4D)$ focal lengths of 0.15–0.2 m are achievable.

For highly polar molecules, the possibility arises of selecting rotation-vibrational states through the rather large change of dipole moment with vibrational quantum number. Thus, $(\mu(n = 0) - \mu(n = 1))/\mu_0$ is ½ per cent for CsCl (from the beam resonance method) and 1 per cent for CsF. However, the focal length is essentially determined from Equation 4.43 by $(\mu^2 I)^{\frac{1}{2}}$ and this quantity may be expected to change by 2–3 per cent upon going from the nth to the $(n + 1)^{th}$ vibrational state. Thus, groups of perhaps two or three vibrational levels might be separated. The fraction of molecules

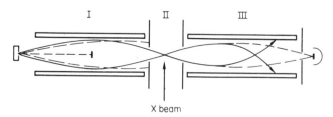

X beam

Fig. 4.9 A quadrupole system for detecting rotational transitions. The selecting field I focuses molecules in the $(1,0)$ state (trajectory ———) and molecules in the $(2,0)$ (————) and higher states either miss the exit aperture or hit the axial stop for molecules entering on the axis. In region II a uniform field establishes the axis of quantisation and a cross-beam intersects the focused beam, inducing rotational transitions. The analysing quadrupole, III, is set for the $(2,0)$ state, which is focused onto the detector.

in these low rotational states at the high oven temperatures is very small; for CsF .03 per cent of the molecules are in the $(1, 0)$ state.

More promising for the selection of vibrational states is a technique adapted from single beam resonance experiments (L. Wharton et al., 1963). A highly polar linear molecule is prepared in, say, the $(1, 0)$ state by passage through a quadrupole lens and led adiabatically into a uniform field region where it is pumped by microwave radiation at the resonant frequency for the $(n, j, m) = (0, 1, 0) \rightarrow (1, 2, 1)$ transition. A second quadrupole lens is then set to pass the $(2, 1)$ rotational state, thereby also selecting the $n = 1$ vibrational state. The experimental arrangement would be that of Fig. 4.9 with the cross-beam replaced by a microwave cavity. Nearly equal populations of the two levels can be obtained in the C-field region and sufficient intensity of vibrationally excited molecules for scattering experiments seems obtainable (T. G. Waech et al., 1968).

Single beam deflection experiments have been performed with non-polar molecules using the force arising from the interaction of the induced electric moment with the external field. The induction energy is quadratic in the field strength (2nd order Stark effect) and so the focusing conditions are analogous to those for linear molecules discussed above. For an isotropically polarisable molecule, polarisability α, the interaction energy is

$$W^{(2)} = -\tfrac{1}{2}\alpha E^2 \tag{4.47}$$

However, molecular polarisabilities are roughly $10^{-28}-10^{-29}$ m^3 and so $W^{(2)}$ in the non-polar case is $10^{-3} - 10^{-4}$ less than that arising from the permanent moment. Although the absence of a rotational state factor from Equation 4.47 increases the fraction of the parent population that can be focused, the focal length of a quadrupole lens operating on non-polar molecules will be approximately ten times greater than that designed for polar molecules and scattering experiments have not yet been carried out with beams selected by this means.

CHAPTER FIVE

Detection and Measurement

As in nuclear scattering the final link in any beam experiment is the detection of the particles after scattering. Unfortunately at the low energies appropriate to molecular scattering, the detection methods are severely handicapped. The fundamental problem is in distinguishing the molecules of the beam from the overwhelming background (pressure) inevitably present in our detectors. For the nuclear or elementary particle physicist the very high energy of the particles of interest serve to distinguish them from the background and efficient devices such as scintillation counters responding to this energy can be used. In contrast at thermal energies no such simple differentiation is possible and the beam properties of direction of motion and chemical species provide a much inferior distinction between beam and background.

Since Dunoyer's first experiments (L. Dunoyer, 1911) when he detected a sodium beam by condensing it upon a cooled surface, a wide range of devices has been used to detect molecular beams. In general these devices measure either the molecular beam flux as in Dunoyer's experiment or the molecular density. Most detectors currently in use convert the molecular current into an electric current, though for some applications condensation targets are still useful. Thus, Kinsey used a condensation target followed by radioactive counting to detect scattered tritium (L. R. Martin, J. L. Kinsey, 1967).

In general the most successful detectors have been those providing a high degree of differentiation between beam and background molecules. Unfortunately such selectivity is usually bought at the price of severe limitations on the range of materials that can be detected.

The overall performance of a detector is a function not only of the actual

122

beam sensor itself but also of the whole experimental configuration including any filtering or correlation processes that may be used. Nevertheless it is convenient to divide the discussion into two parts and consider first the beam detectors proper.

5.1 Beam detectors – Introduction

The most important parameters characterizing beam detectors are sensitivity, noise and response time.

Sensitivity is the output current or number of events per sec (in the case of ion counting systems) in response to a unit incident flux. The range of materials detectable, and their relative sensitivities must also be considered.

Noise is the random electrical output of the device, it can be conveniently measured in terms of the resulting uncertainty in beam flux: this uncertainty will depend not only upon the actual amplitude of the noise current but also upon the statistics of its time variation. Thus, if σ_N is the standard deviation of the noise measured with unit bandwidth then with 95 per cent confidence the uncertainty in a measurement will not exceed:

$$\pm 2\sigma_N/t^{\frac{1}{2}}\, \text{s}^{-1}, t > \frac{1}{\Delta v} \quad \text{or} \quad \pm 2\sigma_N \Delta v^{\frac{1}{2}}\, \text{s}^{-1}, t < 1/\Delta v \qquad (5.1)$$

where Δv is the bandwidth of the detector and t is the observation time. Contributions to σ_N arise from many sources, if the standard deviations for these processes are known the total will be

$$\sigma_N{}^2 = \sum_i \sigma_i{}^2 + \sum_j \sum_i \text{cov}_{ij} \qquad (5.2)$$

or if these different sources are uncorrelated $\text{cov}_{ij} = 0$ and

$$\sigma_N{}^2 = \sum_i \sigma_i{}^2 \qquad (5.3)$$

In almost all detectors one component of the noise output arises from the random motion of background gas molecules. If the motion of these molecules is entirely uncorrelated we may use the de Moivre Laplace limit theorem to estimate their contribution to the standard deviation of the noise. Thus if the noise current, I_N, from the background gas pressure (assuming a flux dependent detector) is:

$$I_N = \sum_i n_i q_i \sqrt{\frac{RT}{2\pi M}} \qquad (5.4)$$

where n_i is the background gas number density of species i and q_i is their detection efficiency, then the theorem leads to the result that:

$$\sigma_N \longrightarrow \left(\sum_i n_i q_i \sqrt{\frac{RT}{2\pi M}} \right)^{\frac{1}{2}} \qquad (5.5)$$

In practice the background atom motion is not entirely uncorrelated and macro pressure fluctuations in the detector due to pumping irregularities etc., can occur. Such fluctuations will depend upon the size of the vacuum chamber and its pumping speed. The contribution from this source has been discussed by S. N. Foner, (1966) in terms of an electrical analogue (Fig. 5.1).

The following identifications are made, where S is the pumping speed and V the chamber volume

$$\text{Beam flux} = I, \qquad R = 1/S, \qquad C = V.$$

E_s is then the signal output from the detector and E_b the noise output (due to pressure fluctuations). The noise output can clearly be minimized by decreasing the impedance of the RC circuit across which E_b is developed.

The impedance of this RC circuit is:

$$|Z| = R/[1 + \nu^2 C^2 R^2]^{\frac{1}{2}} = 1/S[1 + \nu^2 V^2/S^2]^{\frac{1}{2}} \qquad (5.6)$$

where ν is the frequency of the signal current I.

Thus the impedance and hence the noise output E_b can be decreased by moving the signal frequency ν to a suitably high value. In practice this corresponds to modulating the molecular beam at a frequency such that $\nu V \gg S$. The noise output is then reduced to about $S^2/\nu V$ times the zero

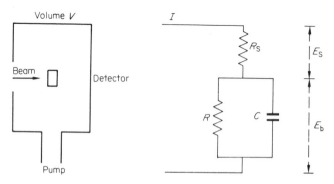

Fig. 5.1 Electrical analog for noise arising from background pressure fluctuations.

frequency level. Noise from this source is thus far from Gaussian and is concentrated primarily at low frequencies.

Noise due to both effects is best combated by lowering the partial pressure of the background material to which the detector responds (typically by installing additional liquid N_2 shielding). Beam modulation methods will also be useful in dealing with other sources of fluctuation noise and will be discussed in more detail later.

Response time τ is defined as the time taken for the output of the detector to rise to 63 per cent, $(1 - e^{-t/\tau})$, of its final value in response to a step change in input. This time will limit the rate at which the incident beam can be varied, e.g. by modulation or velocity scans.

Types of Detectors

5.2 Ionization detectors

The most widely used class of detectors operate by ionizing the molecule and then measuring the resultant ion current. Several techniques may be used to accomplish the initial ionization.

(i) Hot wire detectors

In this type of detector beam molecules with a low ionization potential are ionized by collision with a hot wire of high work function such as tungsten. The operation of this device can be understood in terms of the Saha-Langmuir equation (E. Ya Zandberg, N. I. Ionov, 1959) which relates the temperature T, the ionization potential E_b of the beam material and the work function of the hot wire surface ϕ_w to the proportion of molecules ionized by the collisions as:

$$\frac{\text{number of ions emitted}}{\text{number of neutrals}} = \frac{(1 - \gamma_+)}{(1 - \gamma_n)} \frac{j_+}{j_n} \exp - \left(\frac{E_b - \phi_w}{kT}\right) \quad (5.7)$$

where j_+, j_- are the reflection coefficients and γ_+, γ_n the degeneracies of the ion and neutral particle states respectively. Equation 5.7 is, of course, an equilibrium relation and its useful temperature range in this connection is limited to that over which the neutral atoms do not permanently condense on the surface.

Values for $(E_b - \phi_w)$ for various combinations of wire and beam material are given in Table 5.1.

Table 5.1

Wire Material	ϕ_w eV	Beam Material $(E_b - \phi_w)$ eV							
—	—	Li	Na	K	Rb	Cs	Ga	In	Tl
W clean	4.58	+0.81	+0.56	−0.24	−0.40	−0.71	1.42	1.21	1.5
W oxygenated	5.9	−0.51	−0.76	−1.56	−1.72	−2.03	0.1	−0.11	0.2
Re	5.17	+0.22	−0.03	−0.83	−0.99	−1.30	0.83	0.62	0.9
Ionization Potential E_b	—	5.39	5.14	4.34	4.18	3.87	6.00	5.79	6.1

The agreement between the predicted and observed behaviour is illustrate
by Figs. 5.2 and 5.3 (S. Datz and E. H. Taylor, 1956) which show th
percentage ionization found for alkali metals on tungsten and on platinum
Alkali metal compounds such as halides can also be ionized by suitable ho
wires. In this case the molecule is dissociated and the alkali metal emitted a
an ion. The mechanism for this process is rather less clear. Figs. 5.4 and 5.
show the ionization of some alkali halides on tungsten and on platinum. It i
apparent that the W surface is a fairly efficient ionizer, the platinum muc
less so. An especially valuable fact becomes apparent if we compare Figs. 5.
and 5.4 and Figs. 5.3 and 5.5. The tungsten surface is approximately equall
effective at ionizing both alkali metals and their halides whereas the platinum
surface at temperatures in the $1200°K$ region ionizes the metals almos
exclusively (with the exception of KF). Thus in a mixed alkali/metal halide
flux the difference in signals recorded from tungsten and the platinum wire
is a measure of the alkali halide flux. This differential hot wire detector ha
played a most important role in the study of chemical reaction by molecular
beam methods. Recently, however, K. T. Gillen and R. B. Bernstein (1970)
have found that highly vibrationally excited alkali halides are also quite
readily ionized on a platinum filament, the ionization efficiency varying
exponentially with excitation energy and approaching 20 per cent for highest
states.

This observation has important implications in the original interpretation
of the wide angle elastic scattering from reactive systems. In experiments,
using alloy filaments the K flux was considerably overestimated.

Surface ionization detection has also been used in the reverse sense. Thus
the collision of an atom or molecule having a large electron affinity with a
hot wire of low work function can lead to electron transfer from the metal
and the formation of a negative ion. Such negative surface ionization is a
much less efficient process than the formation of positive ions. For ionization

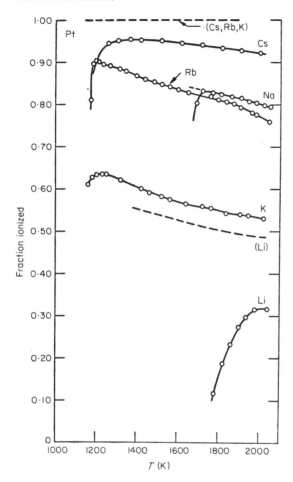

Fig. 5.2 Ionization of alkali metals on platinum. Dotted lines are the calculated behaviour (S. Datz and E. H. Taylor, 1956).

on a carburretted thoriated tungsten wire efficiencies of 1–2 per cent for CBr_4 ranging downwards for other electronegative species were found by E. F. Greene et al., 1968. Apart from the rather low efficiency this method also suffers from the drawback that some form of mass spectrometer is required to distinguish negative ions from the otherwise overwhelming thermionic electron current. Greene found a simple magnetic field configuration highly effective for this purpose at low background pressures. Some typical sensitivities found in his work are listed in Table 5.2.

Table 5.2 Relative negative ionization efficiencies on thoriated
tungsten wire (K on Re at 1 200 K $\equiv$ unit efficiency)

KI	1.8×10^{-3}	CBr_4	1.9×10^{-2}
CCl_4	1.5×10^{-2}	I_2	6.3×10^{-8}
C_2Cl_6	1.4×10^{-3}	HI	1.8×10^{-4}
C_6H_5Cl	2.6×10^{-3}	C_2H_5I	7.7×10^{-4}
Br_2	4.5×10^{-3}	C_6H_5I	1.5×10^{-3}

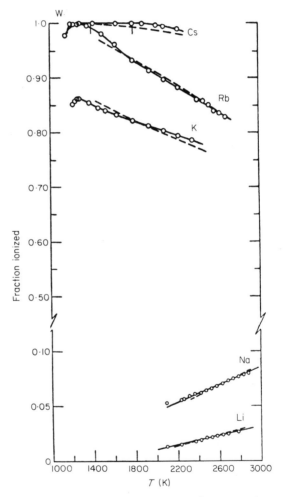

Fig. 5.3 Ionization of alkali metals on tungsten.
Dotted lines are the calculated behaviour (S.
Datz and E. H. Taylor, 1956).

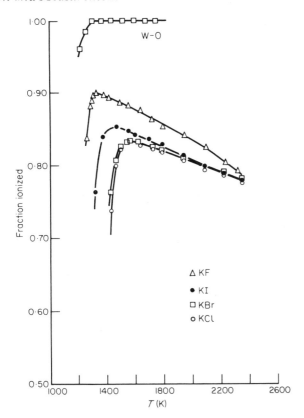

Fig. 5.4 Ionization of alkali halides on tungsten (S. Datz and E. H. Taylor, 1956).

Construction

The most usual form of hot wire detector is shown in Fig. 5.6. The hot wire is suspended under spring tension between two insulating mounts which also provide the feed for the d.c. heating current. The two ends of the wire are screened by small earthed cylinders to prevent the cooler end regions of the wire being exposed to the beam flux. A cylindrical collector slotted in two places to allow the beam to enter and leave is mounted on alumina insulators and biased about 40 volts negative with respect to the filament. The ions formed on the wire surface are thus attracted to the collector and the resulting current measured on an electrometer. A metal screen finally surrounds the whole assembly to form an electric shield.

The normal operating temperatures for tungsten and platinum filaments are 1870 K and 1290 K respectively. For 0.003″ wires these correspond to

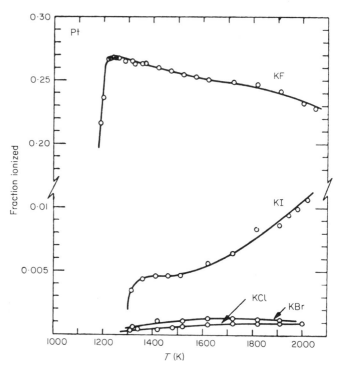

Fig. 5.5 Ionization of alkali halides on platinum. Slow response noted at temperatures below vertical dashed lines. (S. Datz and E. H. Taylor, 1956).

0.600A and 0.200A currents. Oxygenated filaments of tungsten are prepared either by running the filament at 1500 K in a slight pressure of oxygen or alternatively by allowing a capillary jet of oxygen from a reservoir at about 5×10^{-3} torr to play upon the filament during use.

Filaments with a high platinum content have two different surface states. In one with a high work function they can ionize alkali halides, in the other known as mode N (T. R. Trouw and J. W. Trischka, 1963) the work function is lower and the filaments ionize essentially only the alkali metals or highly excited species, e.g. KI. Mode N can be prepared by ageing the Pt wire at 1520 K for several hours and then running it at 1600 K for a few minutes in methane at a partial pressure of $\sim 5 \times 10^{-4}$ torr.

Several variations of the basic device described have been used. Thus the collector can be replaced by the first dynode of an electron multiplier and the bias increased to 2–3 kV. In this way advantage can be taken of the low noise amplification provided by such devices. In other cases (Fig. 5.7) the hot wire

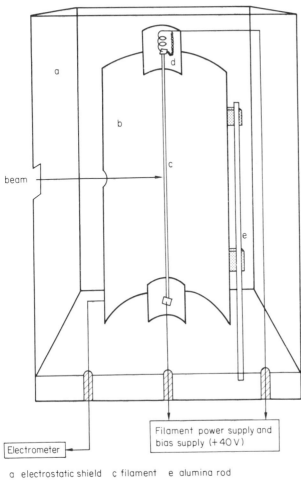

Filament power supply and
bias supply (+40 V)

Electrometer

a electrostatic shield   c filament   e alumina rod
b collector   d spring and current by-pass

Fig. 5.6 Hot wire beam detector with electrometer to
measure a positive ion current.

is mounted at the entrance to a mass spectrometer so that the various alkali
ions etc. can be distinguished. Careful design of the focusing and extraction
lenses is required if the ion collection efficiency is to approach 10–50 per
cent.

Sensitivity

Positive surface ionization detectors perform with good efficiency when the
work function is greater than the ionization potential. They are thus

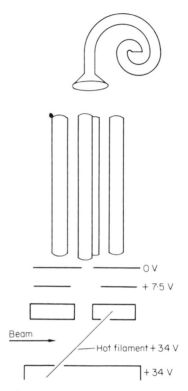

Fig. 5.7 Hot wire detector and quadrupole to detect alkalis selectively. A lens focuses the positive ions from the ribbons into the quadrupole. Total detection efficiencies of the order ~50% can be achieved.

primarily limited to the alkali metals and their compounds together with In, Ga, Tl, Pr, Al and Ba. For the alkali metals the detection efficiency is 80–100 per cent, i.e. ~1.6×10^{-19}A per unit incident flux per m^2 of detector surface. Our 'standard beam' of 5×10^{10} molecules sec^{-1} mm^{-2} at one metre from the source would thus produce a current of 8×10^{-9}A mm^{-2} or for a 1 cm tall beam on a 0.003″ wire a current of ~6×10^{-10}A.

Linearity

The detector is linear over a wide range. At the highest beam fluxes (~10^{-8}A) where surface coverage by the alkalis is significant some decrease in efficiency has been observed (K. Wilson, 1964).

Noise

There are two principal sources of noise in the hot wire detector. The first, common to all detectors, is due to those background gas molecules that are ionizable on a hot wire and has already been discussed. The noise from this source can be estimated from kinetic theory considerations. The number of ions produced will be approximately the number of collisions of ionizable material with the hot wire (of the appropriate mass if a mass spectrometer is used), i.e. number of ions s^{-1} = I = 1/3 $n_b \bar{v}$ cm^{-2} of detector surface, where n_b is the number density and $\bar{v}$ the average molecular velocity.

Then as before:

$$\sigma(I) = (\tfrac{1}{3} n_b \bar{v})^{\frac{1}{2}} \tag{5.8}$$

Thus a background partial pressure of 10^{-15} torr on the surface of a typical detector (5 x 10^{-3} cm^2) will produce an average ion current of

$$I = 10^{-15} A$$

and the standard deviation of the noise rate from this source would be:

$$\sigma(I) \sim (2 \times 10^4)^{\frac{1}{2}} \cong 140 \text{ counts s}^{-\frac{1}{2}}$$

The second noise source is specific to this class of detector and arises from alkali metal impurities in the wire. These diffuse to the surface during operation and are ionized. Tungsten wires are especially prone to this since some KCl is incorporated during manufacture. Fortunately pure tungsten wires drawn from a single crystal of the metal are now available and are much less noisy. In all cases it is standard practice to 'age' wires by running them at an elevated temperature for a few hours. Typically tungsten is aged at 2030 K and platinum alloy at 1520 K; the noise decreases very markedly during this procedure.

The statistics of diffusion noise are very far from Gaussian; the emission of impurities from the interior of the wire appears as sharp pulses of current in which up to 10^8 ions may be released in less than 100 μs (i.e. a current peak of ~10^{-9}A). (The time width of the pulses is related to the wire temperature – at the lowest operating temperatures they may spread over ~50ms). (R. E. Minturn, et al., 1960). In the case of tungsten wires the impurities are very largely potassium so that if the beam material is different a considerable noise reduction can be achieved by using a mass spectrometer. Clipping or limiting circuits have also been used to reduce this form of noise.

Table 5.3 Noise count s^{-1} arising from impurities in tungsten ribbon*

	Operating current	
	1A	1.4A
Na	434	17,942
K	121,332	137,889
Rb	437	1,148
Cs	122	264

* Ribbon was $0.020'' \times 0.001''$ 92% W/8% Pt alloy

Table 5.3 shows a typical distribution of noise from a Tungsten alloy filament. The much lower noise level obtained for Rb is clearly seen. Platinum or single crystal purity W filaments are much less noisy and will normally be used whenever possible.

Response time

The response time of hot wire detectors varies roughly inversely with the wire temperature and ionization efficiency (F. Knauer, 1949; H. Lew, 1953; H. L. Daley et al., 1969). At the very lowest temperatures at which ionization can be observed the emission of an ion may follow in the order of seconds after the neutral atom collision with the surface. For the usual operating temperatures alkali metals are ionized with delays ranging from 10^{-2} seconds for Platinum at 1200 K to 10^{-5} seconds on tungsten wires at high temperatures. Unfortunately the noise pulses from wire impurities decrease in time width in rather a similar way; modulation at a sufficiently high frequency to deal with diffusion noise is therefore difficult. For d.c. experiments, i.e. without modulation the build up of beam material in the detector chamber will also contribute to the response time. Using the electrical analogue again we see that the pumping time constant is RC or chamber volume/pumping speed.

(ii) Surface ionization of fast alkali beams

For very fast alkali beams of >3 eV collision energy the efficiency of the hot wire detector begins to drop off; probably due to reflexion effects.

Fortunately it has been found that ionization of these energetic alkalis can be accomplished on a cold filament of high work function. (E. Hulpke and C. Schlier, 1967.) This process has two important advantages in comparison with a hot wire ionizer. Firstly there is virtually no noise from the ribbon or from the thermalized alkali background, i.e. the detector is highly specific for the beam. Secondly the response time is very small < 0.1 μs so that a detector using this process can be used in time of flight experiments. The disadvantage of this detector is the rapid change in ionization efficiency which occurs between threshold at about 7 eV and 50 eV above which the efficiency becomes relatively constant (Fig. 5.8). This loss of sensitivity arising from an increased reflection of neutral particles at energies between 3 eV–50 eV both on hot and cold surfaces has been circumvented in a detector described by Politiek. In this detector (J. Politiek and J. Los, 1969) the fast atoms enter a heated tungsten cylinder via a narrow slit and hence suffer multiple collisions with the surface during which ionization can be achieved.

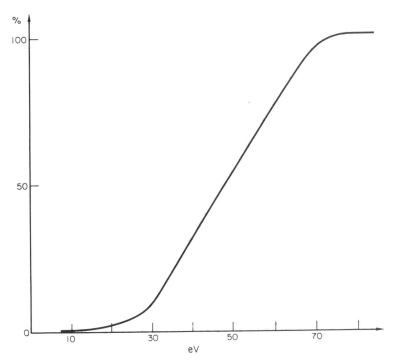

Fig. 5.8 Efficiency of ionization for fast neutrals striking a cold tungsten wire (data from R. K. B. Helbing and E. W. Rothe, 1969).

In practice the ribbon is normally operated 'warm', i.e. just below the threshold for thermal ionization in order to prevent contamination of the ribbon surface. The construction of detectors using this approach is similar to the hot wire pattern; an electron multiplier would normally be incorporated, e.g. Fig. 5.7, take advantage of the fast response time.

(iii) Electron bombardment detectors

This type of detector in its essentials is the same as the sources used in conventional mass spectrometers. A high density of electrons with sufficient kinetic energy to ionize the beam molecules is arranged to intersect the molecular beam. The resulting ions are extracted from the ionizing region – usually via a mass spectrometer and the ion current measured. Since the partial pressure of beam material in the device will be very low, careful attention must be paid to the efficiency of the source.

The number of ions produced from a beam flux of $F(v)$ molecules cm^{-2} s^{-1} with a velocity v is related to the detector parameters by:

$$N_j = \frac{i}{e} \frac{Q_j(E)B}{\bar{v}} k_j F(v) \text{ s}^{-1} \tag{5.9}$$

where i is the electron current in amps, e the electronic charge (1.6×10^{-19} coloumbs), and $Q_j(E)$ the ionization cross-section for molecules of species j at a collision energy E. A and l are the width and length of the high electron density region and B is the height of the beam lying in the area Al. Finally k_j is the mass spectrometer transmission for species j.

The number of ions from the background will similarly be:

$$N_n = \frac{i}{e} B \sum_h n_h Q_h(E) k_{(j-h)} \text{ s}^{-1} \tag{5.10}$$

Where n_h is the number density of molecules h and $k_{(j-h)}$ is their transmission through the mass spectrometer (tuned to mass j).

The signal to noise ratio after 1 second (neglecting pressure fluctuation contributions) will thus be:

$$S/N = N_j/(N_n)^{1/2}$$

$$= \left(\frac{i}{e} B\right)^{1/2} Q_j k_j F(v)/\bar{v} \left(\sum_h n_h Q_h(E) k_{(j-h)}\right)^{1/2} \tag{5.11}$$

The primary design considerations may be summarized as:

(1) To match the beam and ionizing volume cross-sections i.e. A = beam width.

(2) To achieve the highest electron density in the beam path.

(3) To reduce the background gas pressure (especially that appearing at the same mass number as the beam material).

(4) To obtain high extraction into and transmission through the mass spectrometer.

(5) To minimize fluctuation noise by modulation methods.

Further problems can also arise from fragmentation of the parent molecule in the ionizer. In some cases only a small fraction may appear as the parent ion.

Construction

Several designs for beam detectors using electron bombardment have appeared in the literature, e.g. (R. Weiss, 1961). A design due to G. O. Brink (1966) is shown in Fig. 5.9. The electrons produced by the filament oscillate through the molecular beam region several times before ultimate collection on the grid. To improve the stability of the device the d.c. filament heating current is controlled by an emission regulator which samples the grid current and varies the heating current through the filament to maintain constant emission.

The detailed design of sources such as these is a difficult problem in ion and electron optics especially since space charge effects are large because of the high electron density required. The reader is referred to more specialized texts.

Sensitivity

The detector is number density dependent with a sensitivity inversely proportional to velocity as seen from Equation 5.11; and is therefore not very suitable for detecting fast (super thermal) beams.

Inserting typical values into Equation 5.10 we see that we can expect to ionize between 1 in 10^2 and 1 in 10^3 of the molecules in a beam at thermal velocities. In comparison Weiss reported 1 in 40 for argon and Brink 1 in 600 for argon and 1 in 800 for krypton. Ionization cross-sections do not vary very widely from molecule to molecule and electron bombardment ionizers are

Fig. 5.9 Typical high efficiency electron bombardment ionizer (reproduced from G. O. Brink, 1966).

therefore of universal application; though particular mass numbers may be virtually impossible to detect if coincident with persistent background gases.

Linearity

The device is likely to be linear over the usual range of beam fluxes though non-linearities due to space charge effects can occur if operated in a high background pressure.

Noise

The noise in bombardment detectors is due almost entirely to background gas, both low frequency fluctuations (which have already been dealt with) and random 'white' contributions being important. The number of ions from the background is N_n:

$$N_n = \frac{i}{e} B \sum_h n_h Q_h(E) k_{(j-h)} \text{ s}^{-1} \tag{5.12}$$

and the standard deviation of the noise $(N_n)^{1/2}$.

Noise reduction thus depends principally upon vacuum technique and in particular the partial pressure of background gas falling in the mass spectrometer transmission band. U.H.V. techniques, using oil free bakeable equipment, and possibly including liquid He cryogenic pumping are therefore mandatory. Chemical getter pumps to handle particular contaminants or beam material may also be useful. Typical background pressures as a function of mass numbers are shown in Fig. 5.10.

Response time

At thermal beam speeds the most important factor in determining the response time is the length of the region over which ionization can occur. Thus a rectangular step in beam flux will produce a ramp output of duration:

$$\tau = \frac{l}{v_b} - \frac{l}{v_i} \tag{5.13}$$

where v_b is the beam velocity, v_i is the average velocity of the ion and l the length of the ionizer. If $v_i \gg v_b$ then $\tau \approx l/v_b$. Response times are thus typically 10^{-5} seconds, by making $v_i \approx v_b$ the dispersion of the pulse can be minimized, a result which is often more important than reduction of the actual delay between the arrival of a beam pulse and the output of the signal. In some ionizers in which the high electron density is achieved by trapping

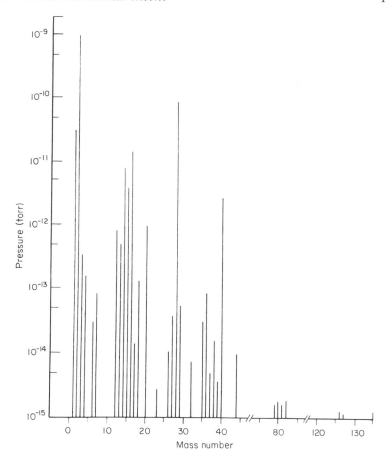

Fig. 5.10 Background partial pressures in an electron bombardment detector (reproduced from Y. T. Lee et al, 1969).

the electrons in a potential well, the net field in the ion may be very small. The response time can then rise to ~10^{-2} s.

(iv) Field ionization detector

The use of the field ionization sources in conventional mass spectrometry is a comparatively recent innovation and as yet this technique has not been much used in molecular beam work. Nevertheless field ionization seems likely to offer important advantages over electron bombardment sources and, when certain problems are overcome, may find very wide use in beam detectors.

The actual process of field ionization has been the subject of several reviews (e.g. E. W. Muller, 1960; H. D. Beckey, et al., 1963). Ionization is brought about by quantum mechanical tunnelling of an electron through a distorted atomic or molecular potential, this distortion being brought about by a very intense electric field (of the order 10^7-10^9 Vm^{-1}). This intense field may be generated around a needle point (as in the original experiments) 5000°A in radius or by a thin wire 2×10^{-4} cm in diameter biased 3–20 kV positively. The actual collecting area is considerably larger than the surface of the point or wire since molecules in a region round about are polarised by the field and attracted inwards. The size of this collection region can be estimated as the distance r_c at which the polarization due to the field balances the centrifugal motion of the molecules about the wire. (R. Gomer and M. G. Ingram, 1955.)

Thus for a needle point radius r_0:

$$\frac{1}{2} M v^2 = \frac{1}{2} \alpha F_0^2 \left(\frac{r_0^2}{r_c^2}\right)^2 \tag{5.14}$$

Where M is the mass and α the polarizability of a molecule moving with velocity v and F_0 is the field strength at the tip. The number of ions N_s produced by a needle point exposed to a unit incident flux of molecules is thus:

$$N_s = \pi r_c^2 = \pi \left(\frac{\alpha}{M v^2}\right)^{1/2} F_0 r_0^2 \ s^{-1} \tag{5.15}$$

The ions formed by field emission are usually predominantly the parent ion; much less fragmentation occurring than is common with electron bombardment ionizers. The chief difficulties with this type of ionizer arise from instabilities in the ionization efficiency due either to erosion of the surface or condensation of polar molecules upon it. The wide angle over which the ions are emitted from the edge or point also makes their extraction into a mass spectrometer difficult. Elaborate lens system compensated for spherical aberration are required to achieve a high efficiency (H. D. Beckey, 1961).

Construction

The construction of a beam detector using this principle has been described by W. D. Johnston and J. G. King (1966). Their device is shown in Fig. 5.11. The ions emitted from the needle point follow field lines and strike a phosphor screen. The screen is viewed by a photomultiplier, scaling circuits are then used to count the ions arriving at the screen. Low frequency noise in the phosphor was reduced by beam modulation.

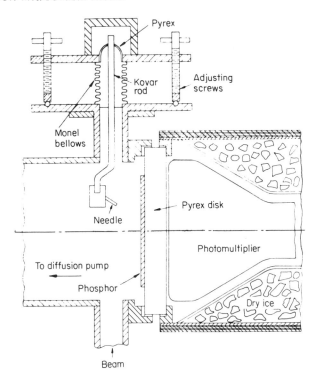

Fig. 5.11 Universal detector using field emission ionization and scintillation counting (reproduced from W.
D. Johnston and J. G. King, 1966).

Another source consisting of a series of thin wires approximately 2μ in
diameter has been described by H. D. Beckey et al, (1963), to replace a
conventional mass spectrometer source.

Sensitivity

The principal factors governing the sensitivity are the matching of the
ionizing region bounded by r_c with the beam cross-section and the extraction
of the ions into the mass spectrometer.

Noise

For the background gas the number of ions formed will be just the number of
molecules crossing a sphere of surface area $4\pi r_c^2$ centred on the point, i.e.

$$N_n = 2\pi r_c^2 \, \bar{v} n_b \qquad (5.16)$$

where n_b is the number density of the background gas and $\bar{v}$ its average
velocity.

The signal to noise ratio for a single needle point detector from background contributions of this type after mass selection is thus:

$$S/N = \frac{N_j k_j F(v)}{(\Sigma k_{(j-h)} N_h)^{\frac{1}{2}}} = \frac{\pi r_c^2 k_j F(v)}{(\Sigma 2\pi r_{c(h)}^2 \, \bar{v} \, n_h k_{(j-h)})^{\frac{1}{2}}} \qquad (5.17)$$

where k_j is the mass spectrometer transmission and $r_c^2{}_{(h)}$ is the critical distance for species h.

Response time

The actual period required for ionization is short of the order 10^{-11} s and the ionization region is relatively small so that response times in the range of 10^{-7} s might be expected.

5.3   Other types of detector

(i) Bolometer detectors

Thus far we have considered only detectors in which the beam molecules are ionized and differentiated from the background either by a mass spectrometer or by selective ionization. Other properties of the beam molecules however can be used. Thus detectors sensitive to the energy of the beam particles have been successful. The bolometers used for this purpose respond either to the kinetic energy of the beam or to some exothermic reaction of the material catalyzed by the bolometer surface, e.g. $2H \rightarrow H_2$ on a platinum surface (M. A. D. Fluendy, 1964). Bolometer detectors are likely to be of especial value in detecting super thermal beams for which electron bombardment ionization is inefficient. However, a superconducting bolometer operating at liquid He temperatures and capable of detecting thermal energy beams of 2×10^{14} molecules m^{-2} s^{-1} has been described (M. Cavallini, et al., 1967).

Construction

Bolometers used for molecular beam detection have usually been commercial devices designed for IR radiation detection. Both semiconductor and metal strip bolometers have been used. Their detailed construction will not be discussed further.

Sensitivity

The device is flux dependent — an important advantage.

A flux $F(v)$ of molecules mass M will yield a power to the bolometer of:

$$N_s = \tfrac{1}{2}Mv^2 F(v)\alpha \, (\tfrac{1}{2}Mv^2 - kT) \qquad (5.18)$$

where T is the temperature of the bolometer and α is the accommodation coefficient of the beam material on the bolometer surface. If a reaction occurs between the beam molecules on the bolometer surface a power

$$W = \Delta H \beta F(v) + N_s \qquad (5.19)$$

will be available. Where ΔH is the exothermicity and β is the sticking coefficient. (It is assumed that the whole of ΔH is available to the surface, i.e. the reaction products leave the surface completely accommodated.) In the case of H atoms, a detection limit of 5×10^{14} atoms m^{-2} s^{-1}, using their heat of recombination, was achieved.

Noise

Noise in bolometer detectors arises in several ways. Low frequency flicker noise is as usual minimized by modulating the beam and using a lock in amplifier. Other noise is due to collisions of the background gas with the bolometer and to Johnson noise in the bolometer itself. Ultra high vacuum technique using liquid helium will be especially valuable, since the low temperature will not only lower the background pressure but will also decrease the energy carried by the individual molecules to the bolometer. The lower operating temperature will also decrease the Johnson noise of the bolometer itself. Unhappily very low temperatures may inhibit surface diffusion and reaction so that detectors responding to an exothermic surface reaction may not be operable at these low temperatures.

Response time

Response times are typically 1–20 ms.

Stability

Instabilities in detector performance due to surface contamination can occur (especially in catalytic detectors). Improved vacuum technique is the usual solution.

5.4   Detection of excited atoms and molecules

Experiments with excited atoms or molecules have been rather popular since the problem of generating a beam of excited species are more than offset by the relative ease of detection. This ready detectability is due to two factors. Firstly the excited species commonly possess sufficient internal energy to differentiate them from the background gas by the ease with which they are ionized or bring about electron ejection from surfaces. Secondly their efficient de-excitation on collision with surfaces means that a 'background' of excited molecules does not develop in the apparatus.

The detection of excited atoms has been reviewed by J. B. Hasted, 1965, and also by E. E. Muschlitz, Jun., 1966. The most frequent method of detection is via electron ejection from a metal surface and measurement of the resulting current.

If E_a is the excitation energy of the species, ϕ the work function of the metal and D_q the depth of the lowest electron level, ejection will occur if:

$$E_a > \phi < D_q - \phi \qquad (5.20)$$

For $2^3 S$ He atoms Stebbings found an ejection efficiency of 0.29 from a gold surface. Lichten has used a surface plated with sodium (by evaporation) to detect mercury metastables (M. N. McDermott and W. C. Lichten, 1960). The sensitivity of these devices can be increased by incorporating an electron multiplier. Thus E. W. Rothe et al. (1965) has used a resistive strip multiplier to detect He $2^3 S$, the excited atom ejecting electrons from the multiplier strip itself. Metastables have also been detected by quenching the excited state in an electric field and detecting the photon liberated, e.g. W. L. Fite et al. (1959) quenched $2^2 S_{1/2}$ hydrogen atoms to the radiating state $2^2 P_{1/2}$. The detection of highly vibrationally excited alkali halides (where the radiative lifetime is long enough to enable beam formation) also appears possible. K. T. Gillen and R. B. Bernstein (1970) found that on a Pt/W (92.8 per cent) alloy filament, the fractional increase in KI ionized, was approximately $\exp(E_{ex}/4\,kT)$, where E_{ex} is the excitation energy carried by the KI. There would thus seem to be a possibility of a sensitive, though not highly selective detector for these states.

(i) Construction

Fig. 5.12 shows a detector for low energy metastables, e.g. Hg $6^3 P_2$. A low work function surface is prepared by plating a surface with alkali metal. Electrons ejected from this surface are focused into a channel electron multiplier. The tungsten peg shown in the figure may be withdrawn a few cms to be plated with potassium from a small effusive source A located close by. In an alternative pattern the peg is replaced by a rotating drum so that plating may proceed simultaneously with detection, this procedure being more successful in systems where contamination occurs rapidly.

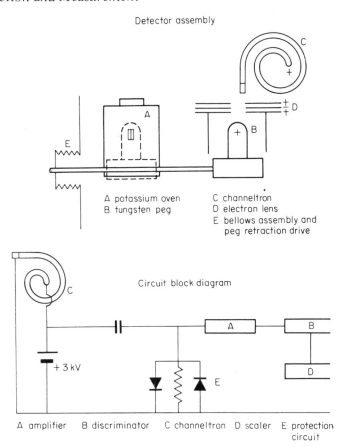

Fig. 5.12 Detector for metastable species using Auger electron ejection and particle counting

(ii) Sensitivity

Sensitivities in the range 0.5 electrons ejected per incident excited atom have been reported.

(iii) Noise

The noise is usually very small and may be largely electronic in origin, e.g. multiplier dark currents or response to photons.

(iv) Response time

For a detector using a multiplier the response time is largely a function of the multiplier construction and may be as short as a few nanoseconds. These detectors are thus the fastest available.

(v) Stability

Electron multipliers are rather sensitive to contamination by hydrocarbon or mercury vapour. As a result their initial gain may drop rapidly from say 10^7 to 10^5 or less, the final value being moderately stable. The resistive strip or channel multipliers are less sensitive to contamination than BeCuO types and are to be preferred in most applications. The stability problem can also be overcome by isolating the multiplier vacuum from the experimental system. Thus in Fig. 5.13 the electrons ejected from the surface by ion impact are accelerated through 40 kV to strike a phosphor surface. The resulting light pulses enter a sealed photo multiplier tube and are detected in the usual way.

5.5 The theory of detection systems

So far in this chapter we have discussed only the detectors themselves. In practice the actual sensors form only one element in the experiment and any meaningful analysis of their performance and capability must consider the system as a whole. To do so, we must digress briefly to consider the rate at which information can be obtained from experiments.

In principle we can achieve any desired precision provided we are prepared to observe our experiment for long enough. Unfortunately there is quite a restrictive practical limit to this procedure and we cannot normally extend our observation time by very many orders of magnitude. The *rate* at which we can acquire information from an experiment is therefore crucial. For a particular experimental configuration there will be a maximum possible rate at which information can be collected. This rate will depend upon the bandwidth (or response time) of the detector, the ratio of signal to noise powers and the statistics or frequency spectrum of the signal and noise. This result is due to Shannon who showed that if both signal and noise were Gaussian in distribution the maximum information rate was:

$$I = \Delta\nu \lg_2(1 + S^2/N^2)$$

where ν is the bandwidth and S^2 and N^2 are the signal and noise powers. In contrast to the maximum rate, the useful rate at which information can be accumulated will depend upon the rate at which the experimental variables are changed, e.g. the rate at which velocity or angle scans are made. If these are made too rapidly, the signal will vary faster than the detector response producing distortion and attenuation. On the other hand, scanning too slowly will not utilize the full bandwidth of the detector and the noise power will be

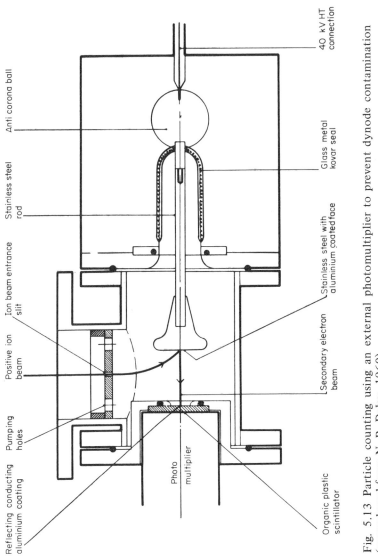

Anti corona ball

Stainless steel rod

Ion beam entrance slit

Positive ion beam

Pumping holes

Reflecting conducting aluminium coating

Photo multiplier

Organic plastic scintillator

Secondary electron beam

Stainless steel with aluminium coated face

Glass metal kovar seal

40 kV HT connection

Fig. 5.13 Particle counting using an external photomultiplier to prevent dynode contamination (reproduced from N. R. Daley, 1960).

147

higher than necessary (as we shall see, white noise increases linearly with bandwidth). The detector bandwidth should therefore be matched to the rate of scanning, the limit to Fourier terms in the expression of the signal output being set by the bandwidth.

Unfortunately a calculation of the maximum information rate possible in an experiment does not provide a prescription for achieving this efficiency. It does, however, provide a yardstick against which we can compare any filtering or analysis process we care to contrive.

(i) Frequency and time domains

Before we can go on to discuss methods of filtering etc., which may improve the rate at which information can be acquired we must discuss the representation of the signal and the noise.

For periodic signals it is possible to use a Fourier transform between frequency and time. Thus a wave-form having a time dependence $I(t)$ (in the time domain) may be equivalently written as a sum of harmonic sine waves:

$$I(t) = \frac{a_0}{2} + \sum_{n=1}^{\infty} \left(a_n \cos\left(\frac{2\pi nt}{\tau}\right) + b_n \sin\left(\frac{2\pi nt}{\tau}\right)\right) \qquad (5.21)$$

where τ is the period of $I_{(t)}$ and:

$$\left. \begin{array}{l} a_n = \dfrac{2}{\tau} \displaystyle\int_{-T/2}^{T/2} I(t) \cos\left(\dfrac{2\pi nt}{\tau}\right) dt \\[3mm] b_n = \dfrac{2}{\tau} \displaystyle\int_{-T/2}^{T/2} I(t) \sin\left(\dfrac{2\pi nt}{\tau}\right) dt \end{array} \right\} \qquad (5.22)$$

Thus for periodic $I(t)$ we can work either in a time or frequency domain with complete equivalence and we are able to consider filtering analysis techniques in either domain. This technique is powerful enough when dealing with signals which are periodic but is clearly inadequate to deal with signals and noise with random periods.

The Wiener Khintchine theorem generalizes these transformations to handle random signals and relates two functions, the auto correlation function:

$$F(\tau) = \int I(t)\, I(t+\tau)\, dt \qquad (5.23)$$

and the power density spectrum:

$$W(f) = 4 \int_0^{\infty} F(\tau) \cos(2\pi f\tau)\, d\tau \qquad (5.24)$$

The auto correlation function is a measure of the 'memory' or correlation of the signal $I(t)$ over the time τ. It varies from the mean square value of the signal $\bar{I^2}(t)$ at $\tau = 0$ to $\bar{I}(t)^2$ (or zero if the signal is pure a.c.) at $\tau = +\infty$ and contains all the information about the distribution of amplitudes in $I(t)$. Thus Gaussian white noise containing an infinite range of frequencies, is entirely uncorrelated so that the signal at time t has no predictive value for the signal at t + dt and the auto correlation function is zero except at $\tau = 0$. Conversely an entirely non-random periodic signal produces an $F(\tau)$ with a similar period extending over all τ for an infinite wave train.

The power density spectrum $W(f)$, in contrast to the representation of periodic signals in Equation 5.21, where only discrete harmonic frequencies appeared, represents a continuous distribution of frequencies with an energy $W(f)$ in the range f to $f + df$. This power density spectrum will not in general be a unique representation of $I(t)$, many $I(t)$s will exist which yield the same $W(f)$.

The bandwidth and response time of the detector can be related by these methods. Thus if the detector output is a time function $S(t)$ it can be shown that $S(t)$ can be uniquely determined by a sequence of only $2\Delta v$ points per second where Δv is the bandwidth. In other words the change in S over an interval $1/2\Delta v$ is determined completely by the speed of response limitations and not at all by changes in the 'message'. This result is known as the *Sampling Theorem*, i.e., we only need the input S at a discrete series of $2\Delta v$ points per second to generate the continuous output $S(t)$.

(ii) Noise

The noise forms $(n(t))$ we can expect to confront can be divided into two classes. The first comprises the 'highly organized' man made forms coming perhaps from adjacent experiments. Such interference is normally dealt with by shielding, turning off equipment etc., and need not concern us further.

The second class of noise is more fundamental in origin and as already discussed arises from the statistics of the devices used in the experiment and the random thermal motion of the electrons, atoms, etc., in the experimental arrangement. At absolute zero this noise will reach a minimum. There will also be a contribution to the noise due to the movement of electrodes, mechanical vibrations etc., this is often known as flicker noise.

Nyquist was able to show on thermodynamic grounds that the correlation of the thermal noise was zero except for extremely short times, i.e. the auto-correlation function = 0 except for $\tau = 0$ since positive and negative deviations cancel. For such noise we can see from Equation 5.24 that the power density is independent of frequency. The noise is 'white'.

The noise voltage developed across a resistor, R, in a band of Δv at frequency v is:

$$S(v) = \left(4kTR\,\Delta v\right)^{\frac{1}{2}} \tag{5.25}$$

For other types (e.g. flicker) $n(t)$ may be correlated for much longer periods and such noise will be far from white. In general we shall need to investigate the statistics or power density spectrum of both signal and noise before desiging an analysis or filtering method that will improve the information acquisition rate.

(iii) Beam detection

To proceed further let us consider a specific experiment in which we are concerned to distinguish between the signal due to a molecular beam which itself has short term fluctuations and contributions arising from background noise etc. At least two sorts of measurement are required. One with the beam running (beam flag open) the other with the beam off (flag closed). If we represent the signal due to the beam as a time function $s(t)$ and the background noise as $n(t)$ the two measurements will be:

$$I_1 = \frac{1}{T_3 - T_2} \int_{T_2}^{T_3} (s(t) + n(t))\,dt$$

$$I_2 = \frac{1}{T_2 - T_1} \int_{T_1}^{T_2} n(t)\,dt \tag{5.26}$$

Where the flag is open during $T_3 - T_2$ and closed during $T_2 - T_1$ the times being long in comparison to the response time of the detector. The estimate[*] of the steady beam signal where:

$$\bar{S} = \underset{T \to \infty}{\text{Lim}}\; \frac{1}{2T} \int_{-T}^{T} s(t)\,dt \tag{5.27}$$

will be:

$$\hat{S} = I_1 - I_2 \tag{5.28}$$

---

[*] We make the assumption that both the signal and the noise are stationary distributions, i.e. their average properties are time independent. This is likely to be a good approximation in most steady state experiments.

If the bandwidth of the detectors is $\Delta\nu$ we may use the central limit theorem to estimate the accuracy of this estimate $\hat{S}$. Ninety-five per cent confidence limits for $\hat{S}$ after N cycles of observation of I_2 and I_1 will be:

$$\pm 2\left(\frac{\text{Var}(\hat{S})}{N}\right)^{\frac{1}{2}} s^{-1} \qquad (5.29)$$

and the figure of merit for this detection system defined as the minimum particle current that can be measured with 95 per cent confidence to ± 20 per cent in an integration time of 100 seconds will be:

$$D = (\text{Var}(\hat{S}))^{\frac{1}{2}} / C \ \ s^{-1} \qquad (5.30)$$

where C is the sensitivity of the sensor. More usefully we can express $\text{Var}(\hat{S})$ in terms of the functions $s(t)$ and $n(t)$†
Thus

$$\text{Var}(\hat{S}) = \text{Var}(I_1 - I_2)$$
$$= \text{Var}(I_1) + \text{Var}(I_2) - 2 \ \text{Covar}(I_1 I_2) \qquad (5.31)$$

But

$$\text{Var}(I_2) = \frac{\text{Var}(n)}{t_c} = \text{Var}(\hat{n}) \text{ if } \Delta\nu > 1/t_c$$

where $\text{Var}(\hat{n})$ is the variance or square of the standard deviation of the population of samples t_c long viewed through a bandwidth window $\Delta\nu$ wide — t_c and t_o being the flag closed and open times respectively.
Similarly

$$\text{Var}(I_1) = \text{Var}(\hat{s}) + \text{Var}(\hat{n}) - 2 \ \text{Covar}(\hat{n}, \hat{s}) \qquad (5.32)$$

and

$$\text{Var}(\hat{S}) = \text{Var}(\hat{s}) + 2 \ \text{Var}(\hat{n}) - 2 \ \text{Covar}(\hat{n}, \hat{n}(t + t_0))$$
$$+ 2 \ \text{Covar}(\hat{n}, \hat{s}) - 2 \ \text{Covar}(\hat{s}, \hat{n}(t + t_0))$$

If the signal and noise are uncorrelated

$$\text{Var}(\hat{S}) = \text{Var}(\hat{s}) + 2 \ \text{Var}(\hat{n}) - 2 \ \text{Covar}(\hat{n}, \hat{n}(t + t_0)) \qquad (5.33)$$

† $(\text{Covar}(x, y) = \overline{xy} - \bar{x}\,\bar{y})$.

In this equation the final term represents the correlation between the noise during t_c and during t_o when the beam is on. It is thus a measure of the noise memory. For purely white or Gaussian noise covar $(\hat{n}(t)\,\hat{n}(t + \tau)) = 0$. In most experiments however, this is not true, though if the alternation between beam on and off is made slowly enough there will be zero correlation between the noise in the two intervals. Thus for these dc experiments the Equation 5.33 becomes:

$$\mathrm{Var}(\hat{S}) = \mathrm{Var}(\hat{s}) + 2\,\mathrm{Var}(\hat{n}) \qquad (5.34)$$

The optimum strategy for the ratio between beam on and off conditions is clearly that which will yield equal absolute precision in the two sub estimates I_2 and I_1. The best ratio of times t_o and t_c for beam on and beam off will be

$$\frac{t_0}{t_c} = \frac{\mathrm{Var}(\hat{s}) + \mathrm{Var}(\hat{n})}{\mathrm{Var}(\hat{n})} \qquad (5.35)$$

The dc experiment is far from optimum if the noise is correlated, i.e. its auto-correlation function is non zero for a range of τ.

Considerable improvement can be effected in this event. Looking again at Equation 5.28 we can rewrite the estimate of S as:

$$\hat{S} = \int_{T_0}^{T_1} \left\{ s(t) + n(t) - n(t + \tau) \right\} dt \qquad (5.36)$$

where $\tau = T_1 - T_0$; here we have combined the two equations (5.26) assuming equal on-off times. The variance for this estimate can be written with the covar $(n, n',)$ term replaced by:

$$\mathrm{Covar}\ (n, n') = F_n(T_1 - T_0) - \bar{n}^2 \qquad (5.37)$$

where $F_n(\tau)$ is the auto correlation function

$$F_n(\tau) = \underset{T \to \infty}{Lim}\ \frac{1}{2I} \int_{-T}^{T} n(t)\,n(t + \tau)\ dt, \qquad (5.38)$$

or in the case of successive measurements occupying a finite time as here

$$F_{\hat{n}}(j) = \sum_{i=0}^{i=\infty} \hat{n}_i \hat{n}_{i+j}$$

Depending upon the behaviour of $F_{\hat{n}}(\tau)$ and the period $(T_1 - T_0)$ the covar term Equation 5.37, will vary from covar $(\hat{n}, \hat{n}') = \mathrm{Var}(\hat{n})$ at $T_1 - T_0) = 0$, to zero when $(T_1 - T_0)$ is large. Thus if the period $(T_1 - T_0)$ can be made sufficiently short the Var $(\hat{n})$ and Covar (n, n') terms can be made to cancel, and a considerable reduction in variance is obtained.

$$\mathrm{Var}(S) \rightarrow \mathrm{Var}(\hat{s}) \qquad (5.39)$$

The particular period chosen for $(T_1 - T_0)$ will depend upon the auto-correlation function of the noise. This modulation frequency* is usually picked by using the Wiener-Khintchine theorem to find the power density spectrum of the noise. The frequency at which minimum noise power is found is then the optimum modulation frequency (subject of course to detector response time limitations). In practice, the covariance term will not completely counterbalance the variance due to the noise. Nevertheless, the modulation process is almost always advantageous. Fig. 5.14 shows a typical arrangement.

In many applications the noise and signal can be quite highly correlated. It is then important to modulate that feature of the experiment which has the

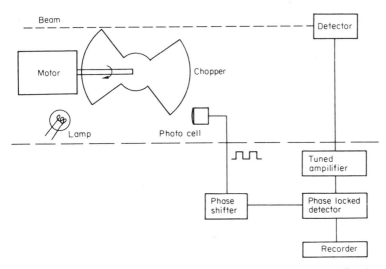

Fig. 5.14 Modulated beam system with a phase locked amplifier in the detection chain.

* Normally the open and closed periods are taken equal in the modulation process for electronic convenience and the beam is interrupted by a rotating disc driven by a synchronous electric motor.

minimum correlation with the additive noise. Thus if we are detecting K scattered from a cross beam of another species we should modulate the cross beam. Only in this way can we distinguish the K scattered from the cross beam from that scattered into the detector by collisions with the background gas.

Still further improvements to the filtering of the detector output are possible. Consider the two estimates I_1 and I_2 again, but now suppose that we continuously divide the detected signal by some time dependent quantity $f(t)$.

$$I_1 = \frac{1}{T_3 - T_2} \int_{T_2}^{T_3} \left(\frac{s(t)}{f(t)} + \frac{n(t)}{f(t)} \right) dt$$

$$I_2 = \frac{1}{T_2 - T_1} \int_{T_1}^{T_2} \frac{n(t)}{f(t)} dt$$

(5.40)

If $f(t)$ is strongly correlated with $s(t)$, for example if $f(t)$ was the main beam signal and $s(t)$ the signal scattered at some angle (θ). Then the differential cross-section $\sigma(\theta)$ is given by:

$$\sigma(\theta) \propto \frac{s(t)}{f(t)}$$

so that

$$\sigma(\theta) \propto \mathrm{Lim} \, (I_1 - I_2)$$

(5.41)

and the relative cross-section can be estimated directly. The variance of this estimate will be:

$$\mathrm{Var}\,(\sigma(\theta)) = 2 \, \mathrm{Var}\left(\frac{\hat{n}(t)}{f(t)} \right) - 2 \, \mathrm{Covar}\left(\frac{\hat{n}(t)}{f(t)}, \frac{\hat{n}(t+\tau)}{f(t+\tau)} \right)$$

(5.42)

We have removed the variance introduced by changes in the beam intensity of Equation 5.34. Experimentally this involves recording the output from two detectors simultaneously. One detector recording the main beam and the other $s(t)$. This system of analysis is known as cross correlation. Since the main beam signal will be large we can neglect the additive noise and treat the recorded signal from this detector as being purely due to beam fluctuations.

As before, beam modulation can be used to reduce the noise arising from the background. The appropriate auto-correlation function will be:

$$F(\tau) = \int \left(\frac{n(t + \tau)}{f(t + \tau)} \right) \left(\frac{n(t)}{f(t)} \right) \mathrm{d}t \qquad (5.43)$$

An alternative procedure might rely upon the signal statistics. For normal beam sources the signal auto-correlation is appreciable for quite large τ. Consequently we could use a modulation technique in which a single detector measures the signal intensity sequentially under two different conditions. Thus if these different observations are:

$$I_1 = \int_{T_0}^{T_1} (s(t) + n(t)) \, \mathrm{d}t$$

$$I_2 = \int_{T_0}^{T_1} n(t + \tau) \, \mathrm{d}t$$

$$I_3 = c \int_{T_0}^{T_1} s(t + 2\tau) \, \mathrm{d}t \qquad (5.44)$$

where $cs(t)$ is the 'normalising' signal condition and $\tau = T_1 - T_0$. The estimate of σ relative to the normalising condition is:

$$\hat{\sigma} = (I_1 - I_2)/I_3$$

averaged over many periods.
The variance of this estimate is:

$$\mathrm{Var}\,(\sigma) = \frac{1}{c^2} \mathrm{Var} \left(\frac{I_1 - I_2}{I_3} \right) = \frac{1}{c^2} \left[\int \left(\frac{s(t)}{s(t + 2\tau)} \right)^2 \mathrm{d}t - \left(\int \frac{s(t)}{s(t + \tau)} \mathrm{d}t \right)^2 \right.$$

$$\left. + \frac{2}{S^2} (\bar{n}^2 - \phi_n(\tau)) + 2 \frac{\bar{n}}{S} \int \frac{s(t)}{s(t + 2\tau)} \, \mathrm{d}t \quad (5.45) \right.$$

The variance due to beam fluctuations has thus been replaced by a measure of its auto-correlation so that if τ can be made short enough the variance from this source will be reduced.

Filtering

The techniques for signal analysis discussed are examples of auto and cross correlation. The procedures described are by no means exhaustive. A more comprehensive theory has been developed by N. Wiener (1949). We shall see that it is in principle possible to design an optimum filter for any application for which the statistics of the signal and noise are known.

In any experiment we are in general concerned to measure the scattered intensity as a function of one or more experimental variables such as collision energy or scattering angle. The problem is to determine the optimum filtering operation which when applied to the primary measurements will yield the closest approach to the correct result.

Consider a set of $m + 1$ observations:

$$b_0, b_1, \ldots b_k, \ldots b_m$$

representing a series of intensity measurements at values of the variable $0, 1, \ldots k, m$. Further let us suppose that the exact values that we should have observed if our measurements had been made under noiseless conditions are:

$$M_0, M_1, \ldots M_k, \ldots M_m$$

We perform a linear filtering operation with a lag s on the observed values to yield an output.

$$a_{k-s} = \sum_{n=0}^{n=h \leqslant m} A_n b_{k-n} \tag{5.46}$$

Where the coefficients A_n represent our filter function of h elements.

The error between the exact value and the output filtered results is therefore:

$$I_{k-s} = M_{k-s} - a_{k-s}$$

$$I_{k-s} = M_{k-s} - \sum_{0}^{h} A_n b_{k-n}$$

The mean square error over the whole series will thus be:

$$I = \frac{1}{m+h} \sum_{k=0}^{m+h} \left(M_{k-s} - \sum_{n=0}^{n-h} A_n b_{k-n} \right)^2 \tag{5.47}$$

The filter can be optimized in the sense of providing an output with the least mean square error by differentiating Equation 5.47 with respect to each filter coefficient and equating each differential coefficient to zero:

$$\frac{\partial I}{\partial A_1} = \sum_{k=0}^{m+h} (m_{k-s} - \sum_{n=0}^{h} A_n b_{k-n})(-b_{k-j}) = 0$$

so

$$\sum_n A_n \sum_k b_{k-n} b_{k-j} = \sum_k M_{k-s} b_{k-j} \qquad (5.48)$$

But $(m+h)^{-1} \sum_k b_{k-j} b_{k-n}$ is the discrete signal form, $F_b(n-j)$, of the auto-correlation function Equation 5.25 for a lag of $(n-j)$. Similarly, $(m+h)^{-1} \sum M_{k-s} b_{k-j}$ is the cross-correlation function (defined as $M(t)b(t+\tau)dt$), $X_{Mb}(s-j)$. Thus we obtain:

$$\sum_{n=0}^{h} A_n F_b(n-j) = X_{Mb}(s-j) \qquad (5.49)$$

as our optimising equation from which the optimum set of filtering coefficients can be obtained. For an additive noise N_i:

$$b_i = M_i + N_i \qquad (5.50)$$

we can write the auto- and cross-correlation functions in Equation 5.49 as the sum of the individual functions for the noise and 'message':

$$F_b(n-j) = F_M(n-j) + F_N(n-j) + 2X_{MN}(n-j)$$

and

$$X_{Mb}(s-j) = F_M(s-j) + X_{MN}(s-j) \qquad (5.51)$$

Thus information on the message (M) and noise statistics can be applied directly to the calculation of an optimum filter. The best lag and length for the filter are usually determined by letting s and m increase until the mean square error shows little further decrease.

In the event that the filtering scheme is required not to produce as closely as possible the noiseless 'message' but merely to yield some parameter of it such as its arrival time similar techniques can be used but will yield smaller mean square errors. For a more detailed discussion the reader is referred to C. A. Robinson (1967).

5.6 Ion counting systems

The foregoing analysis has been made for continuous or analog signals but can be extended to include the output of particle counters. The primary signal in such counting systems however is still in analog form, e.g. the output of an electron multiplier. This signal is digitized by a discriminating circuit which has an output only when the input signal exceeds a certain level. The signal can thereafter be handled digitally and without fear of adding any electronic noise. The optimum threshold for the discrimination depends upon the amplitude and statistics of the noise and signal. The larger the difference in amplitude between noise and signal pulses the less important the setting of the discriminator threshold (Fig. 5.15).

To extend our analysis to deal with this type of pulse output we must interpret the signal and noise time dependent functions used in interpreting analog signals as probability density functions. These describe the probability of a pulse occurring in a period t to $t + dt$, i.e. as instantaneous count rates. Thus for the simple experiment already discussed in which the beam flag is alternately opened and closed at near zero frequency we have

N_n = average number of noise counts sec^{-1}

S = average number of signal counts sec^{-1}

C = neutral particle counting efficiency (counts molecule^{-1})

σ_n = standard deviation of the noise count rate.

The figure of merit* for the detector (minimum particle current measurable to ±20 per cent in 100 secs with 95 per cent confidence) will be:

$$D = \sigma_n/C$$

For white noise, i.e. uncorrelated arrivals of the noise pulses the de Moivre

---

* The *maximum* rate at which counts may be accumulated depends upon the 'resolving time' or time after counting one pulse during which the system will not respond to another. Due to the random arrival of the pulses some counts will inevitably be lost due to overlap. For uncorrelated pulses, if S is the observed count rate, t the resolving time, the true count rate n will be

$$n = \frac{S}{1 - St} \qquad (5.52)$$

The counting loss should not be allowed to exceed a few per cent or the accuracy of the measurements will be badly affected. Particular care is needed if the pulse statistics are not Gaussian, thus emission of ions from a hot filament occurs in 'bursts' during which the instantaneous count rate may be very large. The counting loss may then greatly exceed that calculated from Equation 5.52.

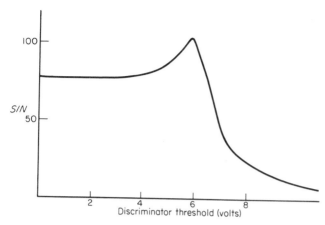

Fig. 5.15 Plot of signal/noise ratio versus pulse height transmitted showing the optimum discriminator setting. A sizeable fraction of the noise has a lower peak height than the average signal pulse.

Laplace theorem asserts that $\sigma_n \approx \bar{N}_n^{1/2}$, i.e. for white noise the figure of merit is:

$$D = \bar{N}_n^{1/2}/C \qquad (5.53)$$

The optimum threshold for the discriminator can thus be determined by optimizing D above. Improvement in the sensitivity can be achieved either by increasing C or by decreasing the noise background. In both cases however, the overall improvement in sensitivity will only vary as the square root since the noise count is also proportional to C.

The counting efficiency depends upon the detector (the average number of ions or electrons ejected per incident molecule), the transmission to the multiplier and the multiplier gain. Conventional multipliers using BeCuO plates are sensitive to contamination (particularly by reactive chemical species) and are best avoided. Resistive strip or channel multipliers are much less sensitive and very much more suitable.

If the rate of arrival of the noise pulses is non Gaussian, and in particular, if low frequency noise components are present, modulation methods similar in principle to those already described may be used. In these systems the phase sensitive detector is replaced by two or more pulse counters. Each counter is then opened for a different phase of the modulation. This type of system can be fairly readily extended to encompass quite complicated modulation schemes. As an example Fig. 5.16 (L. T. Cowley et al., 1969)

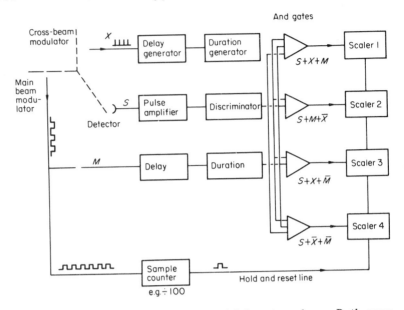

Fig. 5.16 Counting analog of a 'lock in' detector scheme. Both cross and main beams are modulated at different frequencies.

shows a cross-beam experiment in which both beams are modulated, one at a convenient multiple of the frequency of the other.

If $m(t)$ and $x(t)$ are functions representing the main and cross-beam signals, $n(t)$ is the background signal from the species being detected and $V(t)$ is linearly related to the pressure in the scattering chamber. Then the detector output $Si(t)$ will be given approximately by the following table:

Cross beam	Main beam	
on	on	$S_1(t) = Km(t)\,x(t) + n(t) + V(t)m(t) + V(t)x(t)$
off	on	$S_2(t) = n(t) + m(t)V(t)$
on	off	$S_3(t) = n(t) + x(t)V(t)$
off	off	$S_4(t) = n(t)$

Where $m(t)V(t)$ and $x(t)V(t)$ represent the noise contribution produced by scattering the main and cross-beam respectively from the background gas. The scattered signal $Km(t)x(t)$ containing the differential cross-section information will thus be $I = S_1 - S_2 - S_3 + S_4$. Arguing as before we can see Var(I) will include a number of terms describing the co-variation of $x(t)$, $m(t)V(t)$ and $n(t)$ during the observation periods of $S_1 S_2 S_3 S_4$. Thus if the time spent in observing S_1 to S_4 can be made short compared to the time over which the functions $x(t)$, $m(t)$, $V(t)$, $n(t)$ are appreciably auto-correlated then the variance of I will be reduced. In the figure each of the four scalers is driven via a coincidence, anti-coincidence gate so that counts corresponding to the four possible beam flag conditions can be accumulated.

(i) Coincidence and time of flight systems

The use of coincidence gates can be extended to obtain much more detailed information. For two body collisions the centre of mass motion is conserved and two particles of mass M_1 and M_2 emitted from such a collision and scattered through angles θ_1 and θ_2 to the incident beam direction must have specific velocities v_1 and v_2. Thus if two detectors are sited on a radius of l at θ_1 and θ_2 the two emitted particles will produce signal pulses at times $l\,v_1$ and $l\,v_2$ one from each detector. In general, pulse pairs will arrive with time delays determined by the energy transferred in the collision. A system which responds to pulses from different detectors spaced in time by an appropriate amount will thus yield information on the exothermicity of the collisions. A further advantage is the large reduction in signal variance that can be achieved.

Let the number of collisions of the specified sort (i.e. given exothermicity channel and differential cross-section) be N per second and the number of background particles striking at detectors A and B be M_A and M_B. If ϵ_A and ϵ_B are the efficiencies with which the detectors convert particles incident upon them to pulses then the number of signal and noise pulses will be:

At Detector A

Noise $= M_A \epsilon_A$　　　　Signal $= N\epsilon_A$

At Detector B

Noise $= M_B \epsilon_B$　　　　Signal $= N\epsilon_B$

Thus for random arrival of noise pulses the figure of merit for each detector will be:

$$\sqrt{M_A/\epsilon_A} \qquad \text{and} \qquad \sqrt{M_B/\epsilon_B}$$

and the minimum number of potentially detectable events that could be measured with the specified precision would be:

$$N = \sqrt{\frac{M_A}{\epsilon_A}} \qquad \text{and} \qquad \sqrt{\frac{M_B}{\epsilon_B}}$$

at each detector.

If we now use a coincidence detection system such that an output is only taken if detector B has a pulse present in a period τ some specified time after a pulse has occurred in detector A. Then the noise and signal will be:

$$\text{Noise} = \epsilon_A M_A \ \tau M_B \epsilon_B$$

$$\text{Signal} = N \epsilon_A \epsilon_B$$

(Assuming $N \ll M_A$ and M_B which is the interesting case.)

The minimum number of potentially detectable collisions that must occur to be measured with our standard precision is:

$$N = \sqrt{\frac{M_A M_B \tau}{\epsilon_A \epsilon_B}} \tag{5.56}$$

Thus if τ can be made sufficiently short and ϵ_A and ϵ_B are not too different from unity a large improvement in sensitivity can be achieved. As an example let

$$\epsilon_A \sim \epsilon_B \sim 0.5, M_A \sim M_B \sim 10^4 \text{ and } \tau = 10^{-7} \text{ s}$$

The individual detectors would have a figure of merit of:

$$\sqrt{\frac{M_A}{\epsilon_A}} \sim 140 \text{ counts s}^{-1}$$

As a coincidence system the minimum count rate would be:

$$\sqrt{\frac{M_A M_B \tau}{\epsilon_A \epsilon_B}} = 6.3 \text{ counts s}^{-1}$$

For the coincidence system additional information as to the exothermicity of the collision would also be available. Unfortunately the detector requirements of high efficiency and very fast response time are met by few detectors, essentially only those involving direct excitation of the multiplier, either by the collision of an energetic particle or by a photon being suitable. Relatively low backgrounds are also required if the gated detector is not to be permanently open, i.e. $M_A \tau$ must be small compared to 1 s.

Fig.5.17 shows a suitable arrangement for coincident detection. By using beam choppers and suitable additional logic units modulation could be superimposed on the coincidence detector.

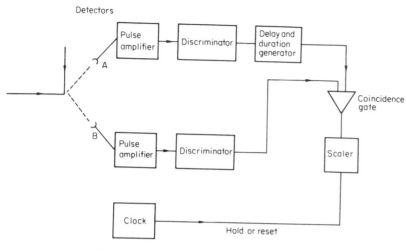

Fig. 5.17 Coincident detection scheme.

The delayed coincident detection system suffers from the drawback that only one particular exothermicity is accepted for each setting of the delay. In some experiments a range of post collision velocities are present and it may be desired to examine their distribution experimentally. The simplest but slowest procedure would be to use the coincident system and take a range of measurements for different delay times. Another alternative would be to use additional delay generators, coincidence gates and scalers, each chain corresponding to a different delay time. Unfortunately if many observation points are required this arrangement becomes very expensive. In these circumstances the arrangement shown in Fig. 5.18 may be used. This system employs a pulse height analyzer which is capable of sorting input pulses into a large number of separate scalers according to the pulse amplitude. The pulses

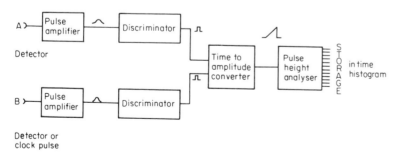

Fig. 5.18 Time of flight analysis using a time to amplitude converter followed by pulse height analysis.

are amplified and discriminated in the usual way and then both detector pulses pass to a time to amplitude convector which produces pulses whose amplitude is proportional to the time difference between successive pulses in channels A and B. The PHA then accumulates the output pulses in accordance with their amplitude (i.e. time difference in this case). The random noise pulses in both detectors are uncorrelated and produce a flat distribution. A disadvantage of this system is the relatively slow speed of the PHA so that counts and hence data can only be accumulated fairly slowly. Of course, if the available signal count rates are already low, this is no additional disadvantage.

As an alternative to coincident detection a single detector may be employed. One of the beams is then pulsed to provide a time reference and the received signal gated after a suitable delay. This technique of 'time of flight' is discussed in more detail in Chapter 4.

CHAPTER SIX

Quantum Mechanics of Scattering

6.1 Introduction

This chapter is largely devoted to deriving the more commonly used formulae that relate elastic scattering to intermolecular potentials and to indicating how the forward calculation, from assumed potential to scattering pattern, can be made. At the outset the notation has been made formal enough to allow the framework to cover inelastic collisions, though in practice the analysis of such events is much more subject to approximation than is elastic scattering. Elementary scattering theory is nowadays treated in all textbooks of wave mechanics for physicists and notable among these are those by E. Merzbacher (1961) and L. D. Landau and E. M. Lifshitz (1958), for their treatment of scattering; a fuller development can be found in L. S. Rodberg and R. M. Thaler (1967), T. Y. Wu and T. Ohmura (1962) or R. Newton (1966).

The evidence for the breakdown of classical mechanics in calculating the details of elastic molecular collisions can be summarized as follows:

(1) The existence of finite rather than infinite total cross-sections. Experimentally (Chapter 7), the differential cross-section $\sigma(\chi)$ reaches a finite limiting value as the scattering angle tends to zero and so the measured total cross-section also tends to a finite value as the angular resolution is improved.

(2) The observation that rainbow structures have a finite amplitude that becomes independent of the resolution as the resolution is improved. Classical mechanics (Chapter 2) predicts a divergence in $\sigma(\chi)$ at the rainbow.

(3) The observation of undulations in $\sigma(\chi)$, especially at small angles, where classical mechanics predicts monotonic behaviour.

(4) The existence of undulations in the energy dependence of the total cross-section, when classical mechanics predicts a monotonic dependence (this point will turn out to be closely related to (3)).

Finally when a cross-section is measured for scattering accompanied by a specific change in internal quantum state, then wave mechanics will have to be used, if only to treat the internal motion.

In general, the differences in behaviour predicted by classical and quantum mechanics for the details of thermal collisions are very pronounced – unlike, say, the quantum corrections to gas compressibilities or transport properties at room temperature. The essential factor here is resolution; under conditions of poor angular or energy resolution, quantum molecular scattering patterns will be close to those predicted by classical mechanics if both results are averaged over the appropriate apparatus functions. However, partly because absolute cross-sections are difficult to measure, the usefulness of elastic scattering data lies in resolving and interpreting the angular or energy structure. Here wave mechanics is essential, although low resolution experiments can yield a great deal of information when applied to gross effects such as chemical reaction.

With the insight given by wave mechanics we can see two reasons why classical mechanics might break down when applied to an actual molecular scattering experiment. The first is that the best wave packet we might construct to represent the classical particle by a wave function, does not move along a well defined trajectory in the presence of the intermolecular field. The second difficulty is that classically a particle reaching the detector might have followed one of several paths resulting in the same angle of deflection. This is a similar situation to the hypothetical interfering slit experiment discussed in wave mechanics and the absence of any information as to the actual path leads to mutual interference.

Treating first the approximation of replacing a wave packet by a classical particle, there are two aspects of the problem. If we are to use classical mechanics for the radial motion associated with any particular trajectory, we require that the equivalent wave packet does not spread appreciably during the collision, either in the forward or transverse direction. Such a wave packet is constructed from a range of momentum states and if the classical property, such as deflection angle or time delay, varies appreciably among the constituent waves of the packet, classical mechanics cannot give a reliable picture of the behaviour of the whole wave packet, merely of its centroid.

If the change in time delay induced by the collision in constituent plane waves of slightly differing velocity is too large, the wave packet will begin to spread rapidly after the collision. Under these conditions both the classical approximation and the concept of interference between different parts of the scattered wave front, frequently used in this chapter, breaks down (T. Y. Wu and T. Ohmura, 1962). We saw in Chapter 2 that the classical time delay is related to the phase shifts by

$$\tau_l = \frac{1}{\hbar} \frac{\partial \eta_l}{\partial E} = \frac{2\mu}{\hbar k} \frac{\partial \eta_l}{\partial k}$$

The spread in time delay across a wave packet constructed from a range of wave numbers thus depends upon $[\partial^2 \eta_l / \partial k^2] \Delta k$. If this quantity becomes too large, the 'resonance' must be considered separately (L. D. Landau and E. M. Lifschitz, 1958). Fortunately, the maximum time delay normally associated with molecular scattering at thermal speeds is $\lesssim 10^{-12}$ s, which is much shorter than the time taken for the whole wave packet to pass the target. Long delay times, associated with classical orbiting, do occur but affect only a small part of the incident wave front.

A wave packet also ceases to behave like a classical particle if the predominant wavelength λ ($= 1/k$) becomes comparable to the range of the scattering potential. Under these conditions reflection occurs from the regions of more rapidly changing potential — an entirely non-classical phenomenon. At thermal energies $\lambda/\sigma_{LJ} \lesssim 0.2$ and so such reflections (and associated tunneling phenomena) should not cause a widespread breakdown of classical mechanics.

A rather different reason why we might not be able to construct a wave packet that moves along the expected classical trajectory, lies in the precision with which we must specify the impact parameter and the effect this has on the uncertainty in the transverse momentum of the wave packet, p_x. Let the angle of deflection in CM coordinates be χ; the transverse momentum transferred from projectile to target is

$$\Delta p_x \approx \mu v_z \sin \chi \approx \mu v_z \chi \qquad (6.1)$$

where the initial velocity is in the z-direction. In theory we can construct a wave packet with as precise a transverse velocity as we wish, but the price is paid in the growing uncertainty of the lateral displacement, b. Like all relationships based upon wave packet considerations, the result is given by the appropriate uncertainty principle,

$$\delta b \delta p_x \sim \hbar. \tag{6.2}$$

For the classical trajectory to be well defined, we require $\delta b \ll b$ and so the wave packet must be constructed from a range of momentum states of width $\delta p_x \gg \hbar/b$. This uncertainty δp_x implies, from Equation 6.1, an uncertainty in the angle of deflection $\delta \chi$ given by

$$\delta \chi \approx \delta p_x / \mu v_z. \tag{6.3}$$

From Equation 2.31, χ is related to b at small deflections by

$$\chi \approx s C_s / (E b^s) \sim V(b)/E, \tag{6.4}$$

the first relationship holding for a potential of the form $V = C_s R^{-s}$. If the fractional uncertainty in the angle of deflection is to be small, $\delta \chi / \chi \ll 1$, combining the above relationships gives

$$\lambda/b \ll \chi \tag{6.5}$$

But, from Equation 6.4, $\chi \propto b^{-s}$ and so whatever the value of λ, Equation 6.5 imposes a lower limit on χ beyond which the scattering cannot be classical. At thermal energies $\lambda \sim 10^{-8}$ mm and so the breakdown of classical scattering can be expected for angles less than $\sim 1°$. When the partial wave analysis of scattering is discussed, it will emerge that at very small angles, in contrast to larger angle scattering, the scattered intensity cannot be attributed to a narrow range of impact parameters centred around the value corresponding classically to the angle of observation.

　　For molecular scattering, a much more important deficiency of classical mechanics is its failure to take into account interfering trajectories. These arise when two or more impact parameters lead to the same angle of deflection. In an actual scattering experiment the target is bombarded by a beam of macroscopic dimensions that, however well collimated, contains a virtually infinite number of angular momentum states. Even if the beams are stopped down to 0.1 mm (which would be very good collimation) the range of possible impact parameters would extend to $\sim 10^6$ molecular diameters. If the beam were made so narrow that it extended over only the dimensions of a molecule, diffraction effects at the slit (themselves a scattering phenomenon) would be so pronounced that the measured differential cross-section could not be defined with respect to a parallel incident beam.

No measurement is made of the impact parameter during the collision and we must make any wave function of the system reflect this virtually complete uncertainty. Adopting the terminology of optics for a moment, a detector in a beam experiment receives contributions from all the secondary scattered waves originating across a virtually infinite wave front. The amplitudes of each partial wave must be added before squaring to calculate the resulting intensity. If we choose to analyze the problem in terms of angular momentum states, the scattered amplitude resulting from each state must be added to calculate the final scattered amplitude. It will emerge that in molecular scattering there are, over a wide angular range, frequently two or three groups of angular momentum states with almost stationary phase and these correspond to classical interfering paths in R. P. Feynmann's and A. R. Hibbs' (1965) sense.

6.2 Boundary conditions for solutions of the wave equations

The wave mechanical problem is discussed in the relative co-ordinate system that was used for the classical treatment, augmented by whatever internal co-ordinates are necessary to cover inelastic events. The motion of the centre of mass of the whole system is factored out of the wave function, leaving the wave function for relative motion $\psi(\mathbf{R})$ to satisfy

$$\{-\hbar^2/2\mu \nabla^2 + V(R)\}\, \Psi(\mathbf{R}) = E\Psi(\mathbf{R}) \tag{6.6}$$

where, as for most of this chapter, the colliding particles are assumed to be structureless. $\psi(\mathbf{R})$ must have the following asymptotic form outside the range of the potential $V(R)$;

$$\Psi(\mathbf{R}) \xrightarrow[R \to \infty]{} \frac{1}{\mathcal{N}^{1/2}} \left\{ e^{ikz} + \frac{1}{R} f(\chi) e^{ikR} \right\} \tag{6.7}$$

and also satisfy

$$\Psi(\mathbf{R}) \xrightarrow[R \to 0]{} 0 \tag{6.8}$$

This type of wave function can be interpreted with the aid of the momentum operator,

$$\mu v = -i\hbar \partial/\partial \mathbf{R} \tag{6.9}$$

and the derived flux Equation 6.10 below. The gradient in Equation 6.9 is taken in the direction in which the component of the velocity of the equivalent classical particle mass μ is required.

The first term in Equation 6.7 represents a plane wave travelling with velocity $v = \hbar k/\mu$ in the z-direction and the second term is an outgoing spherical wave with an angle dependent amplitude $f(\chi)$. The function $f(\chi)$ contains all the information about the scattering process and it is central to the discussion of all scattering processes. The plane wave function $\exp(ikz)$ represents a uniform density of particles extending from $z = -\infty$ to ∞; Equation 6.7 thus represents a steady state solution with a continuous input of particles. The plane wave in Equation 6.7 also has an infinitely broad front, unlike the well collimated beams of actual experiments, but no error will result if interference terms between the incoming and outgoing waves are neglected except in the region where they do in fact overlap along the positive z-axis.

Before the calculation of $f(\chi)$ is discussed, the use of Equation 6.7 is illustrated by deriving the formula for the elastic differential cross-section $\sigma(\chi)$ in terms of $f(\chi)$. The asymptotic flux at a point (R, χ, ϕ) other than on the z-axis is given solely by the second term in Equation 6.10 as $R \to \infty$, provided that the incident beam is of finite width. Applying the standard formula for the flux,

$$ \mathbf{j} = -\frac{\hbar}{2i\mu}\left\{ \Psi \, \nabla \, \Psi^* - \Psi^* \, \nabla \, \Psi \right\} \tag{6.10} $$

(Note that the normalization factor $\mathcal{N}$ in Equation 6.7 must have the dimensions of volume in order to give $\mathbf{j}$ the dimensions of flux and it is conveniently assigned the value 1 cm^3), the plane wave gives a flux of v particles cm^{-2} in the z direction and the spherical wave in Equation 6.7 yields

$$ j_R = |f(\chi)|^2 v/R^2 \tag{6.11} $$

Only the radial component of $\mathbf{j}$ is non-zero (as can be verified later) after the scattering is over. From the definition (see Section 2.1) of the differential cross-section $\sigma(\chi)$ in terms of the number of particles dn scattered into a solid angle $d\omega$ per second per unit incident flux, Equation 6.11 gives

$$ dn = |f(\chi)|^2 \, d\omega $$

and so

$$ \sigma(\chi, \phi) = dn/d\omega = |f(\chi)|^2 \tag{6.12} $$

The total cross-section follows from the integration of $\sigma(\chi)$ over a sphere centred on the scattering centre:

$$\sigma_{tot} = \int_0^{2\pi} \int_0^{\pi} |f(\chi)|^2 \sin \chi \, d\chi \, d\phi \qquad (6.13)$$

We can discuss some aspects of the conservation of matter during collision. In order to generalize the discussion a little, we will suppose that the target has internal states $\Phi_n(\mathbf{r})$ and that these can be excited during collision. Equation 6.7 is then readily generalized to

$$\Psi \xrightarrow[R \to \infty]{} e^{ikz}\Phi_0(\mathbf{r}) + \frac{1}{R} \sum_{n=0} f_n(\chi) e^{ik_n R} \Phi_n(\mathbf{r}) = \sum_n \Psi_n(\mathbf{R})\Phi_n(\mathbf{r})$$

$$(6.14)$$

where the normalization factor has been dropped and the wave number k_n is given by

$$k_n = \sqrt{2\mu E_n}/\hbar \qquad (6.15)$$

where $E_n = E_0 - \epsilon_n$ is the relative kinetic energy after exciting the nth state. The conservation of energy is thus built into the wave function. To ensure the conservation of particles, the total current across a closed surface s surrounding the scattering centre must vanish:

$$\sum_n \int_S \mathbf{j}_n \cdot d\mathbf{s} = 0 \qquad (6.16)$$

where $\mathbf{j}_n$ is the flux of particles scattered with excitation of the nth state and the integration is conveniently over the surface of an infinitely large sphere. In principle, we can measure separately the fluxes associated with exciting different internal states by placing a velocity or state selector in front of the detector. If this is not done, the total signal i received by the detector is the sum of the contributions from the different states:

$$i(\chi) = \sum_n i_n(\chi), \qquad (6.17)$$

since there is no interference between the signals, just as the total cross-section is the sum of the cross-sections contributed by different exit channels rather than the square of the sum of the scattered amplitudes. **We** thus extend the flux formula slightly to the inelastic case by writing

$$j_n = -\frac{\hbar}{2i\mu}\left\{\Psi_n \nabla \Psi_n^* - \Psi_n^* \nabla \Psi_n\right\} \qquad (6.18)$$

where the orthogonality of the internal states Φ_n ensures that there is no asymptotic interference between different exit channels.

The expression 6.18 is most conveniently evaluated by changing completely to spherical polar co-ordinates, and so the plane wave component is written $e^{ikR\cos\chi}$. The number of particles scattered per second that leave the target in its original state, i_0, is then

$$i_0 = \int_s j_0 \, dS = \frac{\pi\hbar}{i\mathcal{N}\mu}\int R^2 \sin\chi d\chi \left\{ e^{+ik_0 R\cos\chi} \nabla_R e^{-ik_0 R\cos\chi} \right.$$
$$+ R^{-1} e^{ik_0 R\cos\chi} \nabla_R f_0(\chi) e^{-ik_0 R} + R^{-1} e^{ik_0 R} f_0(\chi) \nabla_R e^{-ik_0 R\cos\chi}$$
$$\left. + R^{-2} |f_0(\chi)|^2 e^{ik_0 R} \nabla_R e^{-ik_0 R} - \text{complex conjugate} \right\} \qquad (6.19)$$

The reader should follow through each term in Equation 6.19. Thus, the first term reduces to $(\pi\hbar R^2/\mathcal{N}\mu)\int_0^{2\pi} k_0 \cos\chi \sin\chi \, d\chi$, which vanishes by symmetry. The second and third terms together with their complex conjugates represent interference between the plane and spherical waves. Upon repeated integration by parts, an expansion in $1/R$ is developed. Retaining only the leading term as $R \to \infty$, the result is

$$i_0 = \frac{4\pi v_0}{k\mathcal{N}} \text{Im} f_0(0) + \frac{2\pi v_0}{\mathcal{N}} \int_0^\pi |f_0(\chi)|^2 \sin\chi d\chi \quad (v_i = \hbar k_i/\mu) \qquad (6.20)$$

where the first term comes from the second and third terms in Equation 6.19 and the second term from the fourth and fifth terms in Equation 6.19. We note that, in accord with experimental conditions, the interference term (the first one in Equation 6.20) between the plane wave and the spherical scattered wave depends only on the forward scattered amplitude, $f(0)$. For particles scattered inelastically, the interference term is absent and

$$i_n = 2\pi v_n \mathcal{N}^{-1} \int_0^\pi |f_n(\chi)|^2 \sin\chi d\chi \qquad (6.21)$$

Then, the inelastic differential cross-section is

$$\sigma_n(\chi) = i_n(\chi) \cdot \mathcal{N}/v_0 = v_n/v_0 |f_n(\chi)|^2 \qquad (6.22)$$

and the total cross-section, obtained by generalising Equation 6.13, is

$$\sigma_{tot} = 2\pi \sum_n \frac{v_n}{v_0} \int_0^\pi \sigma_n(\chi) \sin \chi d\chi \qquad (6.23)$$

The conservation of particles results in

$$\sum_{n=0} i_n = 0 \qquad (6.24)$$

and so

$$\sigma_{tot} = \frac{4\pi}{k_0} \text{Im} f_0(0) \qquad (6.25)$$

which shows that the conservation requirement is fulfilled by the interference between the incoming and outgoing elastic channels in the forward direction. The result Equation 6.25 is known as the optical theorem and also holds in the presence of reactive scattering, which simply adds other exit channels.

6.3 The formal solution of the wave equation

We now come to the problem of solving the wave equation itself, subject to the boundary condition of Equation 6.7, so that the scattered amplitude can be extracted. The wave equation can either be solved as a differential equation or converted to an integral equation. The former turns out to be the more convenient path for molecular scattering problems, but the integral equation approach leads directly to Born's approximation which occupies an honoured place in scattering theory – though in its full form it has little application to molecular as opposed to electron scattering. The wave equation for elastic scattering, Equation 6.6 can be re-arranged in the form

$$(E - H_0) \Psi(\mathbf{R}) = V(\mathbf{R}) \Psi(\mathbf{R}) \qquad (6.26)$$

where H_0 is the kinetic operator for relative motion,

$$H_0 = -\frac{\hbar^2}{2\mu} \left\{ \frac{1}{R^2} \frac{\partial}{\partial R} R^2 \frac{\partial}{\partial R} + \frac{1}{R^2 \sin \chi \partial \chi} \sin \chi \frac{\partial}{\partial \chi} + \frac{1}{R^2 \sin^2 \chi} \frac{\partial^2}{\partial \phi^2} \right\} \qquad (6.27)$$

and $V(\mathbf{R})$ is the potential energy of interaction. If the terms on the r.h.s. of

Equation 6.26 are for the moment regarded as known functions of the co-ordinates, $\rho(\mathbf{R})$, the whole equation assumes the form of an inhomogeneous second order differential equation but with a particularly simple differential operator on the l.h.s.

$$(E - H_0)\,\Psi(\mathbf{R}) = \rho(\mathbf{R}) \tag{6.28}$$

Now a general solution of such an equation having any required asymptotic form can be constructed from the appropriate Green's function, $G(\mathbf{R}, \mathbf{R}')$, which in turn is a solution of the inhomogeneous equation

$$(E - H_0)\,G(\mathbf{R}, \mathbf{R}') = \delta(\mathbf{R} - \mathbf{R}') \tag{6.29}$$

Direct substitution into Equation 6.28 shows that

$$\Psi(\mathbf{R}) = \int G(\mathbf{R}, \mathbf{R}')\,\rho(\mathbf{R}')\,d\mathbf{R} \tag{6.30}$$

is a particular solution of Equation 6.28 when the following property of the delta function is used:

$$\rho(\mathbf{R}) = \int \delta(\mathbf{R} - \mathbf{R}')\,\rho(\mathbf{R}')\,d\mathbf{R}' \tag{6.31}$$

A complete solution of Equation 6.28 is then the sum of the particular integral, Equation 6.30 and the solution of the homogeneous equation

$$(H_0 - E)\,\chi_0(\mathbf{R}) = 0 \tag{6.32}$$

giving

$$\Psi(\mathbf{R}) = \chi_0(\mathbf{R}) + \int G(\mathbf{R}, \mathbf{R}')\,\rho(\mathbf{R}')\,d\mathbf{R}' \tag{6.33}$$

We choose $\chi_0(\mathbf{R})$ to be $e^{i\mathbf{k}_0 \cdot \mathbf{R}}$ and so a Green's function having the asymptotic R dependence $e^{ik_0 R}/R$ is needed. The required result is:

$$G(\mathbf{R}, \mathbf{R}') = -\frac{\mu}{2\pi\hbar^2}\,\frac{e^{ik_0|\mathbf{R} - \mathbf{R}'|}}{|\mathbf{R} - \mathbf{R}'|} \tag{6.34}$$

Then, letting $\mathbf{R} \to \infty$ so that over effectively the whole field of integration in Equation 6.33 $R \gg R'$, the following result for $f(\chi)$ (the coefficient of

e^{ik_0R}/R in Equation 6.33) is obtained:

$$f(\chi) = -\frac{\mu}{2\pi\hbar^2} \int e^{i\mathbf{k}\cdot\mathbf{R}'} V(\mathbf{R}') \Psi(\mathbf{R}') \, d\mathbf{R}' \tag{6.35}$$

where $k_0|\mathbf{R} - \mathbf{R}'| \approx k_0(R - \mathbf{R}'\cdot\mathbf{R}/R) = k_0R - \mathbf{k}\cdot\mathbf{R}'$ has been used and $\mathbf{k}$ is the wave number vector in the direction of observation $\mathbf{R}$. The angle of scattering, χ, is the angle between $\mathbf{k}$ and $\mathbf{k}_0$. It may not seem that much progress has been made in Equation 6.35 because the exact wave function still appears in the expression. However, the way is now open for the development of a series expansion of the scattered amplitude in terms of $V(\mathbf{R})$ – the Born expansion. The first Born approximation gives $f(\chi)$ to $0(V)$ and is obtained by substituting the undistorted plane wave function for the exact wave function $\Psi(R')$ in Equation 6.35. In general the nth order approximation to $f(\chi)$ is obtained by substituting the $(n - 1)^{th}$ approximation to the wave function into Equation 6.35 but only the first and second order approximations are at all used. Pursuing the 1st order approximation we have

$$f(\chi) = -\frac{\mu}{2\pi\hbar^2} \int e^{-i(\mathbf{k}-\mathbf{k}_0)\cdot\mathbf{R}'} V(\mathbf{R}') \, d\mathbf{R}' \tag{6.36}$$

Then with

$$|\mathbf{k} - \mathbf{k}_0| = 2k \sin \chi/2 = q \tag{6.37}$$

we may take the direction of the vector q as a new polar axis to replace the z-axis and carry out the angular integration in Equation 6.36 with respect to this new axis with α as the new polar angle. The volume elements of integration transform as

$$R^2 \sin \chi \, d\chi d\phi dR = R^2 \sin \alpha \, d\alpha d\phi' dR$$

and the scattered amplitude becomes for a central potential

$$f(q) = -\frac{2\mu}{\hbar^2 q} \int_0^\infty \sin (qR) \, V(R)R \, dR \tag{6.38}$$

This is the first Born approximation. It suffers from one formal fault and one practical disadvantage. Firstly, it gives a scattered amplitude that is wholly real and so cannot satisfy the optical theorem; this is the result of using an undistorted plane wave in the source function $\rho(\mathbf{R})$ without taking into account the attenuation of the incident wave. The second difficulty is that the integral in Equation 6.38 diverges for all commonly used molecular potentials (more precisely, for all functions $V(R)$ that vanish more rapidly than R^{-1}). From a physical point of view, all molecular potentials have a hard core extending out to several times λ at thermal energies which causes a major distortion of a considerable part of the wave front and which cannot be conveniently treated by perturbation methods. It is indeed a pity that the first Born approximation for $f(\chi)$ is not applicable to molecular scattering because if the phase as well as the magnitude of $f(q)$ can be obtained experimentally over the complete angular range, the inversion of Equation 6.38 to yield the potential directly is possible, but this route to $V(R)$ is only open for electron scattering, since the potential is then a shielded Coulomb one. To proceed further we must make a partial wave analysis of the problem.

6.4 The partial wave expansion

The standard procedure for separating the variables in a wave equation governing the relative motion in polar co-ordinates is to write

$$\Psi(\mathbf{R}) = g(R)\,\Theta(\chi)\Phi(\phi) \tag{6.39}$$

For the central potential problem, the wave equation 6.26 then separates into three equations familiar from bound state problems (e.g. the hydrogen atom), the only difference being in the functional form of the potential and the fact that the total energy is positive. The separated equations for radial and angular motion are:

$$-\frac{\hbar^2}{2\mu}\frac{1}{R^2}\frac{d}{dR}R^2\frac{dg_l}{dR} + V(R)\,g_l + \frac{\hbar^2}{2\mu}l(l+1)\,g_l = Eg_l \tag{6.40}$$

$$\begin{cases} \sin\chi^{-1}\dfrac{d}{d\chi}\sin\chi\,\dfrac{d\Theta_{lm}}{d\chi} - m^2\sin^{-2}\chi\,\Theta_{lm} = l(l+1)\Theta_{lm} \\ d^2\Phi_m/d\phi^2 = m^2\Phi_m \end{cases} \tag{6.41}$$

The last two equations have as solutions the spherical harmonics, $Y_{lm}(\chi, \phi)$

closely related to the Legendre polynomials, $P_{lm}(\cos \chi)$;

$$\Theta_{lm}(\chi)\Phi_m(\phi) = Y_{lm}(\chi, \phi) = (-1)^m \left[(2l + 1)/4\pi\right]^{\frac{1}{2}} \left(\frac{l - m}{l + m}\right)^{\frac{1}{2}} P_{lm}(\cos \chi)e^{im\phi}$$

(6.42)

We now see if a solution of the form

$$\Psi(R) = g_l(R) Y_{lm}(\chi, \phi)$$

(6.43)

where g_l is the radial wave function of the lth angular momentum state, can be made an acceptable solution of the scattering problem. In comparing Equations 6.43 and 6.7 a difficulty at once emerges in that the asymptotic form of Equation 6.7 does not refer to a particular angular momentum state but to the totality of all such states that make up an infinite plane wave, i.e. the angular momentum quantum numbers must be introduced into Equation 6.7. Clearly, in order to arrive at Equation 6.7, a linear combination of degenerate terms of the type Equation 6.43 will have to be taken

$$\Psi(R) = \sum_{l, m} A_{lm} g_{lm}(R) Y_{lm}(\chi, \phi)$$

(6.44)

The weighting A_{lm} that is given to each state must be such that asymptotically, the wave function ψ contains only an incoming plane wave and an outgoing spherical wave without an incoming spherical wave. Once the coefficients A_{lm} have been found, then the scattered amplitude is determined. To find these coefficients we need the expansion of a plane wave in terms of the spherical harmonics

$$e^{ikz} = (4\pi)^{\frac{1}{2}} \sum_{l=0}^{\infty} (2l + 1)^{\frac{1}{2}} i^l j_l (kR) Y_{l0} (\chi, \phi)$$

(6.45)

where the polar axis has been taken to be the z-axis and the spherical Bessel functions $j_l(kr)$ are one class of the solutions, f_l, of the radial wave equation with zero potential:

$$\frac{1}{\rho^2} \frac{d}{d\rho} \rho^2 \frac{d}{d\rho} f_l(\rho) - \frac{l(l + 1)}{\rho^2} f_l(\rho) + f_l(\rho) = 0$$

(6.46)

where $\rho = kR$ and $k\hbar = \mu v$.

The solutions of Equation 6.46 can be made the building blocks of the solution of any problem in the continuum, just as bound state problems are conveniently expanded in terms of the more familiar Laguerre or Hermite polynomials. Two different types of solution can be distinguished by their behaviour at $\rho = 0$, the regular (i.e. tending to zero) solution j_l behaving as ρ^l and the irregular or Neumann functions n_l behaving as $\rho^{-(l+1)}$; a few of their properties are listed in Appendix 1. The functions j_l and n_l, being entirely real, do not represent any net flow of particles. Their asymptotic form of large ρ, however, suggests that they can be decomposed in the manner of ordinary trigonometric functions to give two complex functions which represent incoming and outgoing waves respectively. These are the Hankel functions of the first and second kind

$$h_l^{(1)}(\rho) = j_l(\rho) + i n_l(\rho) \xrightarrow[\rho \to \infty]{} \frac{1}{\rho} e^{i(\rho - (l+1)\pi/2)}$$

(6.47)

$$h_l^{(2)}(\rho) = j_l(\rho) - i n_l(\rho) \xrightarrow[\rho \to \infty]{} \frac{1}{\rho} e^{-i(\rho - (l+1)\pi/2)}$$

The two Hankel functions are complex conjugates, separately satisfying the wave equation 6.46 and the recurrence relationship (A2); $h_l^{(1)}$ and $h_l^{(2)}$ represent a flux that falls off uniformly as R^{-2} — as may be verified by substituting Equation 6.47 into Equation 6.10, the results for $h_l^{(1)}$ and $h_l^{(2)}$ being

$$j_R^{(1),(2)} = \pm \frac{v}{\mathcal{N}} \Big/ (kR)^2$$

(6.48)

Returning to the plane wave expansion of Equation 6.45, we can ask for the probability of finding a particle with angular momentum $l\hbar$ in a plane wave. This is a familiar type of problem in wave mechanics and in Equation 6.45 we have the required expansion in terms of the eigenfunctions of the angular momentum operator. Noting from Equation 6.48 that the flux or particle density represented by the radial part of every angular momentum state is independent of l, inspection of Equation 6.45 shows that the squares of the coefficient of the product eigenfunctions $j_l Y_{l0}$ are proportional to $2l + 1$. This result is often given a simple geometrical interpretation. The classical impact parameter is redefined as being related to l by

$$kb_l = l$$

(6.49)

which at first sight seems to imply that b is quantized through the quantisation of l. The interpretation is that all impact parameters lying between $b_l = l\lambda$ and $(l + 1)\lambda$ correspond to a single quantum state with angular momentum $l\hbar$. Thus, if the wave front is pictured divided by concentric circles into annular zones, the radius of the lth circle being b_{l+1}, the area of the lth zone is, from Equation 6.49 $(2l + 1)\, \pi/k^2$. If the intensity across the wave front is uniform, the number of trajectories passing through the lth zone is proportional to its area and thus the probability of picking at random a trajectory with angular momentum $l\hbar$ is proportional to $2l + 1$ as in the quantum treatment.

In our analysis of scattering in terms of partial waves, we now have the asymptotic form

$$\Psi(R) \xrightarrow[\rho \to \infty]{} \sum_l \left\{ (2l + 1)i^l j_l(\rho) + c_l h_l^{(1)}(\rho) \right\} P_l(\cos \chi) \quad (6.50)$$

where the scattered spherical wave has also been subject to a partial wave analysis,

$$\rho^{-1} f(\chi) e^{i\rho} = \sum_l c_l h_l^{(1)}(\rho) P_l(\cos \chi) \quad (6.51)$$

The program now is to solve the radial wave equation 6.40 for the functions $g_l(\rho)$ and then to compare expressions 6.44 and 6.50 so that the $c_l(\rho)$ can be identified.

The precise asymptotic form of the function $g_l(R)$ can only be found by integration of the differential Equation 6.40 but its general form can be readily found by the following argument. If the potential term in Equation 6.40 has a range that is shorter than the centrifugal term, that is, it falls off more rapidly than R^{-2}, then as $R \to \infty$ the centrifugal term $l^2 \hbar^2/2\mu R^2$ alone need be retained. The wave equation then becomes identical with the radial equation 6.46, the relevant solutions of which have already been identified as the spherical Bessel functions; we thus conclude that the asymptotic solution of the complete radial wave equation must be a linear combination of j_l and n_l,

$$g_l(\rho) \xrightarrow[\rho \to \infty]{} a_l j_l(\rho) + b_l n_l(\rho) \quad (6.52)$$

As the potential term in Equation 6.40 tends to zero, only the regular solution remains and one can say that the effect of introducing the potential term is to mix some of the irregular solution $n_l(\rho)$ with the regular solution.

The fuller significance of this can be seen by writing without loss of generality

$$a_l = d \cos \eta_l \left.\vphantom{\begin{matrix}a\\b\end{matrix}}\right\}$$
$$b_l = -d \sin \eta_l$$ (6.53)

so that

$$g_l \longrightarrow \frac{1}{\rho} \sin (\rho - l\pi/2 + \eta_l),$$ (6.54)

where

$$\tan \eta_l = b_l/a_l.$$ (6.55)

Thus, the only effect of the potential is to introduce a phase shift η_l into the elastically scattered wave.

Before discussing the solution of the radial wave equation subject to the limiting form Equations 6.52 or 6.54, the relationship must be found between the phase shift η_l, or the coefficients a_l and b_l and the differential cross-section, which is the actual measured quantity. To do this, we return to the complete partial wave expansion 6.50 which we write in limit of large R as

$$\Psi(\mathbf{R}) \longrightarrow \sum_l (\mathscr{A}_l h_l^{(1)} + \mathscr{B}_l h_l^{(2)}) P_l(\cos \chi)$$ (6.56)

where

$$a_l = \tfrac{1}{2}(\mathscr{A}_l + \mathscr{B}_l)$$
$$b_l = \tfrac{1}{2}i(\mathscr{A}_l - \mathscr{B}_l)$$ (6.57)

Upon subtracting a plane wave from Equation 6.56 only an outgoing spherical wave must remain if the solution is to correspond to scattering; to facilitate this operation we write Equation 6.50 as

$$\Psi(\mathbf{R}) \longrightarrow \sum_l \tfrac{1}{2}(2l + 1)i^l (h_l^{(1)} + h_l^{(2)}) P_l(\cos \chi) + \sum_l c_l h_l^{(1)} P_l(\cos \chi)$$ (6.58)

In general, the Legendre polynomials are not all zero for any value of χ, so that to match Equations 6.56 and 6.58 we equate coefficients of the $P_l(\chi)$

$$\mathscr{A}_l h_l^{(1)} + \mathscr{B}_l h_l^{(2)} - (2l + 1) i^l \tfrac{1}{2} \{ h_l^{(1)} + h_l^{(2)} \} = c_l h_l^{(1)}$$ (6.59)

and so

$$\mathcal{B}_l = \tfrac{1}{2}i^l(2l+1), \quad c_l = \mathcal{A}_l - (2l+1)i^l/2 \tag{6.60}$$

Restoring the phase shifts η_l from Equations 6.57, 6.55 and 6.60

$$\mathcal{A}_l = \tfrac{1}{2}(2l+1)i^l\,e^{2i\eta_l} \tag{6.61}$$

so that the coefficient of e^{ikR} in Equation 6.7 becomes

$$f(\chi) = \frac{1}{2ik} \sum_l (2l+1)\{e^{2i\eta_l} - 1\}P_l(\cos\chi) \tag{6.62}$$

Instead of writing the important result, Equation 6.62, in terms of the phase shifts, greater symmetry and a more flexible notation results if a new set of quantities is defined that make up the scattering matrix $\{S\}$. The diagonal elements of this matrix $\{S\}$ are the ratios of the amplitudes of the outgoing and incoming spherical waves in l^{th} channel in the limit of large R. In the elastic case the complete wave function can be written

$$\Psi \longrightarrow \sum_l \mathcal{B}_l\rho^{-1}\{e^{-i(\rho - l\pi/2)} - S_{ll}\,e^{i(\rho - l\pi/2)}\}P_l(\cos\chi) \tag{6.63}$$

where, from Equation 6.56

$$S_{ll} = \mathcal{A}_l/\mathcal{B}_l = e^{2i\eta_l} \tag{6.64}$$

The complex elements S_{ll}, form a square array and in the central forces elastic scattering case the conservation of relative angular momentum ensures that only the diagonal elements S_{ll} are non-zero and that the wave equations for different angular momentum states are uncoupled (as in Equation 6.41). The components of the S matrix can be regarded as transforming an incident spherical wave in a particular channel into an outgoing wave in the same or another channel. The S matrix elements thus conveniently store all our knowledge of the scattering effect of any potential and they replace phase shifts and transition probabilities.

We can immediately derive a formula for the scattered amplitude in terms of S_{ll} by substituting Equations 6.61 and 6.64 into 6.62:

$$f(\chi) = \frac{1}{2ik} \sum_l (2l+1)\{S_{ll} - 1\}P_l(\cos\chi) \tag{6.65}$$

If inelastic exit channels open up (those in which the final values of the internal quantum numbers differ from the initial values) then Equation 6.65 still holds if the summation is carried out over only the diagonal elements, $S_{nl:nl}$ where n labels the initial state. The phase shift notation does not adapt quite so readily. To anticipate the results of Chapter 8, the simple factor $e^{2i\eta l}$ in Equation 6.62 must be replaced by $e^{2i\eta l}e^{-\xi_l n}$ in the presence of inelastic events, where $\xi_{l,n}$ is a measure of the attenuation of the lth partial wave.

The total cross-section in terms of the S matrix elements is found by forming $|f(\chi)|^2$ from Equation 6.65 and integrating over all scattering angles:

$$\sigma_{total} = \frac{\pi}{k^2} \sum_l (2l+1) \{|S_{ll}|^2 + 1 - 2\mathrm{Re}(S_{ll})\} \qquad (6.66)$$

where the orthogonality of the Legendre polynomials, has been used.

In writing down the asymptotic form Equations 6.56 or 6.58 we have not made use of our knowledge that elastic scattering cannot lead to net adsorbtion or emission of particles, whereas Equation 6.54 does contain this information. To apply this conservation condition to Equation 6.63 and hence to the S matrix, we substitute Equation 6.63 into the expression for the flux Equation 6.3 and integrate the result over the surface of a sphere at infinity; the resulting current is then placed equal to zero,

$$j_l = 4\pi \frac{\hbar k}{\mu} \left\{ |\mathscr{B}_l|^2 - |\mathscr{B}_l S_{ll}|^2 \right\} = 0 \qquad (6.67)$$

leading to

$$|S_{ll}|^2 = 1 \qquad (6.68)$$

whence Equation 6.66 becomes

$$\sigma_{total} = \frac{2\pi}{k^2} \sum_l (2l+1) \{1 - \mathrm{Re}(S_{ll})\} \qquad (6.69)$$

Applying the optical theorem to Equation 6.65 also yields Equation 6.69 which thus also applies in the presence of inelastic or reactive scattering, provided that the summation is carried out only over the relevant diagonal elements of the scattering matrix, $S_{nl:nl}$, where n agains labels the initial quantum state.

Although it is not of direct use in computing individual elements of the large scattering matrices met with in molecular scattering, the formal description of the S matrix cannot be left without mentioning that it is a *unitary* matrix. For elastic scattering the required result follows immediately from Equation 6.64 that

$$\{S\}\{\tilde{S}*\} = 1 \tag{6.70}$$

More generally (see also Sections 6.14 and 6.15) if the colliding molecules can exist in a variety of internal states with wave functions $\phi_a \phi_b \ldots$ then the asymptotic form of Equation 6.63 becomes

$$\Psi_a \longrightarrow \Phi_a \sum_l \mathcal{B}_l \rho^{-1} \{e^{-i(k_a R - l\pi/2)} - S_{al:al} e^{i(k_a R - l\pi/2)}\} P_l(\cos \chi)$$

$$+ \phi_b \sum_{l,l'} \mathcal{B}_l \rho^{-1} S_{al:bl'} e^{i(k_b R - l\pi/2)} P_{l'}(\cos \chi) + \ldots \tag{6.71}$$

for a collision which began in internal state a, where al, bl′, are said to label the entrance and exit channels. If the system had begun in state b, the formal description of the asymptotic wave function would be similar to Equation 6.71 with the S matrix elements replaced by $S_{bl:al'}, S_{bl:bl'}$ etc. Note that in every case the incoming wave e^{-ikR} would be associated only with the entrance channel.

A colliding system starting in state 'a' is, through the orthogonality of the $\phi_a, \phi_b \ldots$ orthogonal to a system starting in any other state. Furthermore, although the system may emerge in a mixture of states a, b ..., it must remain orthogonal throughout the collision to a system originating in any other entrance channel because the colliding system *as a whole* is not acted upon by external forces and so must remain in the same quantum state until perturbed by the act of observation. At the end the act of observation will force the system to be registered in *one* of the states a, b ... and for any partial wave the probability of emerging in a particular exit channel b from an entrance channel a is

$$\sum_{l'} P_{al \to bl'} = \sum_{l'} |S_{al:bl'}|^2 \tag{6.72}$$

The orthogonality of states is simply expressed for any pair of entrance and exit channels al and bl′

$$\sum_n \sum_{l''} S_{al:nl''} S^*_{bl':nl''} = 0, \quad \text{unless } b = a, l' = l \tag{6.73}$$

Similarly, in order to conserve flux, the complete wave function Ψ_a must remain normalised throughout the collision, i.e.

$$\sum_n \sum_{l''} |S_{al:nl''}|^2 = 1 \qquad (6.74)$$

These conditions are automatically fulfilled when the S matrix is accurately calculated (a very difficult matter for complex systems) and together they result in the unitarity of the complete S matrix.

With the aid of Equation 6.62 the problem of calculating $f(\chi)$ for elastic collisions has been converted to one of finding the phase shifts η_l or, equivalently through Equation 6.56 of finding the relative asymptotic contributions of the spherical Bessel and Neumann functions to the solution of the radial wave equation 6.40.

Defining a slightly modified radial function $G(\rho)$

$$G_l(\rho) = \rho g_l(\rho) \qquad (6.75)$$

so that first derivatives are eliminated in the wave equation,

$$-\frac{d^2 G}{d\rho^2} + \mathscr{V} G_l + \frac{l(l+1)}{\rho^2} G_l = G_l$$

where

$$\mathscr{V}(\rho) = 2\mu \, V(\rho)/(\hbar k)^2 \qquad (6.76)$$

the problem is reduced to solving the second order linear differential Equation 6.76 subject to 6.54. For the general potential there are no analytical solutions to Equation 6.76. For some specially constructed potentials, solutions can be found for $l = 0$ and for the Coulomb, square well, hard sphere and delta function potentials there are solutions for $l > 0$ in terms of known functions. Unfortunately, none of these is a good enough potential form to fit the high resolution data now available. Numerical methods of solving Equation 6.76 are discussed in Section 6.8, but first we pursue a little analysis in order to arrive at some approximations.

6.5   The Born approximation for the phase shifts

It is instructive to convert Equation 6.76 into an integral equation and to do so the inhomogeneous form is again adopted:

$$-\frac{d^2 G_l}{d\rho^2} + \left\{ \frac{l(l+1)}{\rho^2} - 1 \right\} G_l = -\mathscr{V}(\rho) G_l \qquad (6.77)$$

If two linearly independent solutions of Equation 6.77 with $V = 0$ (i.e. two complementary functions) are known, $v_l(\rho)$ and $w_l(\rho)$, then a general solution is

$$G_l(\rho) = W^{-1}\left\{ v_l \int_a^\rho w_l \mathscr{V} G_l d\rho' + w_l \int_\rho^b v_l \mathscr{V} G_l d\rho' \right\} + N f_l(\rho); \quad f_l = v_l \text{ or } w_l$$

$$(6.78)$$

where W is the Wronskian $(v_l w_l' - w_l v_l')$ of v_l and w_l and the constants N, a and b are as yet undetermined. That this is a solution of Equation 6.77 can be verified by direct substitution and it contains the two adjustable constants a and b needed to fit the boundary conditions of a second order differential equation. As $\rho \to 0$, we require that only the regular solution remains so clearly a must be put equal to zero and w_l identified with $\rho j_l(\rho)$. As $\rho \to \infty$ the solution must become a linear combination of the functions j_l and n_l; furthermore, in the absence of a perturbing potential the solution must be everywhere $\rho j_l(\rho)$. Dealing with this latter condition first, it is apparent that whatever values are assigned to a and b, $G_l(\rho)$ will tend to $N f_l$ as V tends to zero; clearly $\rho j_l(\rho)$ must be inserted for $N f_l(\rho)$, (N is not an adjustable constant but a scaling or normalising factor which does not affect the following argument). If, now, b is put equal to ∞, Equation 6.78 becomes

$$G_l(\rho) = \rho \left\{ n_l(\rho) \int_0^\rho \rho' j_l(\rho') \mathscr{V} G_l(\rho') d\rho' + j_l(\rho) \int_\rho^\infty n_l(\rho') \rho' \mathscr{V} G_l(\rho') d\rho' \right\} + \rho j_l(\rho)$$

$$(6.79)$$

and so from Equation 6.55, in the limit $\rho \to \infty$

$$\tan \eta_l = \int_0^\infty \rho j_l(\rho) \mathscr{V} G_l(\rho) d\rho \qquad (6.80)$$

where, it is worth emphasising again, $\rho G_l(\rho)$ must be asymptotically of the form Equation 6.52. If, now, $V(\rho)$ is everywhere small, the dominant term on the R.H.S. of Equation 6.79 is ρj_l, provided that integrals of the type Equation 6.81 below converge and ρ is not too small. Substituting ρj_l for $G_l(\rho)$ in Equation 6.80 gives

$$\tan \eta_l \approx \eta_l \approx \int_0^\infty \rho^2 j_l(\rho)^2 \mathscr{V}(\rho) d\rho \quad \text{(to 0}(V)) \qquad (6.81)$$

which is the first Born approximation for the phase shift. Although the Born approximation to the scattered amplitude, Equation 6.38, diverges for all potentials of the type R^{-s} with $s > 1$, the limiting behaviour of the spherical Bessel functions as $\rho \to 0$ (appendix A) shows that the Born phase shift expression 6.81 is integrable for $l > \frac{1}{2}(s - 2, s - 1)$, ($s$ even, odd). Whether the resulting value of η_l is reliable depends upon the extent of the distortion of the incident plane wave by the intermolecular field and a measure of this is the actual phase shift calculated. Equation 6.81 is commonly held to be unreliable for phase shifts greater than half a radian. For these larger phase shifts the second Born approximation (obtained by including terms $O(V^2)$ in $G_l(\rho)$) is rarely used and instead a semi-classical approximation (Section 6.7) is adopted or the wave equation is solved numerically (Section 6.8).

6.6 Small angle scattering; the random phase approximation

We recall that elastic is always strongly forward peaked and that most of the particles are scattered out of the beam by less than a degree. Thus, regarding the total cross-section as the integral of the differential cross-section, we can hope to get a good approximation for the former if we calculate only the small angle behaviour of $\sigma(\chi)$ accurately and this suggests the use of the Born approximation. Because of the factor $(2l + 1)$ in Equation 6.62 we concentrate on the outermost branch of the deflection function and calculate the contribution to $\sigma(\chi)$ from a potential of the form

$$V(R) = -C_s R^{-s} \tag{6.82}$$

Substituting Equation 6.82 into Equation 6.81 gives a standard integral and yields

$$\eta_l^B = -\frac{\mu C_s}{\hbar^2} \left(\frac{k}{2}\right)^{s-2} \pi \frac{\Gamma(s - 1)\Gamma\left(l - \frac{s}{2} + \frac{3}{2}\right)}{\left(\Gamma\left(\frac{s}{2}\right)\right)^2 \Gamma\left(l + \frac{s}{2} + \frac{1}{2}\right)} \tag{6.83}$$

For some value L of the angular momentum quantum number, η_l^B will reach $\pi/2$ where the Born approximation is unreliable. At smaller values of l, $e^{2i\eta_l}$ oscillates with increasing rapidity. The approximation sometimes called the random phase approximation is now introduced that both the real and imaginary parts of $e^{2i\eta_l}$ are effectively zero for $l < L$. The partial wave summation for the forward scattered amplitude is now

$$f(0) = \frac{i}{2k} \sum_0^L (2l + 1) - \frac{i}{2k} \sum_L^\infty (2l + 1) \{\cos 2\eta_l + i \sin 2\eta_l - 1\} \tag{6.84}$$

and so

$$\sigma_{\text{total}} = \frac{4\pi}{k} \text{ Im } f(0) = \frac{2\pi}{k^2} \left[\sum_{l=0}^{L} (2l+1) + \sum_{l=L}^{\infty} (2l+1)^2 \eta_l^2 \right] \quad (6.85)$$

where in Equation 6.87 the approximation

$$\cos 2\eta_l \approx 1 - 2\eta_l^2, \quad \eta_l \ll \pi/2$$

has been introduced. Then, with the knowledge that for molecular scattering $L \gg 1$, we obtain

$$\sigma_{\text{total}} \approx \frac{2\pi L^2}{k^2} + \frac{8\pi}{k^2} \int_L^{\infty} l\eta_l^2 \, dl \quad (6.86)$$

Substituting Equation 6.83 into Equation 6.86 gives the Massey-Mohr formula (H. S. W. Massey and C. Mohr, 1933)

$$\sigma_{\text{tot}}^{\text{MM}} \cong \pi \left(2 + \frac{\pi^2}{s-2} \right) \left(\frac{f_s C_s}{\hbar v} \right)^{2/(s-1)}, \quad (6.87)$$

where

$$f_s = \frac{1}{2^{s-3}} \frac{\Gamma(s-1)}{(\Gamma(s/2))^2} \quad (6.88)$$

The accumulated effect of the approximations, including the ambiguity in the choice of η_L, is to make the Massey-Mohr formula reliable only to $\sim\pm30$ per cent. It is perhaps worth noting that the problem of assigning a value to η_L can be overcome by evaluating the integral form of Equation 6.69 analytically,

$$\sigma_{\text{tot}} \cong \frac{8\pi}{k^2} \int_0^{\infty} l \sin^2 \eta_l \, dl \quad (6.89)$$

with η_l given by Equation 6.83 over the whole range of l. The result, due to Landau and Lifshitz (LL), is

$$\sigma_{\text{tot}}^{\text{LL}} \cong 2\pi^{s/(s-1)} \sin \left[\frac{\pi}{2} \frac{s-3}{s-1} \right] \Gamma\left(\frac{s-3}{s-1} \right) \left[\frac{\Gamma\left(\frac{s}{2} - \frac{1}{2} \right)}{\Gamma\left(\frac{s}{2} \right)} \right]^{2/(s-1)} \left(\frac{C_s}{\hbar v} \right)^{2/(s-1)} \quad (6.90)$$

and is generally preferred to Equation 6.87. It is to be noted that Equations 6.90 and 6.87 predict a monotonic energy dependence of the total cross-section, $\sigma_{tot}(E) \propto E^{-1/(s-1)}$

If a bipolar potential of the form

$$V(R) = -C_s R^{-s} + C_t R^{-t} \tag{6.91}$$

is used, the Born phase shift is the sum of the contributions from the two parts of the potential, and the scattered amplitude is the sum of long and short range contributions. However, if these phase shifts were used to evaluate the total cross-section in Equation 6.89, we will see in Section 6.10 that important interference effects are neglected and the MM approximation gives only the average behaviour of $\sigma_{tot}(E)$.

Small angle scattering is also dominated by collisions of large impact parameter and there should be a small angle approximation to $\sigma(\chi)$ analogous to the MM and LL formulae for the total cross-section. This hope is only realised after some drastic approximations as we will now see.

The contribution from partial waves inside the random phase region $(l < L)$ to the scattered amplitude is

$$f_<(\chi) = (2ik)^{-1} \sum_{l=0}^{L} (2l+1) P_l(\cos \chi)$$

$$\cong (ik)^{-1} \left(\frac{\chi}{\sin \chi} \right)^{1/2} \int_0^L (l + \tfrac{1}{2}) J_0 [(l + \tfrac{1}{2})\chi] \, dl$$

$$\cong -i \left(\frac{\chi}{\sin \chi} \right)^{1/2} \frac{L}{k\chi} J_1(L\chi) \tag{6.92}$$

where the approximation, useful over the whole range of $l\chi$,

$$P_l(\chi) \cong \left(\frac{\chi}{\sin \chi} \right)^{1/2} J_0 [(l + \tfrac{1}{2})\chi] \tag{6.93}$$

has been used. The contribution to $f(\chi)$ from partial waves with $l > L$ is found using the Born approximation to be

$$f_>(\chi) \cong (ik)^{-1} \int_L^\infty (2l+1) \eta_l^B P_l(\cos \chi) \, dl \tag{6.94}$$

Taking $\eta = \pi/2$ to mark the onset of random phase (which gives close agreement with the LL result for the total cross-section) and writing

$$\eta_l^B = \frac{\pi}{2}\left(\frac{l}{L}\right)^{-s+1}, \quad l \geqslant L \tag{6.95}$$

gives

$$f_> \cong \frac{\pi}{ik}\frac{L^2}{s-3}\left\{1 - \left(\frac{s-3}{s-5}\right)\frac{L^2\chi^2}{4} + \cdots\right\}, s > 5 \tag{6.96}$$

Expanding $J_1(L\chi)$ in Equation 6.92 and combining $f_>$ and $f_<$ gives

$$J_1(L\chi) = \frac{L\chi}{2} - \frac{(L\chi)^3}{16} + \cdots \tag{6.97}$$

$$\sigma(\chi) \cong \frac{L^4}{4k^2}\left\{\frac{2\pi + s - 3}{s-3}\right\}^2\left[1 - (L\chi)^2\frac{(s-3)(4\pi + s - 5)}{4(s-5)(2\pi + s - 3)} + \cdots\right] \tag{6.98}$$

From Equation 6.96, as $s \to \infty$ the contribution from $l > L$ goes to zero and the cross-section can then be assigned the hard sphere (HS) value; for $\chi = 0$,

$$\sigma_{HS}(0) = L^4/4k^2 \tag{6.99}$$

Thus, the small angle differential cross-section is

$$\sigma(\chi) \cong \sigma_{HS}(0)\left\{\frac{2\pi + s - 3}{s-3}\right\}^2\left[1 - k\sigma_{HS}(0)^{1/2}\chi^2\frac{(s-3)(4\pi + s - 5)}{2(s-5)(2\pi + s - 3)} + \cdots\right] \tag{6.100}$$

Writing the coefficient of χ^2 in Equation 6.100 as C, the foregoing result is sometimes summarised by saying that the differential cross-section falls off as $\exp(-C\chi^2)$, but this is only accurate to $0(\chi)^2$.

From Equation 6.100, a plot of $\chi^2\sigma(\chi)$ vs. χ will reach a maximum at $\chi = 1/\sqrt{C}$. Such a plot is illustrated in Fig. 6.1. However, this route to L and hence to C_s is not particularly useful because, for thermal scattering, L is greater than 100 and the extremum in the $\chi^2\sigma(\chi)$ plot occurs at very small angles where the precision in angular measurement is poor. Other authors (E. A. Mason et al., 1964; R. J. Munn et al., 1964) have produced alternative formulae to Equation 6.100.

The full form of $f_<(\chi)$, Equation 6.93 and of $f_>(\chi)$ (when evaluated more accurately) exhibit very pronounced oscillations from the presence of the term $J_1(L\chi)$. However, when $f(\chi)$ is evaluated by exact summation without breaking the partial wave summation these oscillations are much less in evidence (see Fig. 6.1). The exponential form at very small angles is found to join onto the classical envelope with its $\chi^{-(s-2)/(s-3)}$ dependence after only a few oscillations, of which the first two might be detectable for heavy atoms at thermal speeds. The oscillations in $f_{<,>}(\chi)$ and the residual structure in the exactly computed $f(\chi)$ are really a diffraction effect resulting from the rapidly changing gradient of the potential and are discussed more fully in

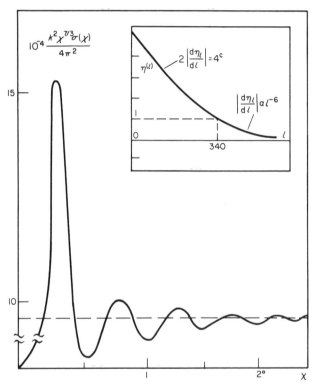

Fig. 6.1 The computed differential cross-section resulting from a monotonic phase shift function (inset), for which the maximum angle of deflection is 4 radians and only one classical branch is present. The very pronounced first maximum is a property of the function $\chi^{7/3} \exp(-C\chi^2)$ and effectively classical scattering sets in soon afterwards. In this particular model calculation roughly 900 partial waves were used.

Section 6.13. Pronounced undulations are indeed observed in $\sigma(\chi)$ but they arise from a different cause and occur outside the very small angle region; they are discussed in Section 6.10.

6.7 Semi-classical phase shifts

If we wish to extend our calculations of $\sigma(\chi)$ to larger angles of scattering via the partial wave summation, a means must be found of evaluating phase shifts that are greater than $\pi/2$. The radial Schrodinger equation 6.40 must be solved subject to the boundary condition of Equation 6.54

$$G_l(\rho) \longrightarrow \sin(\rho - l\pi/2 + \eta_l) \tag{6.101}$$

There are two methods of solution in use, the exact numerical integration of the wave equation and the semi-classical solution, which leads to a simple quadrature for the phase shift.

The use of semi-classical methods is suggested by the fact that for molecular collisions at thermal energies and higher, the wavelength of relative motion ($< 5 \times 10^{-10}$ cm) is comfortably less than the range of the potential ($> 10^{-8}$ cm). The Wentzel-Kramers-Brillouin (WKB) continuum solutions are introduced through the classical action integral $S(\rho)$;

$$S(\rho) = \int_{\rho_c}^{\rho} \xi(\rho)\,d\rho \tag{6.102}$$

where

$$\xi(\rho) = \sqrt{1 - \mathscr{V}(\rho) - (l + \tfrac{1}{2})^{\frac{1}{2}}/\rho^2} = v(\rho)/v(\infty) \tag{6.103}$$

and ρ_c is the classical turning point such that $\xi(\rho_c) = 0$.

Taking as a trial wave function

$$G_l^{\pm}(\rho) = \xi^{-\frac{1}{2}} e^{\pm iS(\rho)} \tag{6.104}$$

The conditions under which Equation 6.104 is a solution of Equation 6.40 are well known (L. D. Landau and E. M. Lifshitz, 1958) and may be summarized as:

$$\frac{\partial \xi}{\partial \rho} \ll 1 \quad \text{and} \quad \xi(\rho) \sim 1 \tag{6.105}$$

over the range of ρ leading to the major contribution to the action integral. The region close to the classical turning point is excluded from this test. For a bipolar potential range σ and well depth ϵ, these two tests are roughly equivalent to

$$\frac{\lambda}{\sigma} \ll 1 \quad \text{and} \quad \frac{\epsilon}{E} \lesssim 1 \tag{6.106}$$

The latter condition is related to the existence of bound states within the potential well and is the subject of Section 6.11.

The next step is to find the linear combination of incoming and outgoing spherical waves G_l^+ that joins smoothly onto an exponential decaying function at the classical turning point. We may replace this by a simpler requirement that the wave function vanishes at the turning point, which is satisfied by

$$G_l = \xi(\rho)^{-\frac{1}{2}} \{ e^{iS(\rho)} - e^{-iS(\rho)} \} \tag{6.107}$$

In order to compare with the asymptotic form of Equation 6.101, the action integral is written as

$$S(\rho) = \rho + l\pi/2 + \left[\int_{\rho_c}^{\rho} \left\{ 1 - \mathscr{V}(\rho) - \frac{(l+\frac{1}{2})^2}{\rho^2} \right\}^{\frac{1}{2}} d\rho - \int_{l+\frac{1}{2}}^{\rho} \left\{ 1 - \frac{(l+\frac{1}{2})^2}{\rho^2} \right\}^{\frac{1}{2}} \right] d\rho \tag{6.108}$$

The second term in Equation 6.108 converges to a finite limit as $\rho \to \infty$ and in writing down the whole expression we have used

$$\int_{l+\frac{1}{2}}^{\rho} d\rho \left\{ 1 - \frac{(l+\frac{1}{2})^2}{\rho^2} \right\}^{\frac{1}{2}} = \rho + l\pi/2 \tag{6.109}$$

So

$$\eta_l = \int_{\rho_c}^{\infty} \left\{ 1 - \mathscr{V}(\rho) - \frac{(l+\frac{1}{2})^2}{\rho^2} \right\}^{\frac{1}{2}} d\rho - \int_{l+\frac{1}{2}}^{\infty} \left\{ 1 - \frac{(l+\frac{1}{2})^2}{\rho^2} \right\}^{\frac{1}{2}} d\rho \tag{6.110}$$

which is the semi-classical expression for the phase shift, derived from plausibility arguments in Chapter 2. The expression 6.110 can be evaluated for any strength of potential and an approximation to the complete phase shift function built up. This absence of any warning signals might lead us to use Equation 6.110 as an approximation for all circumstances, but there is a major deficiency to the semi-classical phase shifts in the presence of orbiting, or when there are three classical turning points. These cases are illustrated in Figs. 6.2 and 6.10. Four types of behaviour are found at energies less than the critical value for orbiting. In the large impact parameter region (III) of Fig. 6.10, the effective potential is monotonic, there is only one classical turning point and the quantum and WKB phase shifts agree to, typically, better than 1 per cent. In region II there are three classical turning points and, although the inner region between R_3 and R_2 is classically inaccessible in a bimolecular collision, its presence has the effect, to a first approximation, of adding π^c, to

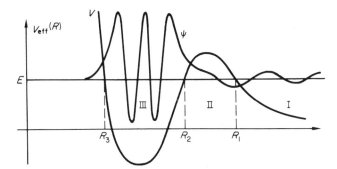

Fig. 6.2(i) A resonant case. The effective potential well, V_{eff}, has a bound state of energy E in resonance with the incident kinetic energy. The resulting wave function ψ has a large amplitude inside the well (region III), leaks through the potential barrier (II) to become the wave function of relative motion of two free particles in region I. The classical turning points are at R_1, R_2 and R_3.

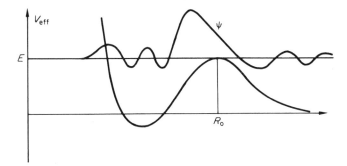

Fig. 6.2(ii) The orbiting case. At the outermost classical turning point R_0, the effective radial force is zero and the classical particle cannot pass this point. The quantum wave function ψ, however, shows that there is a finite possibility of finding the particle inside R_0.

the JWKB phase shift each time a resonance is passed through. This result can be found from a more complete WKB solution of the problem in which the oscillatory solution between R_2 and R_3 is joined smoothly onto the exponentially decaying solutions for $R < R_3$, $R_2 \leqslant R \leqslant R_1$ and thence onto the oscillatory solution for $R > R_1$. As the impact parameter passes through the critical value for orbiting the crude semi-classical phase shifts (from Equation 6.110) jump by several radians due to the sudden change in the turning point from R_1 to R_3. The quantum or exact semi-classical value will change rapidly in this region but, as in passing through the resonances, there will be no discontinuity in the gradient (with l regarded as a continuous variable). For impact parameters less than the orbiting value the crude and exact JWKB phase shifts again nearly coincide.

For any particular bipolar potential, orbiting will only occur at reduced energies E/ϵ below a certain critical value. At energies somewhat above this value e.g. $E/\epsilon > 0.8$ for the Lennard-Jones potential, we may be reasonably confident that the semi-classical phase shifts for all partial waves are reliable, provided that there are no near discontinuities in the potential.

The numerical evaluation of the integrals of Equation 6.110 presents no problems. If the turning point is located sufficiently accurately, any stepwise integration routine may be used. Gauss-Mehler quadrature has been suggested (F. J. Smith and R. J. Munn, 1964) as a quicker method, though convergence at low values of the reduced energy must be carefully tested.

A useful approximation for small phase shifts can be obtained by substituting the JWKB radial wave function for zero intermolecular potential into the quantum Born expression 6.83 where it replaces $j_l(\rho)$ when both incoming and outgoing waves are combined. Thus,

$$j_l(\rho) \approx \frac{1}{2} \frac{1}{\xi^{1/2}\rho} \left\{ e^{iS_0(\rho)} - e^{-iS_0(\rho)} \right\}, \tag{6.111}$$

and so

$$\eta_l \approx \int_{\rho_c}^{\infty} \frac{\mathcal{V}(\rho)\, d\rho}{(1 - (l + \frac{1}{2})^2/\rho^2)^2} \tag{6.112}$$

where terms containing the phase factor $\cos S(\rho)$ that results from squaring Equation 6.111 have been averaged to zero. The numerical results from this approximation differ slightly from those of the quantum Born approximation (they become identical in the limit $l \to \infty$) but, inasmuch as the Born contribution to the scattered amplitude is small, Equation 6.112 is an adequate approximation. Integrating Equation 6.112 by parts results in the 'classical' small phase shift approximation Section 2.2.

6.8 Numerical methods

In the following sections various approximate methods of summing the partial wave expansion will be presented and these yield useful formulae for extracting crude potential parameters from the observed structure in $\sigma(\chi)$. However, when confronted with high resolution plots of $\sigma(\chi)$ over a range of angles and energy, the final fitting must be done by a forward calculation from an assumed potential containing several adjustable parameters. The core of this calculation is that of phase shifts.

The methods available are:—

(1) Numerical solution of the Schrödinger Equation.
(2) Evaluation of the semi-classical phase shifts. (F. J. Smith and R. J. Munn, 1964).
(3) Evaluation of the Born phase shifts, or the contribution of these to $f(\chi)$ directly via Equations 6.95 or 6.97.

The strategy adopted depends upon the particular circumstances and the ingenuity of the programmer, guided by the general consideration that quantum phase shifts will be necessary when there are two or three classical turning points and that Born phase shifts only become reliable at values of $\eta_l < 0.1^c$. The use of semi-classical phases throughout the whole range of l will probably not lead to gross error in $\sigma(\chi)$ except at very low values of E/ϵ and the dominant interference patterns present will be reproduced.

Even without resorting to quantum phase shifts, the time taken to calculate a differential cross-section over a fine enough angular mesh to capture all the structure in the angular range of a typical experiment may well take 5—30 minutes of computer time (IBM 360/50) and the additional calculations required to incorporate any averaging due to apparatus resolution effects will increase this time by a factor of two to five.

If the quantal behaviour is highly developed and the perturbation of the incident wave is large, neither the semi-classical nor the Born approximation will be useful and the wave equation must be evaluated numerically for each partial wave as required. In an elastic scattering problem where strong quasi-chemical forces are involved up to ~50 phase shifts may lie in the quantal regions and a fast numerical technique is therefore essential.

All such methods depends upon replacing the differential in Equation 6.40

by the finite difference formula (using the notation $G_i \equiv G(\rho_i)$

$$\frac{d^2 G}{d\rho^2} \xrightarrow[h \to 0]{} \left\{ G_i - 2G_{i-1} + G_{i-2} \right\} h^{-2} \qquad (6.113)$$

and the wave equation itself is more concisely written as

$$G'' = D(\rho) G. \qquad (6.114)$$

In Equation 6.113 the G_i are discrete values of the wave function tabulated at equal intervals, h, of ρ. The subsequent stage in the calculation then depends upon the nature of the boundary conditions. In the case of bounded motion, negative total energy, the asymptotic value is known at both ends of the range of the function. The finite difference form of Equation 6.114 can then be cast into matrix form describing the conditions which must be fulfilled at each interval and the solution is by normal matrix methods. In the scattering case, however, the situation is very different. The motion is unbounded and though the asymptotic form of G is known boundary conditions can only be placed on $G(\rho)$ at $\rho = 0$. The solution to this type of initial value problem must be obtained by a stepwise integration procedure, until the asymptotic behaviour (Equation 6.101) of the function is achieved.

Since the precision of each step depend upon that of all previous ones accurate finite difference formulae are required. A wide range of such formulae have been suggested and a suitable one is the Numerov,

$$G_i = \frac{2G_{i-1} - G_{i-2} + \dfrac{h^2}{12} [G_{i-2} D_{i-2} + 10G_{i-1} D_{i-1}]}{1 - \dfrac{h^2}{12} D_i}. \qquad (6.115)$$

In the scattering problem $G(\rho)$ is an oscillating function and the integration must be carried over a considerable range before asymptotic behaviour is established and the phase shift can be established. Errors can arise from two sources, firstly from the inevitable truncation errors associated with the finite word length in the computer and secondly from the approximation inherent in the finite difference formula. In some cases the second difficulty can lead to the build-up of an exponentially increasing solution. There is thus an optimum step length for these calculations; if h is too large the finite difference approximation is poor, while if h is too small the build-up in truncation errors can be disastrous.

Fortunately there is often a considerable intermediate range of h where solutions can be obtained without difficulty. In some cases, however, these problems of instability may be severe and special methods are then required (L. Fox, 1962). The obvious solution to these problems, that of using great precision in the numerical calculation, is only of limited value since this ultimately results in a much longer computing time and the calculation becomes impracticable. For atomic or molecular systems these instabilities are not severe except possibly in those cases where integration through a wide potential barrier is involved or if the initial values for starting are not well chosen.

Outside the classical turning point of the motion the wave function is oscillatory. Inside these points, in the classically forbidden region, the wave function decays exponentially. Since we are not interested in the final amplitude of the wave, but only its relative phase, it is sufficient to choose the two starting values inside the classically forbidden region at a point where the wave function is small, the two points being related exponentially as:

$$G_i = \exp(-D_i/(\rho_c - \rho_i)) \qquad (6.116)$$

where ρ_c is the classical turning point. The stepwise numerical integration can then be carried out with arbitrary amplitude from this point. The phase shift could be calculated by continuing the outward integration until the wave function becomes sinusoidal, the phase then being obtained by comparison with the zero potential asymptotic form:

$$G_l \sim \frac{1}{k} \sin (\rho - l\pi/2).$$

It is more expeditious, however, to use the exact free particle wave function:

$$F_l(\rho) = j_l(\rho) + n_l(\rho) \qquad (6.117)$$

and to compare the two solutions before the fully asymptotic form is established. Thus, if R_n is one of the zeros of the calculated wave function $G(\rho)$,

$$\eta_l = \tan^{-1} \left(\frac{j_l(\rho_n)}{n_l(\rho_n)} \right) \qquad (6.118)$$

and estimates of η_l can be made for successive values of n until convergence is obtained.

Instead of finding a polynomial approximation to the wave function over successive intervals (which is the basis of the Numerov method), we can make a polynomial approximation to the *potential* over appropriate intervals such that the simplified wave equation can be solved in terms of known functions. This approach is attractive in that the potential is a smoothly varying function of the interparticle separation whereas the wave function is highly oscillatory. The details will be found in R. G. Gordon 1969.

6.9 Semi-classical scattering

We have seen how the phase shift function η_l can be constructed either from the WKB or exact solutions of the radial wave equation. The effect of actual or near discontinuities in the phase shift function on $\sigma(\chi)$ can be investigated by the method of random phase and the contribution to $\sigma(\chi)$ and σ_{tot} from partial waves of small phase shift has also been discussed. However, most phase shift functions are smooth functions of l and, for thermal scattering, are greater than $\pi/2$ over most of their range so that $e^{2i\eta_l}$ is oscillatory. To handle this situation we introduce the very important technique of stationary phase for approximating the partial wave summation. (K. W. Ford and J. A. Wheeler, 1954.)

The partial wave summation for $f(\chi)$ is first replaced by an integration (permissible when η_l varies little from one l value to the next) and the integral split into two parts;

$$f(\chi) = -\frac{1}{2ik} \left\{ \int_0^\infty (2l+1) \, e^{2i\eta(l)} P_l(\cos\chi) \, dl - \int_0^\infty (2l+1) \, P_l(\cos\chi) \, dl \right\}$$

(6.119)

The second integral is a delta function, $\delta(\chi)$, and so vanishes for $\chi \neq 0$. Next, an approximation for the Legendre polynomials in the first integral of Equation 6.119 is introduced that displays their asymptotic behaviour in the region $l\chi \gg 1$:

$$P_l(\cos\chi) \cong \left[\frac{1}{2} (l + \tfrac{1}{2})\pi \sin\chi \right]^{-\frac{1}{2}} \sin\left[(l + \tfrac{1}{2})\chi + \frac{\pi}{4} \right] + O\left(\frac{1}{l}\right) \quad (6.120)$$

Inserting this into Equation 6.119 gives

$$f(\chi) \cong -\frac{1}{k(2\pi \sin\chi)^{\frac{1}{2}}} \int_0^\infty (l + \tfrac{1}{2})^{\frac{1}{2}} \left\{ e^{i\phi_+(l)} - e^{-i\phi_-(l)} \right\} \, dl, \quad (6.121)$$

where

$$\phi_\pm(l) = 2\eta(l) \pm (l + \tfrac{1}{2})\chi \pm \pi/4. \qquad (6.122)$$

The contribution of a range of l values width Δl around some value l_i to $f(\chi)$ can be examined by expanding $\eta(l)$ in a Taylor series about l_i so that the phase ϕ becomes:

$$\phi_\pm(l) = 2\eta(l_i) + 2\left(\frac{\partial\eta}{\partial l}\right)_{l=l_i}(l - l_i) + \left(\frac{\partial^2\eta}{\partial l^2}\right)_{l=l_i}(l - l_i)^2 \pm (l + \tfrac{1}{2})\chi \pm \pi/4.$$

$$(6.123)$$

We now introduce the important result for semi-classical phase shifts derived in Chapter 2:

$$2 d\eta/dl = \chi, \qquad (6.124)$$

and neglect higher terms than the quadratic as in Equation 6.123 to find that there is a region of stationary phase in $\phi(l)$ centered about l_χ, where l_χ satisfies

$$2(d\eta/dl)_{l=l_\chi} = \pm \chi_{obs} \qquad (6.125)$$

The width Δl of the stationary phase region in which $\phi_\pm$ changes by less than $\sim\pi$ is seen from

$$\phi_\pm(l) \approx 2\eta(l_\chi) - 2(l_\chi \pm \tfrac{1}{2})\eta'(l_\chi) + \eta''(l_\chi)(l - l_\chi)^2 \pm \pi/4, \quad (6.126)$$

to be proportional to $\eta''(l_\chi)^{-\frac{1}{2}}$, but need not be specified if we use the following standard integral to evaluate Equation 6.121 when Equation 6.126 is substituted;

$$\int_{-\infty}^{\infty} e^{\pm iax^2}\, dx = \left(\frac{\pi}{a}\right)^{\frac{1}{2}} e^{\pm i\pi/4}, \qquad (6.127)$$

so that

$$f(\chi) = -k^{-1}\left(\frac{l_\chi}{2\,|\,\eta''(l_\chi)\,|\,\sin\chi}\right)^{\frac{1}{2}} e^{i\alpha_\pm(\chi)} \qquad (6.128)$$

where

$$\alpha_\pm(\chi) = 2\eta(l_\chi) - 2(l_\chi \pm \tfrac{1}{2})\eta'(l_\chi) + \frac{\eta''(l_\chi)}{|\,\eta''(l_\chi)\,|}\frac{\pi}{4}, \qquad (6.129)$$

in which the term $\eta''/|\eta''|$ takes care of a change in sign of $a(=\eta'')$ in Equation 6.127. In arriving at Equation 6.128, the factor $(l + \frac{1}{2})$ in the integrand has been taken out and replaced by l_χ. The leading semi-classical approximation to $\sigma(\chi)$ is then:

$$\sigma(\chi) = |f(\chi)|^2 = l_\chi \left/ \left[2k^2 \left| \frac{d^2\eta}{dl^2} \right|_{l=l_\chi} \sin \chi \right],\right. \tag{6.130}$$

and is identical with Equation 2.10. Upon substituting the large l result for the phase shifts resulting from a potential $V = -C_sR^{-s}$, namely

$$\eta(l) = f_s \left(\frac{C_s}{E} \right) l^{-s+1} k^s \tag{6.131}$$

where

$$f_s = \frac{\pi^{\frac{1}{2}}}{2} \Gamma \left(\frac{1}{2} [s - 1] \right) \left/ \Gamma \left(\frac{s}{2} \right),\right.$$

(a simplified version of Equation 6.83), the following expression is obtained for the small angle semi-classical differential cross-section:

$$\sigma(\chi) \approx \frac{1}{s} \left(2[s - 1] \frac{f_sC_s}{E} \right)^{2/s} \chi^{-(2+2/s)}. \tag{6.132}$$

This result merges with the quantum $\exp(-C\chi^2)$ form at very small angles with some diffraction structure in between, as illustrated in Fig. 1. Thus, to calculate the differential cross-section at some angle χ, it must first be found whether the corresponding phase shift $\eta(l_\chi)$ is appreciably greater or less than 1 radian. In the former case a region of stationary phase will be well developed in the partial wave summation and Equation 6.130 may be used (subject to the reservations in Section 6.10). If the phase shift is $< 1^c$, the parabolic approximation to $\eta(l)$ gives increasingly too large a width Δl to the region of stationary phase, and $\sigma(\chi)$ is best evaluated by direct summation of the partial wave expansion.

For an R^{-s} potential, the angle at which the classical result merges into the quantum form (roughly the position of the first maximum in the function $\chi^{2+2/s} \sigma(\chi)$) can be calculated from Equation 6.131 together with the condition that the critical phase shift is $\eta^* \sim 1$ radian, with the result

$$\chi^* \approx 2(s - 1) \left(\frac{E}{f_sC_sk^s} \right)^{1/(s-1)} \tag{6.133}$$

Typically, at thermal energies $\chi^* \sim 1.5°$ in agreement with deductions from the uncertainty principle (Section 6.1).

6.10 Interfering branches of the deflection function

There is one important respect in which Equation 6.130 may be in error and this arises from the possible presence of more than one region of stationary phase in $\phi_\pm$. The condition for stationary phase is that l satisfies Equation 6.125, and this may well be fulfilled by more than one value of l. In particular, for values of χ less than the rainbow value, there will always be three solutions of Equation 6.125, two corresponding to stationary phase in ϕ_+ and one in ϕ_-, as can be seen from an inspection of Fig. 6.3. It must be remembered that the angle χ that appears in the partial wave summation is the true polar angle of observation (in the CM system) and so must be positive. The deflection function $\chi(l)$, however, can be positive or negative but these alternatives or *branches* cannot be separated experimentally and so both must be included in computing the scattered amplitude at a given angle of observation. If the energy is such that the rainbow angle is greater than 2π, the situation is even more complicated because trajectories that suffer a deflection of $\chi + 2n\pi$ are experimentally indistinguishable from those deflected through χ, and so each contributes a region of stationary phase and is a separate branch of the deflection function. Since the maximum deflection in the orbiting case is ∞ there can be an infinite number of such branches (Fig. 6.4). In order to obtain the correct phase to $|2\pi|$ between all these branches, a new phase β is defined that replaces α in Equation 6.129:

$$\beta = 2\eta(l_\chi) - 2(l_\chi + \tfrac{1}{2})\eta'(l_\chi) - \left(2 - \frac{\eta'}{|\eta'|} - \frac{\eta''}{|\eta''|}\right)_{l=l_\chi} \frac{\pi}{4} \qquad (6.134)$$

where the term $\eta'/|\eta'|\ \pi/4$ provides the relative phase change of $\pi/2$ in passing from the positive to the negative branch of the deflection function, i.e. from ϕ_+ to ϕ_-. Let the three regions of stationary phase be centered on l_1, l_2 and l_3. Each such region gives a contribution to $f(\chi)$ of the form of Equation 6.128 and their sum is the resultant amplitude. The semi-classical differential cross-section then becomes

$$\sigma(\chi) \approx |\sum_n f_n(\chi)|^2 \qquad (6.135)$$

$$= \sum_n |f_n(\chi)|^2 + \sum_n \sum_m |f_n(\chi)| \, |f_m(\chi)| \cos(\beta_n - \beta_m),$$
$$\scriptstyle n \neq m$$
$$\qquad (6.136)$$

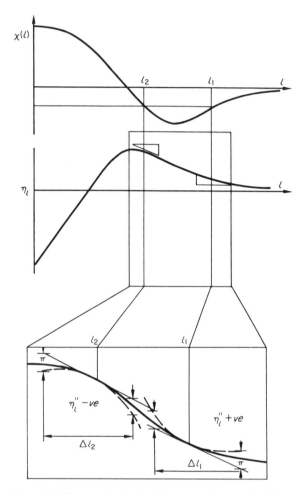

Fig. 6.3 The method of stationary phase applied to two interfering branches of the deflection function $\chi(l)$ at l_1 and l_2. The osculating parabolas are shown as dashed curves and the ranges of l values that lead to coherent scattering, Δl_1 and Δl_2, are determined by the range over which the parabolic approximation departs by less than π from the linear approximation, which is also the phase of the function $P_l(\cos \chi)$.

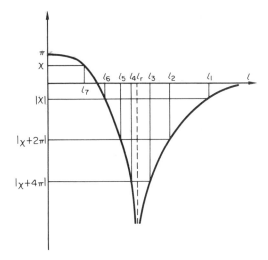

Fig. 6.4 A deflection function exhibiting orbiting. Each of the indicated l values is the centre of a region of stationary phase (for the given value of χ), of which there are an infinite number.

where the second term in Equation 6.136 represents an oscillatory contribution (see Equation 6.138) in the presence of the dominant first term. In fact, we can introduce the classical value of $\sigma(\chi)$ for the non-oscillatory part to get

$$\sigma_{cl}^{(n)}(\chi) = |f_n(\chi)|^2, \qquad (6.137)$$

and so

$$\sigma_{sc}(\chi) = \sum_{\text{all branches}} \sigma_{cl}^{(n)}(\chi) + \text{interference terms between all branches}$$

For heavy particle scattering, the second term in Equation 6.134 is dominant and so, remembering that $\eta'(l_\chi)$ changes sign in passing from ϕ_+ to ϕ_-,

$$\beta_n - \beta_m \approx (l_n \mp l_m)\chi, \qquad (6.138)$$

the upper sign referring to the case in which both branches come from ϕ_+, and the lower sign to one branch from ϕ_+ and the other from ϕ_-. Defining the periodicity Δ of the undulations as

$$\cos(\beta_n - \beta_m) = \cos 2\pi\chi/\Delta \qquad (6.139)$$

one obtains

$$\Delta \approx 2\pi/|l_n \mp l_m|$$

There is a simple picture of the choice of sign in Equations 6.138 and 6.139; from Fig. 6.5 it is seen that the effective grating spacing for trajectories originating on opposite sides of the scattering centre is $b_n + b_m$, whereas for those originating on the same side and experiencing the same deflection the grating spacing is $b_n - b_m$.

If only two branches contribute, the amplitude of $\sigma(\chi)$ oscillates between

$$\sigma_{max} = \{|f_1(\chi)| + |f_2(\chi)|\}^2$$

and   (6.140)

$$\sigma_{min} = \{|f_1(\chi)| - |f_2(\chi)|\}^2$$

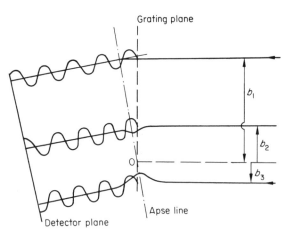

Fig. 6.5 Three trajectories with different impact parameters are shown that emerge at the same angle of scattering. In the simplest approximation they may be regarded as scattered from centres at b_1 and b_2 above the origin O and b_3 below. The effective grating spacings are then $b_1 - b_2$, $b_2 + b_3$ and $b_1 + b_3$. Zero potential wave trains scattered from these points on a hypothetical grating are shown.

In the course of fitting experimental results, the elastic scattering pattern that would be seen under low or intermediate angular resolution is often required. If the complete partial wave summation is evaluated and the resulting differential cross-section averaged over the apparatus angular resolution, the high frequency from the interference of branch 3 with branches 1 and 2 is wiped out. This is a rather clumsy procedure and the following expedient is sometimes adopted to remove the high frequency contribution from the partial wave sum from the outset. In Equation 6.121, the term ϕ_+ contributes the interference terms having $d\eta_l/dl = -\chi/2$ and ϕ_- those regions of stationary phase around $d\eta_l/dl = \chi/2$, i.e. the high frequency ones. Thus, evaluating

$$\sigma(\chi) = (2\pi k^2 \sin \chi)^{-1} \left| \int_0^\infty (l + \tfrac{1}{2})^{\frac{1}{2}} e^{i\phi_+(l)} \, dl \right|^2 \qquad (6.141)$$

will give the appearance of $\sigma(\chi)$ under intermediate angular resolution.

6.11 Glory undulations in $\sigma(\chi)$ and σ_{tot}.

As a first example of the application of the idea of interfering branches, we consider the structure in the differential cross-section at small angles and the related energy dependence of the total cross-section. Referring to Fig. 6.6, strong interference between branches 2 and 3 will arise near $\chi = 0$ because of their almost equal amplitude. This structure will be superimposed on the much stronger scattering from the branch at l_1. Since the two inner branches lead to deflections of opposite sense, the periodicity of their interference pattern is given, from Equation 6.139, by

$$\Delta_{23} \approx 2\pi/(l_2 + l_3) \approx \pi/l_0, \qquad (6.142)$$

and the latter approximation is appropriate to the high frequency structure near $\chi = 0$ (see Fig. 6.8).

Of particular experimental interest is the contribution of the forward glory (i.e. the inner zero deflection branch of $\chi(l)$) to the total cross-section. To tackle this we apply the optical theorem to the semi-quantal forward scattered amplitude $f(0)$:

$$f(0) \cong \frac{1}{2ik} \int_0^\infty (2l + 1)[e^{2i\eta(l)} - 1] \, dl. \qquad (6.143)$$

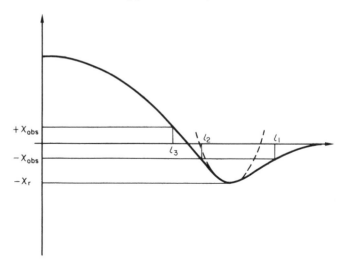

Fig. 6.6 A typical deflection function exhibiting the rainbow phenomenon at $\chi = \chi_r$. Interference effects will be observed near an angle of observation χ_{obs} between the branches at l_1, l_2, and l_3. The osculating parabola at the rainbow angle is shown as a dashed curve.

There are two regions of stationary phase which we subscript (1) and (2,3) the latter two branches having merged at $\chi = 0$ where they are exactly in phase. We require the imaginary part of $f_1(0)$ and so from

$$f_1(0) \cong k^{-1} \int_L^\infty (2l + 1)(\eta^B(l) + i\eta^B(l)^2)\, dl$$

we use

$$f_1(0) \cong e^{i\pi/2} k\sigma_{tot}^B/4\pi \tag{6.144}$$

where the Born phase shifts η^B are adequate and σ_{tot}^B is the contribution of the large impact parameter region to the total cross-section. The contribution of the inner branches is obtained from a parabolic fit to the phase shift function around $l = l_0$:

$$\eta(l) \approx \eta(l_0) + \frac{1}{2}\eta''(l - l_0)^2 \tag{6.145}$$

to give a contribution of the form of Equation 6.128 to the scattered amplitude:

$$f_{2,3}(0) \approx \frac{l_0}{k} \left(\frac{\pi}{\eta''(l_0)} \right)^{1/2} e^{2i\eta(l_0) - i\pi/4} \qquad (6.146)$$

Noting that their relative phase is energy is dependent, the two amplitudes are now combined:

$$\sigma_{tot} = \frac{4\pi}{k} \, \text{Im} \{ f_1(0) + f_{2,3}(0) \} \approx \frac{4\pi}{k^2} l_0 \left(\frac{\pi}{\eta''(l_0)} \right)^{1/2} \sin \left(2\eta(l_0) - 3\pi/4 \right) + \sigma_{tot}^B$$

$$(6.147)$$

Thus, the forward glory gives an oscillatory contribution to the energy dependence of the total cross-section as it passes in and out of phase with the bulk of the forward scattered wave front. The condition for an extremum in the velocity dependence of σ_{tot} is that the wave number k satisfies:

$$\eta_{l_0}(k) = \left(N - \frac{3}{8} \right) \pi$$

where the integer N, running to N_{max}, can be used to index successive maxima. The amplitude of these undulations is $\sim$10 per cent σ_{tot} and examples are given in Chapter 7. N_{max} is of interest in itself in that it is the number of bound states that can be contained in the potential well formed by $V(R)$. The proof of this involves Levinson's theorem, an account of which can be found in M. Wellner, 1964. From a practical point of view, however, it is difficult to extend total cross-section measurements to a low enough energy for N_{max} to be measured and the counting is further complicated by the appearance of resonance spikes at low energies in the structure of σ_{tot} (Appendix B).

The spacing of the structure in the spectrum of σ_{tot} is, of course, a function of the intermolecular potential. The turning point of trajectories that lead to zero deflection lies close to R_m over a range of values of E^* and thus the phenomenon of glory interference probes further into the repulsive part of the potential than the rainbow effect (see Section 6.11). This can be seen in a more quantitative fashion from the limiting high energy expression for η_0. If the Born approximation is applied to both the attractive and repulsive parts of a bipolar potential the high energy expression for the overall phase shift is obtained. For the Lennard-Jones potential the result is

$$\eta(l_0) \cong \frac{240\pi}{847} \left(\frac{231}{160}\right)^{1/6} \epsilon\sigma/\hbar v, \tag{6.148}$$

and so the location of maxima is given by values of v that satisfy

$$N - \frac{3}{8} \cong 0.3012 \, \epsilon\sigma/\hbar v_N. \tag{6.149}$$

Although these expressions only apply for $E^* \gg 1$, they do illustrate the much greater sensitivity of the phenomenon to σ than, say, the magnitude of the envelope or low resolution value of the total cross-section. A fuller analysis of the problem by Bernstein can be found in J. Ross, 1966.

6.12   Rainbow scattering

As the angle of observation approaches the rainbow angle, branches (1) and (2) merge (see Fig. 6.6) and can no longer be considered as separate regions of stationary phase. In order to extend the region of stationary phase over both branches, the deflection function near the rainbow is approximated by an oscillating parabola such that at $\chi = \chi_r$ its curvature and that of $\chi(l)$ are matched,

$$\chi(l) = \chi_r + \frac{1}{2}\left(\frac{d^2\chi}{dl^2}\right)_{l=l_r}(l - l_r)^2, \tag{6.150}$$

or equivalently

$$\eta(l) = \eta(l_r) + \frac{\chi_r}{2}(l - l_r) + \frac{1}{12}\left(\frac{d^2\chi}{dl^2}\right)_{l=l_r}(l - l_r)^3 \tag{6.151}$$

From Equation 2.10 the classical differential cross-section is readily found to be

$$\sigma_{cl}(\chi) = \frac{b_r}{k \sin \chi}\left|2\left(\frac{d^2\chi}{dl^2}\right)_{l=l_r}(\chi - \chi_r)\right|^{-1/2} \tag{6.152}$$

as derived in Chapter 2. However, upon going to the semi-classical formula for the scattered amplitude,

$$f_{sc}(\chi) \cong \left(\frac{l_r + \frac{1}{2}}{2\pi \sin \chi}\right)^{\frac{1}{2}} \frac{e^{i(2\eta_r - l_r\chi)}}{k} \int_{-\infty}^{\infty} \exp\left[i(\chi_r - \chi)(l - l_r)\right.$$

$$\left. + \frac{i}{6}\left(\frac{d^2\chi}{dl^2}\right)_{l=l_r}(l - l_r)^3\right]d(l - l_r), \quad (6.153)$$

where only ϕ_- has been included, an inessential phase factor has been omitted and the factor $l + \frac{1}{2}$ again taken outside the integration in order to cast the integral into a standard form, the Airy integral,

$$Ai(\chi) = \frac{1}{2\pi} \int_{-\infty}^{\infty} \exp\left[i\chi u + \frac{1}{3}iu^3\right]du. \quad (6.154)$$

The Airy function is purely real and so the phase of $f(\chi)$ near the rainbow region is, from Equation 6.153, $2\eta_r + l_r\chi$. The lower limit of integration in Equation 6.154 is extended to $-\infty$ in a completely unphysical fashion, but this has little effect on the value of the integral, to which the major contribution comes from $|u| < \pi$. Finally, then,

$$\sigma_{sc}(\chi) = \frac{b_r}{k \sin \chi} 2\pi |\chi''(l_r)/2|^{-2/3} Ai(\chi)^2 \quad (6.155)$$

where

$$x = |\chi''(l_r)/2|^{-1/3}(\chi_r - \chi)$$

The Airy function is purely real and so the phase of $f(\chi)$ near the rainbow rapid than exponential decay on the dark side $(\chi > \chi_r)$ and an oscillatory behaviour on the bright side. Useful approximations are

(i) $Ai(x) \approx 2^{-1} \pi^{-\frac{1}{2}} x^{-\frac{1}{4}} \exp\{-(\frac{2}{3})x^3{}_2\}$ $x \to \infty$ (6.156)

(ii) $Ai(x) \approx \pi^{-\frac{1}{2}}|x|^{-\frac{1}{4}} \cos\{\frac{2}{3}|x|^{\frac{3}{2}} - \pi/4\}$ $x \to -\infty$

Substituting Equation 6.156 ii into Equation 6.155, replacing the $\cos^2$ factor by $\frac{1}{2}$, yields twice the classical value for $\sigma(\chi)$ given by Equation 6.152. This is because the semi-classical result (for $\chi < \chi_r$) includes both branches of the deflection function on either side of the rainbow. The classical rainbow (at

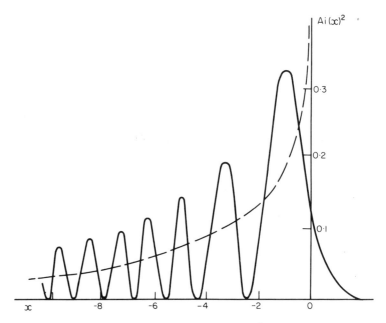

Fig. 6.7 The function $Ai(x)^2$.

$x = 0$) coincides with the point of maximum gradient on the dark side of the semi-classical differential cross-section, not with the maximum of the Airy function. The supernumerary structure arises from the interference of partial waves scattered from either side of minimum of the deflection function, l_1 and l_2 in Fig. 6.6.

In this discussion of the rainbow phenomenon, the third interfering branch coming from positive angles of deflection has so far been neglected. Referring to Fig. 6.6, this contribution comes from impact parameters centered around b_3 and we may use the result of Equation 6.139 to deduce that a high frequency structure will be superimposed upon the rainbow oscillations. If the rainbow contribution is regarded as a single branch (i.e. with branches (1) and (2) merged) and written in the form,

$$f_r(\chi) = |f_r(\chi)| \, e^{i[2\eta_r + l_r|\chi| - 3\pi/4]}$$
(6.157)

then combining with the third branch

$$f_3(\chi) = k^{-1} \left(\frac{l_3}{2 \, |\eta_3''| \sin \chi} \right)^{1/2} e^{i(2\eta_3 - l_3\chi)},$$
(6.158)

gives a scattered amplitude

$$|f(\chi)|^2 = |f_r|^2 + |f_3|^2 + 2|f_r||f_3|\cos[(l_r + l_3)\chi + \delta] \qquad (6.159)$$

which oscillates with approximately the frequency $\Delta = 2\pi/(l_3 + l_r)$. This type of structure is illustrated in Fig. 6.8. As χ approaches zero, the two rainbow branches separate and the inner one merges with the glory branch.

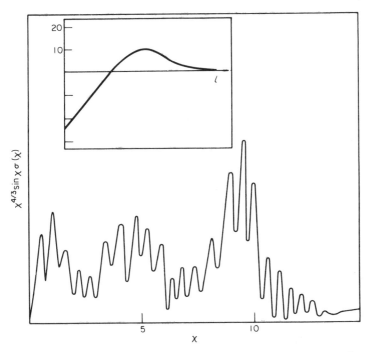

Fig. 6.8 A typical high resolution differential cross-section plot exhibiting the rainbow effect. Both high and low frequency interference effects are evident. The form of the phase shift function is inset. The classical rainbow angle is at $10°$.

The above simple treatment of the rainbow and its supernumerary structure is not valid far from χ_r. For this, a uniform approximation to the integral of Equation 6.121, i.e. one valid with specified precision over the whole angular range in which $P_l(\cos\chi)$ is oscillating, has been given by M. V. Berry (1966) but is inevitably less convenient than Equation 6.153.

6.13   Hard sphere scattering and Fraunhofer diffraction

The phase shifts for the scattering of impenetrable spheres radii a_1 and a_2 are sometimes approximated by (N. F. Mott and H. S. W. Massey, 1965).

$$\eta(l) = -kd + l\pi/2 \quad l \leqslant kd$$
$$\eta(l) = 0(ka/l)^l \quad l > kd \tag{6.160}$$

where the distance of closest approach $d = a_1 + a_2$. The semi-classical value for $l > kd$ are zero, but the quantum value is of the order shown and arise from the fact that the Bessel function decays as ρ^l inside the classical turning point.

Neglecting the phase shifts for $l > kd$, and replacing the partial wave summation, Equation 6.65, by integration over l we have

$$\sigma_{tot} \cong 2\pi d^2, \tag{6.161}$$

a result twice the classical value. This effect was first noticed by H. S. W. Massey and C. Mohr, 1933, and is essentially the result of constructive interference in the forward direction as can be seen by the following analysis. The scattered amplitude can be broken up into two contributions after substituting Equation 6.160 into the partial wave summation with $L = kd$

$$f_c = -\frac{i}{2k} e^{-2ikd} \sum_0^L (-1)^l (2l+1) P_l(\cos \chi) \tag{6.162}$$

$$f_d = \frac{i}{2k} \sum_0^L (2l+1) P_l(\cos \chi) \tag{6.163}$$

These contribute equally to the total cross-section and the reader can readily verify that

$$2\pi \int_0^\pi |f_c(\chi)|^2 \sin \chi d\chi = 2\pi \int_0^\pi |f_d(\chi)|^2 \sin \chi \, d\chi = \pi d^2 \tag{6.164}$$

(the cross term $|f_c| |f_d|$ vanishes through the operation of the $(-1)^l$ factor in f_c). However, their contribution to the differential cross-section is very different as can be seen from the two forward scattered amplitudes $f_c(0)$ and $f_d(0)$;—

$$|f_c(0)| = \frac{1}{2} d(-1)^{kd}$$

$$|f_d(0)| = \frac{1}{2} kd^2,$$

i.e. the contribution from f_d is $O(kd)$ greater than that from f_c. $|f_d(\chi)|^2$ is, in fact, a very sharply peaked function near $\chi = 0$ and contains the interference cone of angular width $1/kd$ described above. f_c is called the classical amplitude because it gives the whole of the classical contribution outside the diffraction cone (assuming the exact $\eta(l)$ to be used).

Using the approximation of Equation 6.94 for the Legendre polynomials, the following approximation for the small angle scattering is derived from f_d with the aid of Equation 6.163:

$$\sigma(\chi) \approx [d^2/\chi \sin \chi] J_1^2(kd\chi). \tag{6.165}$$

The first minimum occurs at $\chi \approx 3.8/kd$ and the complete function is displayed in Fig. 6.9. The undulations in $\sigma(\chi)$ are the result of interference between waves trains scattered from either side of the sphere from (A5) the periodicity is

$$\Delta\chi = \pi/kd \tag{6.166}$$

since the hard sphere diameter is effectively half the spacing of the diffraction grating.

Making use of the asymptotic form of $J_1(x)$ for $x \gg 1$ (Appendix A) shows further that with the phase shifts used above:

$$\sigma(\chi) \xrightarrow{\chi \to \pi} O(d/k) \tag{6.167}$$

while the correct classical limit is $O(d^2)$. In order to obtain the quantum equivalent of this result, a more accurate phase shift function must replace Equation 6.160. Starting from the classical deflection function in Equation 2.63 and using

$$\eta(l) = \eta(0) + \frac{1}{2} \int_0^l \chi(l')\, dl' \tag{6.168}$$

where $\eta(0) = -kd + \pi/4$ for the hard sphere case, we obtain:

$$\eta(l) = l\chi/2 - kd \sin(\chi/2) + \frac{\pi}{4} \tag{6.169}$$

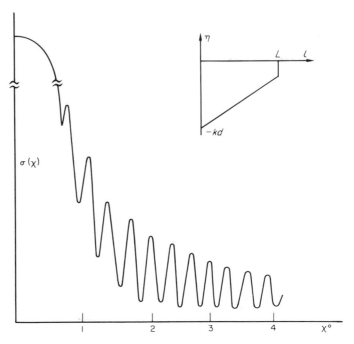

Fig. 6.9 The small angle scattering resulting from a step in the phase shift function (inset), of the type represented by (6.160). The exponential decay of $\sigma(\chi)$ at very small angles is shown, with the quadratic decay of the envelope at larger angles. The function displayed is essentially $J_1(L\chi)$.

where $\chi(l)$ is the classical deflection function. There is a discontinuity in the gradient of this phase shift function at $l = kd$. Once again $f(0)$ is split up into a diffraction term f_d identical to Equation 6.163 and a potential scattering term,

$$f_c(\chi) = \frac{i}{2k} \sum_{l=0} (2l + 1)\, e^{2i\eta_l}\, P_l(\cos \chi) \qquad (6.170)$$

with η_l given by Equation 6.169, $f_c(\chi)$ can be evaluated by the usual semi-classical method (Section 6.9) and the classical result

$$\sigma_c(\chi) = |f_c(\chi)|^2 = \frac{\pi}{2} \frac{d^2}{\sin \chi} \qquad \chi > \frac{1}{kd} \qquad (6.171)$$

obtained. However, the diffraction contribution $f_d(\chi)$ is still present and makes a small oscillatory contribution at large angles, with the envelope determined by Equation 6.171.

In optics this type of interference is familiar as Fraunhofer diffraction. Its molecular manifestation is not limited to the artificial hard sphere potential but may arise from any potential yielding a region in which the phase shift varies discontinuously with l. Thus, scattering from a deep 'chemical' potential well supporting many quasi-bound states will show this effect; in Fig. 6.10 the discontinuities produced by these resonances would merge into a single large step in region II. This edge in the phase shift function at $l = L$ leads to oscillations in the differential cross-section of a frequency from Equation 6.139 of π/L. To a crude approximation $\sigma(\chi)$ can be estimated by assuming random phases for $l < L$ and zero phase shifts for $l > L$, whence

$$\sigma(\chi) = |f_d(\chi)|^2 \tag{6.172}$$

with $f_d(\chi)$ given by Equation 6.163. In practice the phase shifts will not be

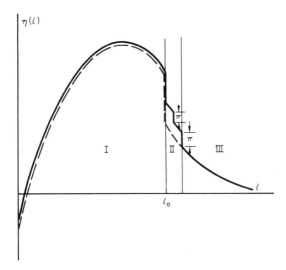

Fig. 6.10 The phase shift function in the presence of orbiting. The orbiting value of l is l_0; for $l < l_0$, region I, there is only one classical turning point and the quantum (full line) & semi-classical (dashed line) phase shifts nearly coincide. In region II there are either two ($l = l_0$) or three classical turning points and resonances occur in the quantum phase shift. In region III the effective potential energy curve is monotonic and the quantum and semi-classical values coincide.

random and interfering branches may exist either side of the 'edge' leading to lower frequency oscillations superimposed upon the Fraunhofer pattern (L. T. Cowley et al. 1969. M. A. D. Fluendy, 1970).

6.14   Resonances

Resonances play an important part in electron and nuclear scattering, but their role so far in molecular scattering has been negligible. One reason for this is that a single resonance affects only a few partial waves, whereas the width of a semi-classical branch of the scattered amplitude in heavy particle scattering typically exceeds 100 partial waves. In contrast, in low energy nuclear and electron scattering, the s-wave contribution to the differential cross-section is usually dominant and a resonance can become of paramount importance. Nevertheless, the theory of resonances and especially their effect on the total cross-section follows identical lines in all cases to yield one of the best known formulae of nuclear scattering, the Breit-Wigner formula (appendix B), thus reminding chemists that their interests are but part of a larger story.

The key to the interpretation of resonances is the relationship between the lifetime Γ of a compound state formed as the result of a collision and the range of energy ΔE over which the total cross-section is perturbed:

$$\Gamma.\Delta E \sim h \qquad (6.173)$$

The most promising area to search for resonances in molecular scattering is in the energy dependence of the total cross-section where the basic structure is simple and slowly varying. Two requirements are then that the potential should be deep enough to support at least one bound state, and that the lifetime of a state (essentially trapped behind the centrifugal barrier) should be sufficiently short for the corresponding energy width, ΔE, to be large, as indicated by Equation 6.173. For the lifetime to be short, the centrifugal barrier must not be too high or too wide, and the frequency of the classical motion inside the barrier must be high. These condition are fulfilled by a pair of particles of small reduced mass near orbiting. Stwalley (W. C. Stwalley, 1969) has thus suggested that the scattering of hydrogen atoms from a variety of species should yield relatively pronounced resonances in $\sigma_{tot}(E)$. In the most favourable case, that with the shortest Γ, we can set an upper limit on ΔE by assuming that the lifetime in the well is equal to the classical periodicity and that the system passes back through the barrier on the first attempt. From Equation 6.173, ΔE is then $\sim 10^{-14}$ ergs; this is to be compared with the typical energy resolution in a total cross-section experiment at thermal energies, which is also $\sim 10^{-14}$ ergs so detection even in the most favourable case is still difficult.

6.15 The scattering of identical particles

Since Equation 6.7 is the wave function for the relative motion of two particles, it must have a definite parity with respect to the interchange of the two colliding particles if these are indistinguishable. The correct wave functions for fermions will be anti-symmetric and for bosons symmetric with respect to this permutation. For the purposes of elastic scattering, the pair wave function is the product of the nuclear spin function and the overall rotational wave function, just as it would be for a Σ state diatomic molecule. Depending on the nuclear spin, a variety of spin wave functions can be constructed that are either symmetric or anti-symmetric with respect to the interchange of nuclear labels. This interchange also results in the inter-nuclear vector, **R** being reversed in sign, which is a symmetry operation on the rotational wave function. Thus, the inversion of the coordinates of particle (1) through the origin results in the change of its polar co-ordinates from (χ, ϕ) to $(\pi - \chi, \pi + \phi)$. Under this transformation, the Legendre polynomials behave as follows:

$$P_l(\cos \chi) \xrightarrow{\chi \to \pi - \chi} (-1)^l P_l(\cos (\pi - \chi))$$

and, from Equation 6.45,

$$e^{ikz} \longrightarrow e^{-ikz}$$

(the purely radial functions e^{ikR} or $j_l(kR)$ are unchanged). The operation of an exclusion principle ensures that for bosons nuclear and rotational states of like symmetry are combined and for fermions only those of unlike symmetry combine. This situation is familiar in spectroscopy where for half integral spin particles the even rotational levels are called para states and the odd levels ortho states.

In the scattering problem we must impose odd or even symmetry on the spatial wave function if the nuclei are identical. For a given pair of atoms in a definite nuclear spin state (which is not necessarily known but which does not change during the collision) only odd or even partial waves can be included in any part of Equation 6.7. The initial plane wave thus becomes

$$e^{ikz} \longrightarrow e^{ikz} \pm e^{-ikz} = 2\sum_{l\ \text{even, odd}} i^l(2l+1)j_l(kr)P_l(\cos\chi), \qquad (6.174)$$

which represents the approach of identical particles from both left and right with equal flux, which is what is occurring physically (Fig. 6.11). The partial wave expansion of the scattered amplitude now reads

$$f_\pm(\chi) = 2\frac{1}{2ik}\sum_{l\ \text{even, odd}} (2l+1)(e^{2i\eta_l}-1)P_l(\cos\chi), \qquad (6.175)$$

(where the factor 2 has come from the doubling of the intensity of each allowed value that results from using Equation 6.174).

To restore the complete summation over l we introduce $P_l(\cos(\pi-\chi))$,

$$2\sum_{l\ \text{even, odd}} (2l+1)(e^{2i\eta_l}-1)P_l(\cos\chi)$$

$$= \sum_{\text{all}\ l} (2l+1)\,(e^{2i\eta_l}-1)\Big\{P_l(\cos\chi)\pm P_l(\cos(\pi-\chi))\Big\}. \qquad (6.176)$$

Then,

$$f_\pm(\chi) = f(\chi) \pm f(\pi-\chi), \qquad (6.177)$$

and so

$$\sigma(\chi) = |\,f(\chi)\,|^2 + |\,f(\pi-\chi)\,|^2 \pm 2|\,f(\chi)\,|\,|\,f(\pi-\chi)\,|. \qquad (6.178)$$

Finally, we must include the weighting of the ortho (+) and para (−) states w_+ and w_- to give

$$\sigma(\chi) = |\,f(\chi)\,|^2 + |\,f(\pi-\chi)\,|^2 + 2(w_+ - w_-)\,|\,f(\chi)\,|\,|\,f(\pi-\chi)\,|. \qquad (6.179)$$

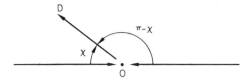

Fig. 6.11 Identical particles approaching from left and right in the cm must be scattered through $(\pi-\chi)$ and χ respectively to reach the detector D.

The partial wave summations for $f(\chi)$ and $f(\pi - \chi)$ can be evaluated in the semi-classical fashion as described in Section 6.9 and the molecular symmetry of the problem has no effect on this stage of the calculation. However, the overall differential cross-section $\sigma(\chi)$ is rendered symmetrical about $\chi = \pi/2$ (CM). Classically, this is because we cannot tell whether a particle reaching the detector has come from the main beam or the cross-beam. Besides this entirely new symmetry in the scattering pattern, novel interference effects have appeared from the cross-term $2f(\chi) f(\pi - \chi)$ in Equation 6.178, but for this term to be important $f(\chi)$ and $f(\pi - \chi)$ must have similar amplitudes and this will only occur near $\chi = \pi/2$.

If the two beams are differently isotopically labelled, we can perform two experiments;

I Detector cannot discriminate between the isotopes, in which case

$$\sigma(\chi) = |f(\chi)|^2 + |f(\pi - \chi)|^2 . \tag{6.180}$$

II Detector is mass sensitive, in which case

$$\sigma(\chi) = |f(\chi)|^2 . \tag{6.181}$$

In either case the special interference effects are destroyed. The total cross-section for the scattering of spinless bosons ($I = 0$) is readily obtained by applying the optical theorem to Equation 6.176

$$\sigma_{tot} = \frac{2\pi}{k^2} \sum_l (2l + 1)(1 - \cos 2\eta_l)(P_l(1) + P_l(-1))$$

$$= \frac{2\pi}{k^2} \left\{ \sum_l (2l + 1)(1 - \cos 2\eta_l) + \sum_l (2l + 1)(1 - \cos 2\eta_l) \cos \pi l \right\}$$

$$= \frac{2\pi}{k^2} \left\{ \sum_l (2l + 1)(1 - \cos 2\eta_l) + \sum_l (2l + 1)(-1)^l \right.$$

$$\left. - \sum_l (2l + 1) \cos 2\eta_l \cos \pi l \right\} \tag{6.182}$$

where the equivalent forms $P_l(-1) = \cos \pi l = (-1)^l$ have been used as needed.

The first term in 6.182 represents the normal contribution that would be obtained for unlike particles without any symmetry requirements. The second term has been seen (Section 6.13) to be negligible. The third term can exhibit a region of stationary phase if the deflection function passes through $\pm \pi$, so that $2\eta_l - \pi = 0$, 2π at $l = l_{\pm\pi}$. The region of stationary phase at $\chi(l) = \pi$, which occurs at $l = 0$, is always present; the occurrence of the other branch depends upon the attractive part of the potential being sufficiently strong. Making a parabolic fit to the phase shift function near $l = 0$ and $l = l_{-\pi}$ results in

$$2\eta(l) - l\pi = \begin{cases} 2\eta(l_\pi) + 2l^2\eta''(l_\pi) \\ 2\eta(l_{-\pi}) + (l - l_{-\pi})^2\eta''(l_{-\pi}) - 2\pi l. \end{cases} \quad (6.183)$$

The range of integration in the Fresnel integral that is obtained when Equation 6.183 is substituted into Equation 6.182 is now $0 \to \infty$ in the first case and $-\infty \to \infty$ in the second (which is similar in all quantitative respects to a forward glory). The scattered amplitude in the forward direction due to these inner branches is now given by

$$f(0) = \frac{l_\pi}{4ik} \left\{ \cos 2\eta(l_\pi) + \sin 2\eta(l_\pi) \right\} \left(\frac{\pi}{2\eta''(l_\pi)} \right)^{\frac{1}{2}}$$

$$+ \frac{l_{-\pi}}{2ik} \left\{ \cos 2\eta(l_{-\pi}) + \sin 2\eta(l_{-\pi}) \right\} \left(\frac{\pi}{2\eta''(l_{-\pi})} \right)^{\frac{1}{2}} \quad (6.184)$$

Then, neglecting the possible presence of a forward glory, the total cross-section is given by:

$$\sigma_{tot} = \sigma_{tot}^{cl} + \frac{\pi l_\pi}{2k^2} \sin \left[2\eta(l_\pi) + \pi/4\right] \left(\frac{\pi}{\eta''(l_\pi)} \right)^{\frac{1}{2}}$$

$$+ \frac{\pi l_{-\pi}}{k^2} \sin \left[2\eta(l_{-\pi}) + \pi/4\right] \left(\frac{\pi}{\eta''(l_{-\pi})} \right)^{\frac{1}{2}} \quad (6.185)$$

The physical interpretation of this result is that a cross-beam particle deflected through $\pm \pi$ into the direction of the main beam, will reach the detector in a total cross-section experiment and cannot be distinguished from a particle originating in the main beam. The two wave trains thus interfere, and a maximum in the total cross-section occurs every time η_π or $\eta_{-\pi}$ passes through $(\pi/4 + 2 \pi n)$.

For very low energy scattering of light particles in which only a few partial waves participate, only the S-wave contribution at $\chi = \pi$ is important and the semi-classical nature of Equation 6.185 would be inappropriate. Such a situation arises in the scattering of He^4 from He^4 (Section 7.4) and very low temperatures. In this case the interatomic potential is essentially purely repulsive and the $\chi = -\pi$ branch is absent. For Ne or Ar, also spinless bosons, the presence of a minimum in the intermolecular potential means that a forward glory must be present and this contributes yet another interfering branch which must be included in Equation 6.185.

In the treatment of identical particle scattering so far it has been assumed that only one intermolecular potential is operating, irrespective of the nuclear spin state. This is a valid assumption for atoms in S states. However, when the scattering of like particles that possess non-zero electronic spin is considered, new phenomena appear which are discussed in Section 6.17.

6.16 Scattering from mixed electronic states; exchange scattering

We now discuss the scattering of excited atoms or ions (M^*, M^+) from the corresponding ground state species (M). The need for a separate treatment of this problem arises from the fact that the electronic energy levels of the two particle system that dissociate to $M^* + M$ are of two kinds and hence two potential energy functions can govern the relative motion of the pair. These electronic states are classifiable with respect to inversion of the electrons in the centre of symmetry of the nuclear charges (i.e. the centre of mass in the present problem). The scattering of a metastable molecule from a ground state partner is a much more complicated situation; the symmetry of the problem depends upon the orientation of the two molecules and there is considerable coupling between molecular rotation and electronic motion.

In a crossed-beam experiment (M^*/M), a diatomic system is in effect prepared in which it is known which of the two atoms is excited initially by the position they occupy in the laboratory. We must first describe this unusual situation in terms of eigenfunctions having the full symmetry of this molecule which are the gerade and ungerade states, ψ_g and ψ_u. For slow collisions we will need only the lowest members of these two classes (the others lying too high in energy to be accessible) and so

$$\psi_{g,u} = \frac{1}{\sqrt{2}} \left\{ \phi_A \phi_B^* \pm \phi_A^* \phi_B \right\} \tag{6.186}$$

where A and B label the two identical atoms, one from each beam, and ϕ_A, ϕ_B are the ground state atomic eigenfunctions. The electronic wave functions in the actual entrance channels of the experiment are

$$\left. \begin{array}{c} \phi_A \phi_B^* \\ \text{or} \\ \phi_A^* \phi_B \end{array} \right\} = \frac{1}{\sqrt{2}} \left\{ \psi_g \pm \psi_\mu \right\} \tag{6.187}$$

Our first approach might be that, equipped with wave function 6.187 we calculate an interatomic potential from 1st order perturbation theory

$$V_{AB*}(R) = V_{A*B}(R) = \frac{1}{2}\left\{\langle\psi_g \mid H \mid \psi_g\rangle + \langle\psi_u \mid H \mid \psi_u\rangle - (E_0 + E_0^*)\right\}$$

(6.188)

where H is the complete electronic Hamiltonian and E_0, E_0* are the energies of the isolated ground and excited atoms. In arriving at Equation 6.188, use has been made of the fact that, by symmetry, $< \psi_g \mid H \mid \psi_u > = 0$. The scattering, we might think, would then be confined to the AB* or A*B channel and in either case proceed under the influence of the potential in Equation 6.188.

The difficulty is that the interaction potential in H, by which an electron on one atom experiences a field due to the neighbouring atom, connects the state AB* and A*B in the sense that the matrix element

$$\langle\psi_A\psi_{B*} \mid H \mid \phi_{A*}\phi_B\rangle = \langle\psi_g \mid H \mid \psi_g\rangle - \langle\psi_u \mid H \mid \psi_u\rangle \qquad (6.189)$$

is not zero. The result of this is that if we were to start the collision in the state AB*, then time dependent perturbation theory (or the method of analysis to follow) tell us that the 'exciton' (labelled*) oscillates between the two atoms during the collision. This problem seems to require the solution of two simultaneous wave equations to replace the single one (Equation 6.6) with which this chapter began, but fortunately there is an equivalent route that decouples the states.

The interatomic potentials for the states described by ψ_g and ψ_u are also well defined

$$V_{g,u}(R) = \langle\psi_{g,u} \mid H \mid \psi_{g,u}\rangle - \frac{1}{2}\ (E_0 + E_0^*),$$

(6.190)

and the Hamiltonian is diagonal in this representation:

$$\langle\psi_g \mid H \mid \psi_u\rangle = 0.$$

Thus, regardless of whether in practice we can prepare the u and g states, we can define a scattering matrix for the collision of the two atoms with entrance and exit channels formally labelled g and u. The advantage of this is that the complete S matrix is now factored into two sub-matrices, one for scattering between (g, l) channels and the other between (u, l) channels. Physically, if we prepare a gerade state, then however violent the collision we cannot possibly end up in an ungerade state because there is no term in the Hamiltonian that couples terms of different symmetry. For the scattering of ground state S atoms, the scattering matrix is completely diagonalised because states of different relative angular momentum (l – value) are not coupled by the Hamiltonian. This remains true to a good approximation for the scattering of excited or ionised $2S$ or $3S$ states, and somewhat less true of P states, where electronic orbital angular momentum is more readily coupled to translational angular momentum, especially with regard to changes in the projection quantum number m_L.

Assuming that the relative angular momentum is separately conserved, we deduce that the S matrix in the g, u description is completely diagonalised, and the lth sub-matrix down the diagonal is of the form

$$\begin{pmatrix} l-1 & & \\ & l & \\ & & l+1 \end{pmatrix} \longrightarrow \begin{pmatrix} e^{2i\eta_l^g} & 0 \\ 0 & e^{2i\eta_l^u} \end{pmatrix} \tag{6.191}$$

The phase shifts $\eta^{g,u}$ can be calculated by any of the methods outlined in Sections 6.5, 6.7 or 6.8 using $V_{g,u}(R)$ as appropriate.

From our knowledge of the S matrix in one basis, (Equation 6.191) we can readily find it in any other orthonormal basis by the appropriate unitary transformation (Section 6.4). In the present case the matrix $\{T\}$ that converts the $\{\psi_u, \psi_g\}$ basis into the $\{\phi_A, \phi_B\}$ basis is, from Equation 6.187.

$$\{T\} = \begin{pmatrix} \dfrac{1}{\sqrt{2}} & \dfrac{1}{\sqrt{2}} \\ \dfrac{1}{\sqrt{2}} & -\dfrac{1}{\sqrt{2}} \end{pmatrix} = \{T\}^{-1}, \tag{6.192}$$

and so the lth factor of the scattering matrix in the $\{\phi_A \phi_B\}$ basis is given by the similarity transformation

$$\{S_l\}_{A,B} = \{T\}^{-1} \{S_l\}_{g,u} \{T\}$$

where the first transformation deals with the exit channels and the second with the entrance channels. The result is

$$
\begin{pmatrix} S_{AB*l:AB*l} & S_{AB*l:A*Bl} \\ S_{A*Bl:AB*l} & S_{A*Bl:A*Bl} \end{pmatrix} = \begin{pmatrix} \dfrac{1}{2}\left\{ e^{2in_l^g} + e^{2in_l^u} \right\} & \dfrac{1}{2}\left\{ e^{2in_l^g} - e^{2in_l^u} \right\} \\ \dfrac{1}{2}\left\{ e^{2in_l^g} - e^{2in_l^u} \right\} & \dfrac{1}{2}\left\{ e^{2in_l^g} + e^{2in_l^u} \right\} \end{pmatrix}
$$

The new S matrix is, of course, unitary but is no longer diagonal. The probability of transition from the entrance channel $(AB*;l)$ to the exit channel $(A*B;l)$, i.e. for the transfer of excitation from one atom to the other is

$$
P_{AB*l:A*Bl} = |S_{AB*l:A*Bl}|^2 = \tfrac{1}{2}\left[1 - \cos 2(\eta_l^g - \eta_l^u)\right]. \qquad (6.193)
$$

The differential cross-section for elastic scattering of either the excited or the ground state is given by

$$
\begin{aligned}
f_{AB*:AB*}(\chi) &= \frac{1}{2ik}\sum_l (2l+1)\left\{\frac{1}{2}(e^{2in_l^g} + e^{2in_l^u}) - 1\right\} P_l(\cos\chi) \\
&= \frac{1}{4ik}\left\{\sum_l (2l+1)(e^{2in_l^g} - 1) P_l(\cos\chi) \right. \\
&\quad \left. + \sum_l (2l+1)(e^{2in_l^u} - 1) P_l(\cos\chi) \right\} \\
&= \frac{1}{2}\left\{f_g(\chi) + f_u(\chi)\right\}
\end{aligned} \qquad (6.194)
$$

The gerade and ungerade scattered amplitudes can be summed separately by any of the methods previously outlined. In particular, if the semi-classical method is used and the regions of stationary phase for a given value of χ located in both $f_g(\chi)$ and $f_u(\chi)$, we can write

$$
\sigma_{AB*:AB*}(\chi) = \frac{1}{4}\left\{\sigma_g(\chi) + \sigma_u(\chi) + 2[\sigma_g(\chi)\sigma_u(\chi)]^{1/2} \cos(\beta_g - \beta_u)\right\} \qquad (6.195)
$$

where it is assumed that there is only one region of stationary phase in each of the $f_g(\chi)$ and $f_u(\chi)$; β_g, β_u are defined analogously to Equation 6.134. A new interference structure has thus emerged, with a frequency

$$
\Delta\chi \approx 2\pi/(l_\chi^g - l_\chi^u), \qquad (6.196)
$$

where the difference between η_l^g and η_l^u in $\beta_g - \beta_u$ has been neglected. This structure will only be pronounced if the amplitudes of $f_g(\theta)$ and $f_u(\theta)$ are similar.

The exchange differential cross-section is similarly found to be given by

$$\sigma_{AB^*:A^*B}(\chi) = \frac{1}{4} \, |f_g(\chi) - f_u(\chi)|^2, \tag{6.197}$$

and so also exhibits interference structure of the same frequency as the direct scattering but $180°$ out of phase. At large separations of the particles, the g and u potentials differ only slightly, as do the associated phase shifts. Re-arranging Equation 6.197 to introduce an average phase shift,

$$\frac{1}{2} (\eta_l^g + \eta_l^u) = \eta_l^{av}$$

gives

$$f_{AB^*:A^*B}(\chi) = \frac{1}{2k} \sum_l (2l + 1) \, e^{2i\eta_l^{av}} \sin (\eta_l^g - \eta_l^u) P_l(\cos \chi) \tag{6.198}$$

For small angle scattering, then, the term $\sin (\eta_l^g - \eta_l^u)$ in Equation 6.198 is but slowly varying and we need only look for stationary phase in η^{av}. The treatment of Section 6.9 will then give an average scattered amplitude $f_{av}(\chi)$ and the exchange cross-section expression becomes

$$\sigma_{AB^*:A^*B}(\chi) \approx |f^{av}(\chi)|^2 \sin^2 (\eta_\chi^g - \eta_\chi^u) \tag{6.199}$$

a formula valid for $\eta_\chi^g - \eta_\chi^u \ll \pi/2$. Thus it can be said that exchange scattering is directly dependent on the difference in gerade and ungerade potentials. In particular, at small angles, when the Born approximation for the phase shifts is applicable, the exchange cross-section is quadratically dependent on the difference in strengths of the two potentials.

Exchange scattering of the type described in this section has been most thoroughly studied in ion/neutral systems, notably He^+/He from 15 eV to 300 eV. In this case it is not an exciton that is exchanged but an electron, but the foregoing treatment remains unchanged, except for the complication of identical nuclei for which the treatment of Section 6.15 can be incorporated as follows. The entire atomic pair wave function

$$\psi = \begin{pmatrix} \psi_{nuclear} \\ spin \end{pmatrix} \begin{pmatrix} \psi_{electronic} \\ co\text{-}ordinate \end{pmatrix} \begin{pmatrix} \psi_{molecular} \\ rotation \end{pmatrix} \begin{pmatrix} \psi_{electron} \\ spin \end{pmatrix}, \tag{6.200}$$

must be either symmetric (bosons) or anti-symmetric (fermions) with respect to interchange of identical particles. The He^+/He system can be treated as a 1-electron one and only the first three factors in Equation 6.200 are relevant (i.e. only doublet molecular states considered). For He^4 ($I = 0$), gerade electronic states are associated with even rotational states and ungerade with odd states. Then,

$$f_g(\chi) = f_g(\chi) + f_g(\pi - \chi) = \frac{1}{ik} \sum_{l \text{ even}} (2l + 1)[e^{2i\eta_l^g} - 1] \, P_l(\cos \chi),$$

$$f_u(\chi) = f_u(\chi) + f_u(\pi - \chi) = \frac{1}{ik} \sum_{l \text{ od}} (2l + 1)[e^{2i\eta_l^u} - 1] \, P_l(\cos \chi)$$

$$(6.201)$$

replace f_g and f_u in Equation 6.194. The number of possible interfering branches of the deflection function has now increased to four or more and the simplicity of the earlier pattern is marred. However, we have seen (Section 6.15) that if the scattering can be described in a semi-classical fashion, nuclear symmetry effects only become apparent at angles somewhat greater than the rainbow value. For the case of He^+/He in the low eV region, many partial waves contribute and a semi-classical treatment is appropriate. In this system it is the ungerade state that possesses a deep potential minimum and the gerade state is effectively everywhere repulsive. There are thus three branches contributing to $f_u(\chi)$ at angles less than the rainbow and only one branch to $f_g(\chi)$.

All these interference effects can be found in the experimental results for the $^4He/^4He^+$ system. The potentials and deflection functions are sketched in Fig. 6.12 together with the calculated (semiquantal) differential cross-section at 15 eV (Fig. 6.13). The observed scattering (D. C. Lorents and W. Aberth, 1965) follows the calculated curve quite closely, although the highest frequency oscillations on the bright side of the rainbow (arising from f_u) have not been resolved.

The radial separation at which gerade and ungerade potentials begin to diverge depends upon the electronic states of the two atoms. Thus, in the case of the He/He^+ system, a typical matrix element that governs the gerade/ungerade splitting is a 1-electron integral;

$$H_{AB} = \int \phi_A(r_A) \left\{ \frac{1}{r_A} + \frac{1}{r_B} - \frac{1}{2} \nabla^2 \right\} \phi_B(r_B) \, dr \qquad (6.202)$$

However, for the system $H(1s)/H(2s)$ or $He(1s^2; {}^1S)/He(1s^1 2s^1; {}^3S)$ a two electron exchange integral is involved, which is a roughly quadratic function of the overlap of the two atomic orbitals. The splitting of the gerade and

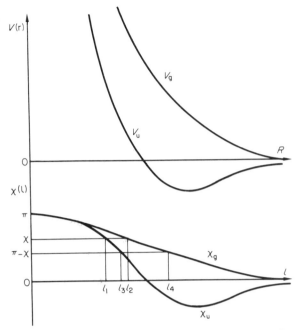

Fig. 6.12 Potentials and deflection functions for ^{4}He, ^{4}He$^+$ scattering. For the angle of deflection, χ, illustrated $(\chi > \chi_r)$, there are four interfering branches of the deflection function centered at $l_1 \ldots l_4$. The gerade potential will have a shallow minimum at a fairly large value of R that arises from the charge-induced dipole interaction and is not shown.

ungerade states thus begins at much closer separations in the latter cases and so the associated interference effects (e.g. from Equation 6.199) appear at larger angles of deflection and are less accessible to observation.

6.17   Scattering from mixed spin states

We now turn to the problem of the mutual scattering of ^2S atoms, i.e. of atoms with one unpaired electron. Two types of experiment have been performed, in the first case one of the beams is spin state selected ($M_s = \pm 1/2$) while the detector has an analyser also tuned to one of the spin states. The other configuration is one in which no spin selection at all is used.

Concentrating on the case of unlike nuclei (labelled A and B) the various atom pair wave functions that fulfill the anti-symmetric rule for the

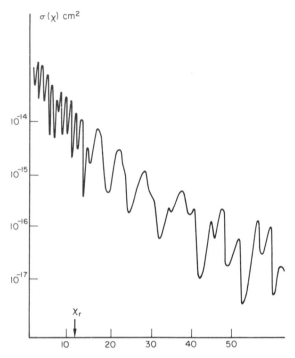

Fig. 6.13 The differential cross-section for $He^+ -$
He scattering at 15 eV, identical nuclei. The high
frequency structure at $\chi < \chi_r$ is apparent, giving
way to a simpler low frequency structure beyond
the rainbow. This, in turn, shows the increasing
interference from the exchange scattering
$(|f(\chi)| \, | \, |f(\pi - \chi)|)$ at larger angles. The pure ex-
change scattering, $|f(\pi - \chi)|^2$ is negligible through-
out this angular range. (Adapted from R. P. Marchi
and F. T. Smith, 1965.)

electronic wave function are the familiar singlet and triplet states;

$$\psi_{00} = \{\phi_A(r_1)\phi_B(r_2) + \phi_B(r_1)\phi_A(r_2)\} \{\alpha(1)\beta(2) - \alpha(2)\beta(1)\}$$

$$\psi_1 \begin{Bmatrix} 1 \\ 0 \\ -1 \end{Bmatrix} = \{\phi_A(r_1)\phi_B(r_2) - \phi_B(r_1)\phi_A(r_2)\} \begin{Bmatrix} \alpha(1)\alpha(2) \\ \alpha(1)\beta(2) + \alpha(2)\beta(1) \\ \beta(1)\beta(2) \end{Bmatrix} \quad (6.203)$$

The potentials associated with these two states are very different, the triplet
potential generally exhibiting only a very shallow minimum and the singlet
state leading to a deep 'chemical' well. However, with no spin selection at all,

or even with the spin of only one atomic partner known, we have no a priori means of knowing whether the colliding pair is in the singlet or triplet state. However, if the spin is not coupled strongly to the relative angular momentum, transitions between singlet and triplet states are unlikely and we can expect the S matrix to be diagonal in the true singlet/triplet representation. The situation is thus very similar to the gerade/ungerade scattering of excited atoms or of ions treated in Section 6.14 and the formalism can be largely carried over.

From an experimental point of view, we need to describe the various atom pair wave functions according to the spin of each atom. Thus, if both atoms have $M_s = +\tfrac{1}{2}(\equiv \alpha)$,

$$\phi_{\alpha\alpha} = \|\, \phi_A \alpha\, \phi_B \alpha \,\|.$$

If atom A has spin α and atom B spin β,

$$\phi_{\alpha\beta} = \|\, \phi_A \alpha\, \phi_B \beta \,\|.$$

and so forth. Expanding these wave functions in terms of the singlet and triplet eigenfunctions ψ_{SM_s} gives:—

$$\phi_{\alpha\alpha} = \psi_{11}$$

$$\phi_{\alpha\beta} = 2^{-\frac{1}{2}}\,(\psi_{00} + \psi_{10}) \qquad\qquad (6.204)$$

$$\phi_{\beta\alpha} = 2^{-\frac{1}{2}}(\psi_{00} - \psi_{10})$$

$$\phi_{\beta\beta} = \psi_{1-1}$$

Clearly, although the singlet and triplet eigenfunctions diagonalize the total energy operator, the basis $(\alpha\beta)$ does not and in particular the matrix element

$$\int \phi_{\alpha\beta}\, V \phi_{\beta\alpha}\, d\tau = \int \psi_{00} V \psi_{00}\, d\tau - \int \psi_{10} V \psi_{10}\, d\tau \qquad (6.205)$$

is not zero. In this situation it is more convenient to evaluate the S matrix elements in the (SM_s) basis and to subsequently transform to the $(\alpha\beta)$ basis. The observed scattering pattern will then be the superposition of the scattering resulting from the $(\alpha\alpha)$ $(\beta\beta)$, $(\alpha\beta)$ and $(\beta\alpha)$ entrance channels weighted according to the spin selection used in the experiment. Thus, if $\sigma_{\alpha\beta:\gamma\delta}$ denotes the cross-section for scattering from the entrance channel $(\alpha\beta)$ to the exit channel $(\gamma\delta)$ we have, using the fact that either spin state is equally likely in an unselected beam (the cross-beam in cases I, II and IV below)

Case I.   Atom A in state α, analyzer for atom A set for state β;

$$\sigma_I(\chi) = \frac{1}{2} \ \sigma_{\alpha\beta:\beta\alpha}(\chi).$$ (6.206)

Case II.   Atom A in state α, analyzer for atom A set for state α;

$$\sigma_{II}(\chi) = \frac{1}{2} \left[\sigma_{\alpha\alpha:\alpha\alpha}(\chi) + \sigma_{\alpha\beta:\alpha\beta}(\chi) \right].$$ (6.207)

Case III.   Atom A in state α, atom B in state β, no spin analysis at the detector;

$$\sigma_{III}(\chi) = \sigma_{\alpha\beta:\alpha\beta}(\chi) + \sigma_{\alpha\beta:\beta\alpha}(\chi).$$ (6.208)

Case IV.   No spin selection or analysis;

$$\sigma_{IV}(\chi) = \frac{1}{4} \left[\sigma_{\alpha\alpha:\alpha\alpha}(\chi) + \sigma_{\beta\beta:\beta\beta}(\chi) + \sigma_{\alpha\beta:\alpha\beta}(\chi) + \sigma_{\beta\alpha:\beta\alpha}(\chi) \right.$$
$$\left. + \sigma_{\beta\alpha:\alpha\beta}(\chi) + \sigma_{\alpha\beta:\beta\alpha}(\chi) \right]$$ (6.209)

In cases III and IV the spin exchange cross-sections must be included because the detector cannot discriminate between direct and exchange scattering.

Relying upon the fact that the interaction potential is diagonal in the (SM_s) representation, we know that the S matrix for scattering from these states will be diagonal.

The lth sub-matrix reads

$$\begin{pmatrix} e^{2i\eta_l^{1\,1}} & 0 & 0 & 0 \\ 0 & e^{2i\eta_l^{1\,0}} & 0 & 0 \\ 0 & 0 & e^{2i\eta_l^{1-1}} & 0 \\ 0 & 0 & 0 & e^{2i\eta_l^{0\,0}} \end{pmatrix},$$

(6.210)

where $\eta_l^{SM_s}$ is the lth phase shift derived from the potential

$$V^{SM_s}(R) = \langle SM_s \mid H(r, R) \mid SM_s \rangle - (E_0^A + E_0^B) \qquad (6.211)$$

and V is independent of M_s. Then, to convert from the (SM_s) to the (M_{s_1}, M_{s_2}) basis:

$$\begin{pmatrix} \alpha\alpha \\ \alpha\beta \\ \beta\alpha \\ \beta\beta \end{pmatrix} = \begin{pmatrix} 1 & 0 & 0 & 0 \\ 0 & 2^{-\frac{1}{2}} & 0 & 2^{-\frac{1}{2}} \\ 0 & -2^{-\frac{1}{2}} & 0 & 2^{-\frac{1}{2}} \\ 0 & 0 & 1 & 0 \end{pmatrix} \begin{pmatrix} 1, & 1 \\ 1, & 0 \\ 1, & -1 \\ 0, & 0 \end{pmatrix} \qquad (6.212)$$

The S matrix in the $(\alpha\beta)$ representation then becomes: (l^{th} factor only shown)

$$\begin{pmatrix} e^{2i\eta_l^{11}} & 0 & 0 & 0 \\ 0 & 2^{-1}(e^{2i\eta_l^{10}} + e^{2i\eta_l^{00}}) & 2^{-1}(e^{2i\eta_l^{10}} - e^{2i\eta_l^{00}}) & 0 \\ 0 & 2^{-1}(e^{2i\eta_l^{10}} - e^{2i\eta_l^{00}}) & 2^{-1}(e^{2i\eta_l^{10}} + e^{2i\eta_l^{00}}) & 0 \\ 0 & 0 & 0 & e^{2i\eta_l^{1-1}} \end{pmatrix} \qquad (6.213)$$

The differential cross-section for case I (pure exchange scattering) is found from

$$f_{\alpha\beta:\beta\alpha}(\chi) = \frac{1}{4ik} \sum (2l+1) \left\{ e^{2i\eta_l^{10}} - e^{2i\eta_l^{00}} \right\} P_l(\cos\chi) \qquad (6.214)$$

to be (with the notation $1 \equiv$ singlet, $3 \equiv$ triplet)

$$\sigma_{\alpha\beta:\beta\alpha}(\chi) = \frac{1}{4} \mid f_1(\chi) - f_3(\chi) \mid^2 \qquad (6.215)$$

$$= \frac{1}{4} \left\{ \mid f_1(\chi) \mid^2 + \mid f_3(\chi) \mid^2 - 2\cos(\alpha_1 - \alpha_3) \mid f_1(\chi) \mid \cdot \mid f_3(\chi) \mid \right\}$$

where (see Equation 6.129)

$$f_{1,3}(\chi) = \frac{1}{2ik} \sum (2l+1) \left\{ \begin{matrix} e^{2i\eta_l^{00}} \\ e^{2i\eta_l^{10}} \end{matrix} \right\} P_l(\cos\chi) = \mid f_{1,3}(\chi) \mid e^{i\alpha_{1,3}} \qquad (6.216)$$

and we have used the off-diagonal element $S_{\alpha\beta:\beta\alpha}$ in Equation 6.213. Equation 6.214 shows that the exchange scattering is determined by the difference between the singlet and triplet potentials.

The scattering in case II is given by:

$$\sigma_{II}(\chi) = \frac{5}{8} \mid f_3(\chi) \mid^2 + \frac{1}{8} \mid f_1(\chi) \mid^2 + \frac{1}{4} \cos(\alpha_1 - \alpha_3) \mid f_1(\chi) \mid \cdot \mid f_3(\chi) \mid.$$

(6.217)

This experiment, without a spin selected cross-beam, is much simpler than the direct observation of spin exchange scattering (case I) and the interference oscillations arising from the last term in Equation 6.217 have been observed by D. E. Pritchard and F. Y. Chu, 1970. It is clear that little is gained by spin selecting the cross-beam; the weighting of the interesting cross-term would increase but no new effects would emerge.

The cross-section in case III is given by:

$$\sigma_{III}(\chi) = \frac{1}{2} \left\{ \mid f_3(\chi) \mid^2 + \mid f_1(\chi) \mid^2 \right\}$$

(6.218)

The cross-section for scattering from unselected beams, case IV, is given by:

$$\sigma_{IV}(\chi) = \frac{3}{4} \mid f_3(\chi) \mid^2 + \frac{1}{4} \mid f_1(\chi) \mid^2$$

(6.219)

The interference terms have disappeared, the oscillations in $\sigma(\chi)$ from the direct and exchange scattering (contributed by $\sigma_{\alpha\beta:\alpha\beta} + \sigma_{\beta\alpha:\beta\alpha}$ and $\sigma_{\alpha\beta:\beta\alpha} + \sigma_{\beta\alpha:\alpha\beta}$ respectively) being $180°$ out of phase. The weighting 3:1 of the triplet and singlet cross-sections is simply the relative probability of finding these states in a random mixture of spins drawn from the two beams. The unselected spin experiment has been performed with sodium scattered from potassium and although it is difficult to deduce both singlet and triplet potential parameters from this sort of experiment alone, they can be extracted when the results are considered in conjunction with the spin selected experiments.

Experiments can also be devised to measure the total cross-section in cases II-IV. In cases III and IV, those without spin analysis at the detector, the measured intensity in the forward direction, besides giving the attenuation of the main beam, also contains a contribution from the exchange scattering, $\sigma_{\alpha\beta:\beta\alpha}(0)$ and $\sigma_{\beta\alpha:\alpha\beta}(0)$ which reduces the apparent total cross-section from the true value given by the optical theorem. The outer branch contributions to the singlet and triplet scattered amplitudes are in phase at $\chi = 0$ (for large impact parameters the difference between the singlet and triplet potentials disappears) and so give no contribution to $\sigma_{exch}(0)$, leaving only the small inner branch contributions of which there may be several. Experimentally, see Fig. 7.20, it is observed that $\sigma_{exch}(0)$ is indeed very small, being less than 1 per cent of σ_{tot} (D. E. Pritchard, et al., 1970).

Calculating σ_{tot} in cases III and IV presents no problems, we can simply integrate expressions Equation 6.218 or 6.219 over χ and add the forward exchange contribution to obtain for the apparent total cross-section Q:

$$Q^{IV} = \frac{3}{4} \sigma_{tot}^{(3)} + \frac{1}{4} \sigma_{tot}^{(1)} - \frac{1}{2} \sigma_{exch}(0). \qquad (6.220)$$

However, when we come to integrate $\sigma_{II}(\chi)$,

$$\int_0^\pi \cos(\alpha_1 - \alpha_3) \, |f_3(\chi)| \cdot |f_1(\chi)| \sin \chi d\chi$$

has to be evaluated. We by-pass this by applying the optical theorem to the relevant scattered amplitude to obtain:

$$\sigma_{tot}^{II} = \frac{3}{4} \sigma_{tot}^{(3)} + \frac{1}{4} \sigma_{tot}^{(1)}, \qquad (6.221)$$

since the forward exchange contribution is clearly zero under the experimental conditions.

Appendix A Some properties of Bessel functions

Useful limiting forms of spherical Bessel functions are:

$$
\left.
\begin{aligned}
j_l(\rho) &\longrightarrow \rho^l / 1.3.5 \ldots (2l+1) \\
n_l(\rho) &\longrightarrow -1.3.5 \ldots (2l+1)/\rho^{l+1}
\end{aligned}
\right\} \rho \ll l
$$

$$
\left.
\begin{aligned}
j_l(\rho) &\longrightarrow \frac{1}{\rho} \sin(\rho - l\pi/2) \\
\\
n_l(\rho) &\longrightarrow -\frac{1}{\rho} \cos(\rho - l\pi/2)
\end{aligned}
\right\} \rho \gg l
\qquad (6.A1)
$$

The Wronskian is

$$j_l \frac{d}{d\rho} n_l - n_l \frac{d}{d\rho} j_l = \frac{1}{\rho^2}. \qquad (6.A2)$$

In generating these functions in the region $\rho \gg l$ on a digital computer (for calculating quantum phase shifts) an upward recursion formula is sufficient:

$$j_{\pm l}(z) = f_{\pm l}(z) \sin z + (-1)^{l+1} f_{\mp l-1}(z) \cos z \qquad (j_{-l} \equiv n_l)$$

$$f_0(z) = z^{-1} \qquad f_1(z) = z^{-2} \qquad (6.A3)$$

$$f_{l+1}(z) = (2l+1) z^{-1} f_l(z) - f_{l-1}(z)$$

If the argument is appreciably greater than the order, the magnitude of successive j_l and n_l is similar (from A.1) and upward recursion may be used without cumulative error.

The first two Bessel functions of integral order, $J_l(\rho)$, encountered in Section 6.6 are expanded thus as $\rho \to 0$;

$$J_0(\rho) \approx 1 - \rho^2/4 + \rho^4/64 + \cdots$$

$$J_1(\rho) \approx \rho/2 - \rho^3/16 + \rho^5/384 + \dots \qquad (6.A4)$$

and for $\rho \to \infty$ the asymptotic behaviour is

$$J_0(\rho) \approx (2/\pi\rho)^{\frac{1}{2}} \cos(\rho - \pi/4)$$

$$J_1(\rho) \approx (2/\pi\rho)^{\frac{1}{2}} \sin(\rho - \pi/4) \qquad (6.A5)$$

Appendix B Resonances

Analytically, the simplest way in which resonances arise is by reflection at an abrupt change in the potential, even though classically there is no barrier to the motion. Thus, a commonly used model of the nuclear potential, the square well, permits the continuum S-wave functions to penetrate the well for some energies but completely reflects the incoming wave at other energies. (Fig. B1). In molecular scattering, potentials that change abruptly over a wavelength of the relative motion are rare and resonances generally arise by reflection and transmission at a centrifugal barrier, Fig. B1(2). In the latter case there are classically bound states of positive energy that are absent from the S-states of the square well. There are, nevertheless very close formal

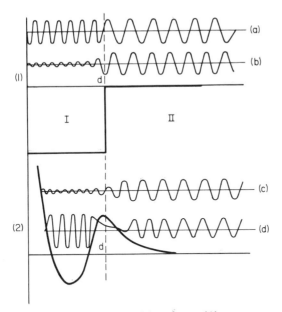

Fig. B1. Resonances arising from (1) a square well potential, (2) a centrifugal barrier. In case (a) the particle passes into the well and experiences a large positive phase shift. In (b), reflection at d prevents the incident particle from passing over the step and the phase shift is that of hard sphere scattering.

In (c), the energy is above the critical value for orbiting, but slight reflection can occur near the potential maximum (vestigial behaviour of type (b)) leading to small perturbations of the quantum cross section. In (d) there is a resonance with a quasi-bound state in the well, where the amplitude exceeds that of the exterior wave function. The phase shift will rapidly increase by π radians at this energy.

similarities between the two cases and we develop in very simple terms the potential step case up to the Breit-Wigner formula and then state the parallel results for the centrifugal barrier case. The first part of the path is a well trodden one and clear treatments are in T. Y. Wu and T. Ohmura, 1962, and E. Merzbacher, 1961.

For the square well potential,

$$V = -V_0, \quad R \leqslant d$$
$$V = 0, \qquad R > d$$

(6.B1)

wave functions of the standing wave type inside and outside the well are, for the case of zero angular momentum,

$$\psi_I = C \sin [KR]$$
$$\psi_{II} = D \sin [kR + \eta_0(E)],$$
(6.B2)

where the asymptotic forms appropriate to regions where the oscillatory behaviour is well developed ($kR \gg 1$) are used. The wave number inside the well, K, is given by

$$K = \frac{1}{\hbar} \sqrt{2\mu(E + V_0)}.$$
(6.B3)

The two solutions for Equation B2 are joined at $R = d$ by matching their gradients and amplitude, generally telescoped into the logarithmic derivative,

$$f = \left(\frac{1}{4}\frac{d\psi}{dR}\right)_{R=d}$$
(6.B4)

In order to make use of standard results, the S matrix elements (of which there is only one for $l = 0$) is found in terms of f. From Equation 6.63,

$$\psi_{II} = \mathscr{B}\{e^{ikr} - S_{00}e^{-ikr}\}$$
(6.B5)

and from Equation 6.B4 applied to the exterior wave function,

$$S_{00} = \frac{f + ikd}{f - ikd}e^{-2ikd}$$
(6.B6)

and so the total cross-section is, from Equation 6.65

$$\sigma_{tot} = \frac{\pi}{k^2}\left|(1 - e^{2ikd}) + \frac{2ikd}{f - ikd}\right|^2,$$
(6.B7)

where the scattered amplitude has been broken up into a hard sphere contribution (phase shift $\eta = -kd$ from Equation 6.160) and a resonance part.

Incorporating the actual wave functions ψ_I and ψ_{II} gives the matching condition

$$f = kd \cot [kd + \eta_0] = Kd \cot Kd$$
(6.B8)

which determines η_0. Referring to Equation B7, the resonance contribution to the total cross-section passes through a maximum every time f passes through zero. $\eta_0(E)$ can be found from Equation B8 to have the following form: in the region $K \gg k$ ($E \ll V$) $\eta_0 = -kd + n\pi$ except when Kd passes through an odd multiple of $\pi/2$, when η_0 rapidly increases by π to sweep $\cot(kd + \eta)$ through zero. In the limit $E \gg V$, $K \approx k$, η_0 tends smoothly to zero, finally to be given by the Born approximation (e.g. from Equation 6.81 with $(kR)^2 j_0(kR)^2$ replaced by $1/2$ in the integral)

$$\eta_0 \approx \frac{V_0}{E} kd. \tag{6.B9}$$

Thus, building up the phase shift function from the high energy end, there is a smooth rise from zero until K/k is appreciably greater than unity when a step-like structure appears in $\eta_0(E)$, the points of maximum gradient occurring at the resonant energies E^* at which

$$\frac{1}{\hbar} \sqrt{2\mu(E^* + V_0)} = (n + \tfrac{1}{2})\pi. \tag{6.B10}$$

We now need an approximation to f in the region of a resonance and take a linear approximation,

$$f \approx (E - E^*) \mid df/dE \mid_{E=E^*} \tag{6.B11}$$

Introducing Equation 6.B8,

$$df/dE \approx \frac{kd\, \partial\eta/\partial E}{\sin^2[kR + \eta_0]} \quad \therefore \quad \mid df/dE \mid_{E=E^*} = kd(\partial\eta/\partial E)_{E=E^*}, \tag{6.B12}$$

where we have used the knowledge that η is much more rapidly varying than k near a resonance. Defining a quantity Γ with the dimensions of energy,

$$\Gamma = 2 \mid (\partial\eta/\partial E) \mid^{-1}_{E=E^*} \tag{6.B13}$$

we have

$$\eta_0 = \eta_0^0 - \tan^{-1} \Gamma/2(E - E^*) \tag{6.B14}$$

where $\eta_0^0 = -kd$ is the phase shift induced by scattering at the boundary d; and so Γ is the range of E over which the phase shift effectively changes by π.

Then, substituting Equations B11 and B12 into Equation B7 gives

$$\sigma_{tot} = \frac{\pi}{k^2} \left| \frac{i\Gamma}{(E - E^*) + i\Gamma/2} + (1 - e^{2i\eta_0^0}) \right|^2 \qquad (6.B15)$$

and if the resonant contribution is dominant near E^*,

$$\sigma_{tot} \approx \frac{\pi}{k^2} \frac{\Gamma^2}{(E - E^*)^2 + \Gamma^2/4} \qquad (6.B16)$$

This has the form of the Breit-Wigner formula. Γ has added significance through its connection with the delay time of the scattering. From Equation 2.41,

$$\tau = 2\hbar \, \partial\eta/\partial E$$

and so

$$\Gamma = 4\hbar/\tau. \qquad (6.B17)$$

Thus, the shorter the delay time, i.e. the shorter the lifetime of the system within a radius d, the broader the resonance. This is the basis of the argument used in Section 6.14. In deciding the best experimental conditions for observing resonances.

We now turn to a qualitative discussion of the changes in the above results when the resonances are associated with states trapped behind a centrifugal barrier, so called shape resonances. There are strong formal similarities between the two cases and these are emphasised in Fig. B1, where the matching boundary at $r = d$ is extended into the potential with a centrifugal term and forms a notional boundary at which interior and exterior solutions are matched in the latter case. A phase sensitive detector situated at $r \gg d$ would see only the step-like behaviour of the phase shift which can always be fitted by the form of Equation B14, with the aid of only two parameters and without a detailed knowledge of the nature of the potential.

Important differences between the two cases are that the amplitude inside the well can now exceed that of the exterior wave and very long lifetimes are encountered. Secondly, at a given energy there may be several partial waves in or near resonance, but generally these will be sparsely scattered and we will continue to assume that only one is present.

The semi-classical approach is to match the three WKB solutions in regions I, II and III of Fig. 2.1, and after some manipulation the form of Equation

312 is regained for the phase shift, but with two changes (J. N. L. Connor, 968). For the nth resonance of the lth angular momentum state,

$$\Gamma_{nl} = \frac{h\nu_{nl}}{2\pi} \ln \left[1 + \exp \left(2\hbar^{-1} \int_{R_1}^{R_2} |p(R)| \, dR\right)\right] \qquad (6.B18)$$

where ν_{nl} is the classical frequency of oscillation in the well of the effective potential. The logarithmic factor in Equation B18 represents the effect of the centrifugal barrier and ranges between zero for very thick barriers to ln2 for a barrier of zero width. Equation B18 is derived for the case of a parabolic barrier, but the dependence on the action integral through the barrier will not be a sensitive function of the barrier shape. The phase shift, far away from resonance, η_0, is now given by the usual semi-classical value, in Equation 6.110.

Finally, the contribution of an isolated resonance at $l = l^*$ to the observed total cross-section can be found by integrating Equation B15 over the energy resolution δE of the experiment to give (for $\delta E \gg \Gamma_{nl}$)

$$\delta \sigma_{l^*} = \frac{1}{\delta E} \int_{E-\delta E/2}^{E+\delta E/2} \sigma_{tot}^{res} \, dE \cong \frac{4\pi}{k^2} (2l^* + 1) \left\{ \sin^2 \eta_l^0 + \pi \frac{\Gamma_{nl}}{\delta E} \cos 2\eta_l \right\}.$$

$$(6.B19)$$

The most favourable conditions for observing a resonance are thus for Γ_{nl} and l^* to be large. This points to a level near the top of the centrifugal barrier, but even so the measure of the resonance is small. Thus, the maximum value for l^* will be that for orbiting and if the orbiting radius is d, $l^* = kd$ and so

$$\frac{\delta \sigma_{tot}^{res}}{\sigma_{tot}} \leqslant \frac{1}{kd} \frac{\Gamma_{nl}}{\delta E}, \qquad (6.B20)$$

generally a small fraction for even the lightest atoms ($1/kd \leqslant 0.01$).

Appendix C Summary of useful formulae

In the partial wave summation the scattered amplitude is

$$f(\chi) = \frac{1}{2ik} \sum (2l + 1)[S_{ll} - 1] P_l(\cos \chi) \qquad (6.C1)$$

and the differential cross-section

$$\sigma(\chi) = |f(\chi)|^2.$$

The total cross-section is

$$\sigma_{tot} = \frac{2\pi}{k^2}\sum(2l + 1)[1 - \text{Re } S_{ll}] \tag{6.C2}$$

$$= \frac{4\pi}{k^2}\sum(2l + 1) \sin^2 \eta_l, \tag{6.C3}$$

where S_{ll} is the diagonal scattering matrix element $e^{2i\eta_l}$ and η_l is the phase shift of the lth partial wave.

The optical theorem connects the imaginary part of the forward scattered amplitude, $\text{Im } f(0)$, with the total cross-section,

$$\sigma_{tot} = \frac{4\pi}{k} \text{ Im } f(0) \tag{6.C4}$$

In the semi-classical approximation the phase shift is given by

$$\eta_l = \int_{\rho_c}^{\infty} \left[1 - \frac{2\mu V(\rho)}{\hbar^2 k^2} - \frac{(l + \frac{1}{2})^2}{\rho^2}\right]^{\frac{1}{2}} d\rho - \int_{l + \frac{1}{2}}^{\infty} \left[1 - \frac{(l + \frac{1}{2})^2}{\rho^2}\right]^{\frac{1}{2}} d\rho \tag{6.C5}$$

The condition of validity of Equation C5 is sometimes expressed in terms of the de Boer parameter Λ^*

$$\Lambda^* = h/[\sigma(2\mu\epsilon)^{\frac{1}{2}}], \tag{6.C6}$$

(closely related to the condition of Equation 6.106 with $E = \epsilon$) and is $\Lambda^* \lesssim 1$.

In the Born approximation the phase shift is given by

$$\eta_l^B = \frac{2\mu}{(\hbar k)^2}\int_0^{\infty} j_l(\rho)^2 V(\rho)\rho^2 d\rho \tag{6.C7}$$

$$\rho = kR$$

and is valid for $\eta \lesssim 0.5$ or $\Lambda^* \ll 1$.

For a potential of the form $V = -C_s R^{-s}$ the Born result reduces to

$$\eta^B = \frac{\mu C_s}{2\hbar^2} \left(\frac{k}{2}\right)^{s-2} \pi \frac{\Gamma(s-1)\Gamma\left(l - \frac{s}{2} + \frac{3}{2}\right)}{\left(\Gamma\left(\frac{s}{2}\right)\right)^2 \Gamma\left(1 + \frac{s}{2} + \frac{1}{2}\right)} \qquad (6.C8)$$

and for the total cross-section:

$$\sigma_{tot}(v) = 2\pi^{s/(s-1)} \sin\left[\frac{\pi}{2}\frac{s-3}{s-1}\right] \Gamma\left(\frac{s-3}{s-1}\right) \left[\frac{\Gamma\left(\frac{s}{2} - \frac{1}{2}\right)}{\Gamma\frac{s}{2}}\right]^{2/(s-1)} \left(\frac{C_s}{\hbar v}\right)^{2/s-1} \qquad (6.C9)$$

For a potential with $s = 6$, this reduces to:

$$\sigma_{tot}(v) \approx 8.083 \left[\frac{C_6}{\hbar v}\right]^{2/5} \qquad (6.C10)$$

At not too small angles of observation, the semi-classical or classical outer branch contribution to $\sigma(\chi)$ is:

$$\sigma(\chi) \approx \frac{1}{s}\left([s-1]\frac{C_s}{E}\right)^{2/s} \chi^{-2+2/s} \qquad (6.C11)$$

If the Born approximation is valid for *all* phase shifts,

$$f(q) = -\frac{2\mu}{\hbar^2}\int_0^\infty q^{-1}\sin(qR)\,R\,V(R)\,dR, \qquad (6.C12)$$

where

$$q = 2k\sin(\chi/2)$$

so that in this case inversion to yield the potential is possible,

$$RV(R) = -\pi\int_0^\infty q\,\frac{\hbar^2}{\mu}f(q)\sin(qR)\,dq. \qquad (6.C13)$$

The extrema in the total cross-section for a Lennard-Jones potential occur at velocities v_N given by:

$$N - 3/8 = 0.3012 \, (\epsilon\sigma/(\hbar v_N)) \qquad (6.C14)$$

where N is an integer for maxima and half integral for minima. The transition between attractive and repulsive behaviour in the total cross section energy dependence occurs at:

$$v \approx 2.5 \, \epsilon\sigma\hbar^{-1}. \qquad (6.C15)$$

The total cross-section is approximately related to the differential cross-section at zero degrees by

$$\sigma_{tot} \approx \frac{4\pi}{k} \, [\sigma(0)]^{\frac{1}{2}} \qquad (6.C16)$$

CHAPTER SEVEN

Elastic Scattering

7.1 Introduction

In the preceding chapters we have discussed mainly the results of collisions between particles without internal structure and interacting via a single potential. These collisions were of necessity elastic in the sense that there was no change in the internal states of the particles after collision. In the real world of atoms and molecules internal states are legion and collisions often result in transitions between them. Furthermore, scattering may not take place under the influence of a single intermolecular potential if the Born-Oppenheimer approximation breaks down. In this situation even collisions which are formally elastic in that the incident and final states are identical, may not be two body collisions in the sense of the theory presented in Chapter 6. Potentials that are apparently velocity dependent would be one indication of behaviour of this sort. Fortunately for the evolution of the field it appears that at thermal energies most atomic and molecular systems can be thought of to a good approximation as interacting according to well defined potentials, i.e. the electronic motion is adiabatic.

Elastic scattering experiments are primarily aimed at extracting intermolecular potentials and, less directly, with any concurrent inelastic or reactive processes. A full discussion of the other experimental techniques and their theory that are relevant to the topic of intermolecular forces would occupy several volumes. Fortunately, a number of recent books have treated this subject in depth (J. O. Hirschfelder, 1967; H. Margenau and N. R. Kestner, 1969; C. Schlier, 1969) and here we shall be concerned only with the scattering aspects of the problem.

The intermolecular potential is usually given a bipolar analytical form, with a long range attractive part and a short range repulsion term. We have seen that the operation of both attraction and repulsion in a molecular collision is responsible for much of the structure in molecular scattering patterns. A purely repulsive potential would be much less rich in quantum interference structure. A very wide range of analytical forms have been proposed for these potentials, the best known being the Lennard-Jones 12-6 potential:

$$V(R) = -C_6 R^{-6} + C_{12} R^{-12} \qquad (7.1)$$

$$= 4\epsilon \left\{ \left(\frac{\sigma}{R} \right)^{12} - \left(\frac{\sigma}{R} \right)^{6} \right\} \qquad (7.2)$$

The advantage of using such a universal formulation lies in the readiness with which comparison between different molecular systems may be made in terms of only two parameters. In addition, the measurement of intermolecular forces reduces to the determination of the coefficients in the potential if a simple parametrised form is adopted. This approach, although widespread, suffers from a number of disadvantages.

Firstly, it is already clear that these forms are over-simplifications. The parameters in the potential, when they do have a clear physical meaning such as a well depth, can only yield the best approximation to the actual value that the form of the potential allows. For instance, in a truncated multipole expansion of the potential the various coefficients C_6, C_8 etc. although having a precise physical meaning alter their apparent value as more terms are included in the potential used to fit the data. A second difficulty with these forms is that they seem to apply to an infinite range of intermolecular separations and energies even though the experiments to which they are fitted have only sampled a very limited range of these variables. Thus, a measurement of the differential cross-section, even over 180 degrees, will only yield information on the potential over the range of R actually sampled by the classical trajectories, and most accurately on values of R near the classical turning points. The cautious experimenter should thus perhaps present his data as a table of values of the potential, defined with varying precision, to which spline functions can be fitted for analytical purposes.

Data on intermolecular potentials has been obtained by a number of techniques other than by scattering methods. The most important of these are (i) bulk measurements of state and transport properties and (ii) spectroscopic methods. Typical bulk data are second virial coefficients and viscosities of gases over a range of temperatures. Unfortunately, the temperature range over which such data can be obtained is limited and the results are relatively structureless, Fig. 7.1. The information about potentials that can be extracted is therefore limited and these methods are perhaps of most value in testing potentials devised by other means.

Spectroscopic methods have been applied in various ways, perhaps most important is the Rydberg-Klein-Rees (RKR) method (J. T. Vanderslice et al., 1959). In this technique vibration-rotation bands are analyzed to yield values of the potential at the classical turning points of the internal motion and no prior assumptions about the potential form are involved. Unfortunately, this

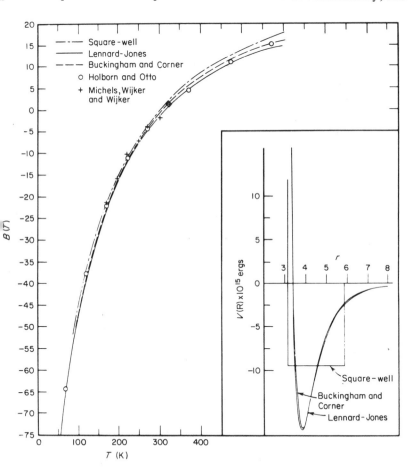

Fig. 7.1 Second virial coefficients for argon calculated for several molecular models. The potential functions obtained from the experimental $B(T)$ data are also shown. The experimental data are those of L. Holborn and J. Otto, *Z. Physik*, **33**, 1 (1925), and A. Michels, Hub. Wijker, and Hk. Wijker, *Physica*, **15**, 627 (1949). (Reproduced from J. O. Hirschfelder et al., 1964).

method is only suitable for relatively deep potentials which can support many vibrational states. The broadening of atomic spectral lines as a function of pressure also yields information on the difference between ground and excited electronic state potentials.

Scattering methods, on the other hand, can readily explore a wide range of relative energies and potential depths. Also, if high resolution experiments are possible, very detailed quantum structure can be observed, e.g. as in Fig. 7.2. The information content is large, and tight constraints can be placed on the form of the potential over the range of separations effectively explored. The major limitations of the method are mundane experimental ones and also that, for atoms not in ^1S states, separation of the various possible molecular states of the colliding system depends upon selecting the (J, m_J) state of the incident atoms, sometimes a difficult task. The extent of this problem is shown in Table 7.1, where the various electronic states arising from different atomic states are shown; each such molecular state will be associated with a rather different intermolecular potential.

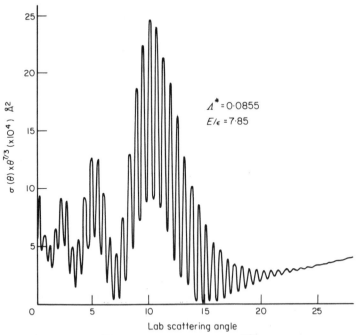

Fig. 7.2 Elastic differential cross-section $\times \theta^{7/3}$ as a function of laboratory scattering angle, calculated for a LJ potential with parameters $E/\epsilon = 7.85$, $\sigma_{LJ} = 4.25$ A; $\Lambda^* = \hbar/[\sigma_{LJ}(2\mu\epsilon)^{1/2}] = 0.0855$ and $\chi_{CM} \approx 1.17 \, \theta_{lab}$. The rainbow angle is $12.5°$ (lab) and two supernumerary bows are visible.

To date, atomic scattering measurements have been largely confined to atoms in Groups I and VIII, mercury and the halogen atoms. For collisions involving molecules, the problem is formally much worse both because of the intrusion of inelastic events and because even if the motion is adiabatic with respect to the rotational and vibrational motion, different potentials might be associated with different internal states. However, these potentials may not be very different and especially in the case of a nearly spherical molecules an average potential is often adequate. In any case, this simplification is normally imposed by experimental considerations.

7.2 Extraction of potential data from scattering measurements

The formal inversion of a differential cross-section to yield a potential is a difficult problem. For cases in which a very few partial waves are involved, e.g. nuclear scattering, rather sophisticated procedures have been evolved (T. Y. Wu and T. Ohmura, 1962). These have not, however, been extended to thermal molecular scattering where the effective range of the potentials is much greater and thousands of partial waves are required. If either classical mechanics or the Born approximation is valid then inversion processes can be formulated directly. The Born approximation gives for the scattered amplitude

$$f(q) = - \int_0^\infty q^{-1} \sin (qR) \mu R V(R) dR / (2\pi\hbar^2) \qquad (7.3)$$

where $q = 2k \sin (\chi/2)$

and so $RV(R)$ is the Fourier transform of $f(q)$:

$$RV(R) = - \frac{2}{\pi} \int_0^\infty q f(q) \sin (qR) \left(\frac{2\pi\hbar^2}{\mu} \right) dq \qquad (7.4)$$

Thus the potential can be determined by observation of the complete energy dependence of $f(q)$ $(= \sigma(\chi)^{1/2})$ in the Born approximation) at a fixed angle of scattering. Unfortunately (see Chapter 6), Equation 7.3 is not valid for potentials that become comparable to the relative kinetic energy over any part of their range, as intermolecular potentials always do because of their hard core. The Born approximation finds its greatest use in electron and X-ray diffraction work where the inversion property Equation 7.4 is the key to its structural exploitation.

If classical mechanics is valid at the energy of observation and the potential is monotonically repulsive, there is a 1:1 correspondence between impact parameter and angle of deflection. The differential cross-section can

Table 7.1 Diatom electronic states: unlike atoms.
Reproduced from R. B. Bernstein and T. J. P. O'Brien, 1963.

Atom 1		Atom 2		
		Group: I	II, VIII	III A
Group	State	State: $^2 S_{\frac{1}{2}}$	$^1 S_0$	$^2 P_{\frac{1}{2}u}$
I	$^2 S_{\frac{1}{2}}$	$^1\Sigma^+, ^3\Sigma^+$.		
II, VIII	$^1 S_0$	$^2\Sigma^+$.	$^1\Sigma^+$.	
III A	$^2 P_{\frac{1}{2}u}$	$^1\Sigma^+, ^1\Pi, ^3\Sigma^+, ^3\Pi$.	$^2\Sigma^+, ^2\Pi$	$^1\Sigma^+(2), ^1\Sigma^-, ^1\Pi(2), ^1\Delta,$ $^3\Sigma^+(2), ^3\Sigma^-, ^3\Pi(2), ^3$
IV A	$^3 P_0$	$^2\Sigma^-, ^2\Pi, ^4\Sigma^-, ^4\Pi$.	$^3\Sigma^-, ^3\Pi$	$^2\Sigma^+, ^3\Sigma^-(2), ^2\Pi(2), ^2\Delta.$ $^4\Sigma^+, ^4\Sigma^-(2), ^4\Pi(2), ^4$
V A	$^4 S_{\frac{1}{2}u}$	$^3\Sigma^-, ^5\Sigma^-$.	$^4\Sigma^-$.	$^3\Sigma^-, ^3\Pi, ^5\Sigma^-, ^5\Pi$.
VI A	$^3 P_2$	$^2\Sigma^-, ^2\Pi, ^4\Sigma^-, ^4\Pi$.	$^3\Sigma^-, ^3\Pi$.	$^2\Sigma^+, ^2\Sigma^-(2), ^2\Pi(2), ^2\Delta,$ $^4\Sigma^+, ^4\Sigma^-(2), ^4\Pi(2), ^4$
VII A	$^2 P_{\frac{1}{2}u}$	$^1\Sigma^+, ^1\Pi, ^3\Sigma^+, ^3\Pi$.	$^2\Sigma^+, ^2\Pi$.	$^1\Sigma^+(2), ^1\Sigma^-, ^1\Pi(2), ^1\Delta,$ $^3\Sigma^+(2), ^3\Sigma^-, ^3\Pi(2), ^3$

then be inverted to yield the potential (I. Amdur, 1968). This approach will clearly be most useful at high energies.

Unfortunately, even this technique is of very limited applicability in molecular scattering. Experimental observations will be limited in angular and energy range, be of less than perfect resolution and will include some noise. Under these conditions any formal inversion procedure is unreliable and what is required is an algorithm for making the connection between an assumed potential and the scattering pattern associated with it. The details will vary, but the components of this algorithm will be:

(1) Apply all available information from other sources to estimate the potential and choose an analytical form for it.
(2) Identify and use any key features in the scattering observations, e.g. rainbows or glories, to refine the original estimates of the potential parameters.

	V A	IV A	VIII A
	$^4S_{\frac12 u}$	$^3P_0$	$^2P_{\frac12 u}$

$), {}^1\Sigma^-, {}^1\Pi(2), {}^1\Delta,$
 triplets and
ntets of above.

$\Pi, {}^4\Sigma^+, {}^4\Pi,$
$+, {}^6\Pi.$ $^1\Sigma^+, {}^3\Sigma^+,$
      $^5\Sigma^+, {}^7\Sigma^+.$

$), {}^1\Sigma^-, {}^1\Pi(2), {}^1\Delta,$ $^2\Sigma^+, {}^2\Pi,$ $^1\Sigma^+(2), {}^1\Sigma^-, {}^1\Pi(2), {}^1\Delta,$
 triplets and   also $^4(\ \ )$ also $^3(\ \ )$ and $^5(\ \ )$
ntets of above.   and $^6(\ \ ).$ of above.

                                                            $^1\Sigma^+(2), {}^1\Sigma^-, {}^1\Pi(2), {}^1\Delta,$
                                                              also $^3(\ \ )$ and $^5(\ \ )$

$\Sigma^-(2), {}^2\Pi(2), {}^2\Delta,$ $^3\Sigma^-, {}^3\Pi,$ $^2\Sigma^+(2), {}^2\Sigma^-, {}^2\Pi(2), {}^2\Delta,$ of above.
$+, {}^4\Sigma^-(2), {}^4\Pi(2), {}^4\Delta.$ $^5\Sigma^-, {}^5\Pi.$ $^4\Sigma^+, {}^4\Sigma^-(2), {}^4\Pi(2), {}^4\Delta.$

(3) If the data is of high enough resolution, carry out some fitting between a forward calculation of the expected scattering pattern (with appropriate averaging to allow for apparatus resolution) and the observed pattern.

In many cases interpretation has stopped at stage (2). However, as better data becomes available the full statistical treatment implied in (3) will become more usual.

Recently an inversion based on classical mechanics and due to Firsov has appeared (V. G. Firsov, 1953) which relates the classical deflection function and the potential†. This has been extended by U. Buck, 1971, who allows the deflection function to have both positive and negative branches, as

†

$$R_c(b) = b \exp \left\{ \frac{1}{\pi} \int_b^\infty \frac{\chi(b')db'}{(b'^2 - b^2)^{\frac12}} \right\}$$

$$V(R_c) = E(1 - b^2/R_c(b)^2); \quad (2R)^{-1} d(R^2 V)/dR < E$$

it should. The deflection function has to be obtained by a fitting process based on a semi-classical approximation to $\chi(b)$ in terms of b. The advantage of this process is that the potential is obtained pointwise rather than as a constrained function.

Elastic scattering measurements fall into two classes, those of the total cross-section $\sigma_{tot}(v)$ by primary beam attenuation, and those of the differential cross-section $\sigma(\chi)$. The latter measurement always involves two beams so that the angular scattering can be measured as a function of collision energy from an accurately defined collision volume. Although $\sigma(\chi)$ in principle contain more information than total cross-section measurements, experimental considerations frequently make the single beam σ_{tot} measurement the most fruitful in practice, but in either case the effect of imperfect angular and energy resolution must be carefully allowed for in any interpretation.

7.3 Total cross-sections

(i) Interpretation

The key features in the dependence of total cross-sections on collision velocity have already been discussed in Chapter 6 and in Fig. 7.3 we show the major features in a plot of σ_{tot} *vs.* velocity. At high energies the major

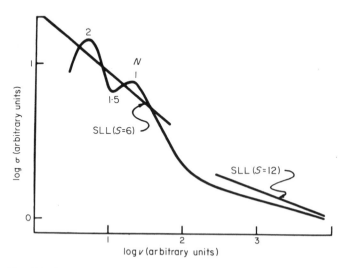

Fig. 7.3 Plot of log total cross-section versus log impact velocity (LJ potential (12:6), $2\mu\epsilon\sigma^2/\hbar = 125$). (Reproduced from R. B. Bernstein, 1966.)

contribution to the cross-section comes from scattering by the repulsive core; this is followed by a transition region where both attractive and repulsive forces are important and then a low energy region where attractive forces dominate. In this region, oscillations in the amplitude of the cross-section arise from the maximum in the phase shift curve passing alternately through odd and even multiples of $\pi/2$. Finally at reduced energies $E/\epsilon < 0.8$ sharp resonance spikes due to quasi bound states may be seen. In the case of angle dependent potentials the situation is more complex. However, if the molecule is rotating either very slowly or very rapidly with respect to the motion of the incident atom, some averaged potential may operate. In the first case the sudden approximation can be used (R. B. Bernstein and K. H. Kramer, 1964), and in the latter case the angular dependence is effectively wiped out by the rotation so that broadly similar features to those of Fig. 7.3 can be expected.

The preliminary interpretation of data such as is shown in Fig. 7.3 will concentrate on the mean slope of the velocity plot and proceed via the Massey-Mohr approximation. We recall that the exact result for σ_{tot}:

$$\sigma_{tot} = \frac{4\pi}{k^2} \sum_l (2l+1) \sin^2 \eta_l \tag{7.5}$$

becomes:

$$\sigma_{tot}^{MM} \approx f_s \left[C_s/(\hbar v) \right]^{2/(s-1)} \tag{7.6}$$

where f_s has been given in Equation 6.C9. Using this approximation,

(i) The gradient of $\ln \sigma_{tot}$ versus $\ln v$ plots will be $-2/(s-1)$ if the observations are made either in the low or high velocity regions. As can be seen from Fig. 7.3 (R. B. Bernstein, 1966), precision is limited by the existence of undulations in the attractive region and by the slow convergence of the gradient to its limiting value at high energies.

(ii) The transition region cannot be accurately located, but for a 12:6 potential:

$$v_{trans} \approx 2.5 \, \epsilon \sigma_{LJ}/\hbar \tag{7.7}$$

so that $\epsilon \sigma_{LJ}$ can be estimated rather crudely.

(iii) An absolute measurement of the total cross-section will yield C_6 since in the MM approximation (with v in cm s^{-1}, σ in cm^2):

$$C_6 \approx 5.76 \times 10^{-30} \, v \sigma_{tot}^{5/2} \, \text{erg cm}^6 \tag{7.8}$$

This approximation is not too accurate, but is probably adequate for the experimental precision (±15 per cent) in the measurement of absolute total cross-sections.

The glory undulations which provide much more precise constraints on the intermolecular potential are not predicted by the MM approximation and it is necessary to go to the semi-classical treatment. We recall from Chapter 6 that these undulations have their origin in the joint operation of the attractive and repulsive parts of the potential, the turning points of the trajectories responsible lying close to R_m, the position of the potential minimum.

Taking the particular case of the 12:6 potential, the relevant Equation 6.147 becomes:

$$\sigma_{tot} = 8.083 \, [C_6/\hbar\sigma_{LJ}]^{2/5} + \frac{4\pi l_0}{k^2} \, [\pi/\eta''(l_0)]^{\frac{1}{2}} \sin \, (2\eta(l_0) - 3\pi/4) \quad (7.9)$$

where maxima in σ_{tot} occur when the wavenumber k satisfies

$$\eta_{l_0}(k_N) = \pi(N - 3/8) \quad (7.10)$$

where N is an integer. The amplitude of the undulations described by Equation 7.9 is determined by $[l_0/\eta_0'']^{\frac{1}{2}}$, but from an experimental point of view the most reliably measured quantities are the extrema wave numbers k_N since the amplitude of oscillation depends very strongly on the apparatus resolution.

In the normal method of analysis, the various extrema are indexed with integers for the maxima, and half integers for the minima, the numbering starting from the high velocity end. The relative velocities v_N corresponding to these extrema constitute an atom impact spectrum and the experimental results are plotted as $\sigma_{tot}(v).v^{2/5}$ versus v. An example of this plot is shown in Fig. 7.4. The indexing may be checked by plotting the index number N against $1/v_N$; the plot should be linear at high velocities and yield an intercept of $N = 3/8$ at $v = \infty$ and if this is not the case, the indexing is probably incorrect. The limiting gradient at high v_N of this latter plot can be calculated using Born phase shifts for $\eta(l_0)$; for the Lennard-Jones (12:6) potential the result is:

$$N - 3/8 = 0.3012 \, \frac{\epsilon\sigma_{LJ}}{\hbar v_N} \quad (7.11)$$

enabling an initial estimate of the product $\epsilon\sigma$ to be made before more detailed fitting is begun.

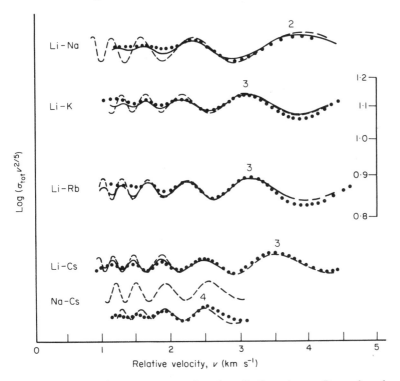

Fig. 7.4 Atom impact spectra for the alkali systems. Reproduced from E. W. Rothe and R. K. B. Helbing, 1968. Integers are the index numbers of the extrema. Dots are experimental values, dashed lines are forward calculations with no allowance for apparatus resolution. The full lines are apparatus averaged calculations.

More detailed analysis is normally based on the Bernstein-O'Brien (BOB) plot in which $(N-3/8)v_N$ is plotted against E_N^{-1} (collision energy) (R. B. Bernstein and T. J. P. O'Brien, 1965, 1967; Fig. 7.5). The data is then fitted numerically to a quadratic form:

$$(N - 3/8)v_N = I - S_1 E_{\bar{N}}^1 + S_2 E_{\bar{N}}^2 \qquad (7.12)$$

to yield values for I and S_1 with good precision and for S_2 with rather poorer accuracy. For any assumed potential form I, S_1 and S_2 can then be interpreted in terms of particular potential parameters. In the Bernstein-O'Brien treatment Equation (7.12) is shown to be equivalent to:

$$(N - 3/8)v_N = \frac{2\epsilon R_m a_1}{\pi h} \left(1 - \frac{A_1 \epsilon}{a_1 E_N} + \frac{A_2 \epsilon^2}{a_1 E_N^2}\right), \qquad (7.13)$$

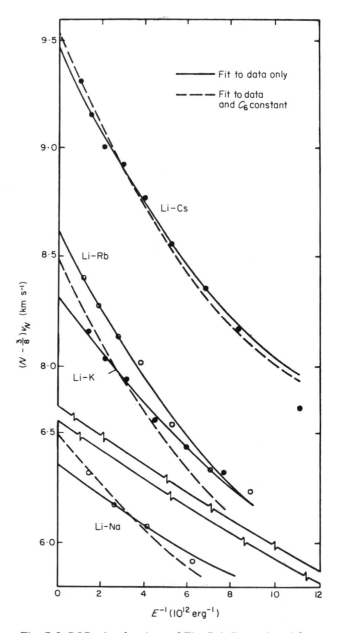

Fig. 7.5 BOB plot for data of Fig. 7.4. Reproduced from E. W. Rothe and R. K. B. Helbing, 1968. The dashed curves are the best fit to the data with values of ϵ and σ that are related by $4\epsilon\sigma_{LJ}^6 = C_6^{calc}$. The fact that rather different values for ϵ and σ are obtained with constrained and unconstrained fits means either that the theoretical C_6 value is wrong or that the potential is not of the Lennard-Jones form.

where

$$\epsilon R_m a_1 = (\pi\hbar/2) I \qquad \text{(A)}$$
$$\epsilon/a_1 = S_1/(A_1 I) \qquad \text{(B)}$$
$$\epsilon^2/a_1 = S_2/(I A_2) \qquad \text{(C)} \qquad (7.14)$$

so

$$a_1 = S_2 A_1^2/S_1^2 A_2 I^2 \qquad \text{(D)}$$

and A_1, A_2 are almost independent of the potential form, having the values $A_1 = 0.1625$ and $A_2 = 0.0801$. On the other hand, the parameter a_1 depends primarily, but still rather weakly upon the curvature of the potential at the minima and only to a much less extent on the actual potential form chosen. The curvature κ at the potential minima is defined as

$$\kappa = \left[\frac{\partial^2 (V/\epsilon)}{\partial (R/R_m)^2} \right]_{R=R_m} = f^{(2)}, \qquad (7.15)$$

i.e. it is the second term in an expansion of the potential about the minimum of the form:

$$V(\gamma)/\epsilon = -1 + \tfrac{1}{2}\kappa\gamma^2 + \sum_{n=3}^{N} \frac{\gamma^n}{n!} f^{(n)}, \qquad (7.16)$$

where $\gamma = R/R_m - 1$ (the reduced displacement). The variation of the parameter a_1 with κ is shown in Fig. 7.6. It can be seen that the curvature can be reasonably well determined without recourse to a specific potential form. Alternatively an assumed potential form can be used to calculate a_1 for a range of curvatures and differing potentials. The data may then be used to determine the other parameters in the potential. A table due to Bernstein for three potentials of the forms:

(1) L.J. n, 6;
$$V/\epsilon = \left(\frac{6}{n-6}\right)\left(\frac{R_m}{R}\right)^n - \left(\frac{n}{n-6}\right)\left(\frac{R_m}{R}\right)^6 \qquad (7.17)$$

(2) Kihara:
$$V/\epsilon = \left(\frac{1-\alpha}{R/R_m - \alpha}\right)^{12} - 2\left(\frac{1-\alpha}{R/R_m - \alpha}\right)^6 \qquad (7.18)$$

(3) Exponential:
$$V/\epsilon = \left(\frac{6}{\alpha-6}\right)\exp\left[-\alpha\left(\frac{R}{R_m}-1\right)\right] - \left(\frac{\alpha}{\alpha-6}\right)\left(\frac{R_m}{R}\right)^6 \qquad (7.19)$$

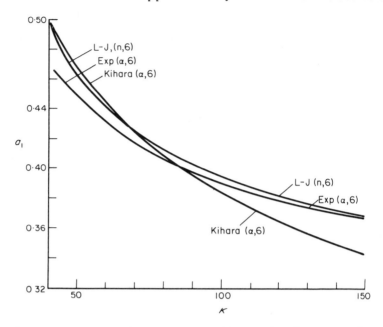

Fig. 7.6 Variation of a_1 parameter with κ, reduced curvature for three potentials; (i) Lennard-Jones (n:6) (ii) Kihara (Equation 7.18) (iii) exp-6 (Equation 7.19).

is shown in Table 7.2. For the L.J. potential the curvature is given by $\kappa = 6n$. For the other potentials the nomogram given by R. B. Bernstein and T. J. P. O'Brien, (1967) may be used. Thus, if a particular potential form is selected, and a_1 estimated, a measurement of I and S_1 enables both ϵ and R_m to be obtained from Equation 7.14A or B and if both S_1 and S_2 can be measured then a_1 can be found from Equation 7.14D and the form of the potential thereby subjected to a test. The product $\epsilon^2 R_m$ is obtained with greater accuracy than ϵ or R_m individually and can provide a very useful constraint in analysing other data (e.g. differential cross-section).

It should be noted that the above interpretation of glory oscillations has not required absolute measurements of the total cross-section — a considerable advantage in view of the experimental difficulties in obtaining absolute scattering data.

A typical BOB plot from Rothe's work (E. W. Rothe and R. K. B. Helbing, 1968) is shown in Fig. 7.5, where some data from alkali systems are plotted. The final confirmatory stage of the analysis is shown back in Fig. 7.4 where the observed data is compared with the results of a forward calculation using the derived potential parameters and the effect of the thermal motion of the target molecules on the total cross-section measurements is illustrated.

Table 7.2 a_1 parameter for various curvatures κ and potentials. The three potentials are defined in Equations 7.17, 7.18, and 7.19. (Reproduced from R. B. Bernstein and T. J. P. O'Brien, 1965).

	a_1		
κ	potential 1	potential 2	potential 3
48	0.47000	0.47421	0.45209
60	0.44113	0.44432	0.43063
72	0.42156	0.42156	0.41462
84	0.40727	0.40338	0.40232
96	0.39630	0.38838	0.39257
108	0.38757	0.37568	0.38465
120	0.38043	0.36474	0.37808
132	0.37446	0.35515	0.37253
144	0.36938	0.34666	0.36776

The interpretation of the velocity dependence of σ_{tot} for the scattering of atoms is now quite well understood.

(ii) Measurement of the total cross-section

The technique for determining total cross-sections by measuring the attenuation of a narrow primary beam by a target gas has already been described. The expression:

$$I/I_0 = e^{-n\sigma_{tot}(v)l} \qquad (7.20)$$

(where I is the attenuated beam flux, I_0 the primary beam flux, nl the number density times path length of the target gas) defines the observed total cross-section. If the velocity is low enough, or if by other arguments we know that inelastic or reactive processes make a relatively small contribution, σ_{tot} can be equated to the total elastic cross-section. If non-elastic channels are important, total cross-section measurements are still informative, but their analysis is reserved until Chapter 8.

Difficulties arise with the measurement of all the observables in Equation 7.20. Firstly, the angular resolution must be sufficient to distinguish between scattered and unscattered material at angles outside the forward diffraction cone. Secondly, the spread of relative velocity between the primary and target molecules must be small enough to avoid blurring any of the structure in the velocity dependence of $\sigma_{tot}(v)$. Finally, if absolute total cross-sections are to be measured, the target density and length must be known.

Angular resolution

If the true quantum total cross-section is to be measured, the angular resolution of the apparatus must be sufficient for the error $\delta\sigma$ (calculated from Equation 3.14) to be small. Since this error estimation involves an integration over $\sigma(\chi)$, information which is unlikely to be available in advance, some approximate treatment is needed. Fortunately, $\sigma(\chi)$ is a steeply falling function of θ so that a small angle approximation to $\sigma(\chi)$ is sufficient. Thus, substitution of Equation 6.100 into Equation 3.14 will enable the apparatus resolution to be determined.

To proceed further, we define an apparatus dependent angle β such that all deflections greater than β in the CM system miss the detector, while all those with $\chi < \beta$ are collected with unit efficiency. Using Equation 6.100 in its exponential form, the fractional error in the total cross-section is:

$$\delta\sigma/\sigma_{tot} \approx \int_0^\beta e^{-\alpha\chi^2}\chi\,d\chi \bigg/ \int_0^\infty e^{-\alpha\chi^2}\chi\,d\chi$$

where

$$\alpha \approx k^2\,\sigma_{tot}/(8\pi) \approx k\sigma(0)^{\frac{1}{2}}/2$$

Integrating we find:

$$\delta\sigma/\sigma_{tot} \approx \alpha\beta^2,$$

so, for good precision in the total cross-section measurement,

$$\beta_{CM} < \frac{1}{k}(\pi/\sigma_{tot})^{\frac{1}{2}} \sim \frac{\lambda}{a} \tag{7.21}$$

For light atoms at thermal speeds β_{CM} is $\leqslant 0.5°$.

The methods of Chapter 2 can now be used to transform β into the LAB system for particular cases.

Calculations of the resolution required with a more realistic apparatus function have been made (R. K. B. Helbing, 1966; F. von Busch, 1966). For an apparatus with a beam and detector of circular cross-section, Helbing found:

$$\theta_a \approx \beta_{LAB}, \tag{7.22}$$

while for tall narrow beams von Busch calculated:

$$\theta_a \approx 0.1\beta_{LAB}, \tag{7.23}$$

where in both cases θ_a is the angular half width of the apparent beam profile. The improvement in resolution between tall rectangular and circular beam geometry is due to out-of-plane scattering. In the case of circular geometry, a much narrower angular range can enter the detector via out-of-plane deflections (see Fig. 3.3 of Chapter 3). The resolution required at thermal energies is therefore typically between 1 and 10 minutes of arc.

Velocity resolution

The velocity resolution required to resolve specific structure in $\sigma(v)$ can be estimated by a forward calculation using guesses of the potential parameters, e.g. Equation 7.13 can be used for the resolution needed for glory undulations.

In general, the attainable resolution is not limited by that of the primary beam and its velocity selector, but by the motion of the target molecules. Averaging arising from this motion not only limits the velocity resolution, obscuring, for example, features with a very narrow energy width such as resonances, but also produces a systematic deviation between the measured and true total cross-section.

There are two configurations of the total cross-section experiment of interest. In the first, target molecules are contained in a scattering chamber and have a Maxwellian distribution of velocities in random directions. The velocity averaging can only be minimized by operating the chamber at as low a temperature as condensation will permit. In the second configuration the target is a cross-beam. If this is well collimated, the velocity averaging introduced can be very small. The use of nozzle cross-beams of high Mach number is particularly attractive here.

For a relative velocity $w(=|\mathbf{v}_1 - \mathbf{v}_2|)$, the probability of a collision in a length l in passing through the target is $n_2 \sigma_{tot}(w)wl/v_1$ and the attenuation of the primary beam from its initial value I_0 is:

$$\frac{I(w)}{I_0(w)} = e^{-n_2 \sigma_{tot}(w)wl/v_1}. \tag{7.24}$$

The measured attenuation is the average of $I(w)/I_0(w)$ over the relative velocity distribution $f(w)$. If a mean total cross-section for a given incident velocity v_1 is defined:

$$\bar{\sigma}_{tot}(v_1) = \int_0^\infty \sigma_{tot}(w) f(w) \frac{w}{v_1} \, dw, \tag{7.25}$$

then the measured attenuation is given to a good approximation $(\Delta I/I_0 < 0.1)$ by:

$$\frac{I(v_1)}{I_0(v_1)} \approx e^{-n_2 \bar{\sigma}_{\text{tot}}(v_1)l} \tag{7.26}$$

Appropriate distributions $f(w)$ are readily worked out for the important case of two crossed effusive beams, when the distribution is quite sharp (see Equation 1.7) and for a monoenergetic beam passing through a thermal scattering gas, when the distribution in w is somewhat sharper than the Maxwellian distribution appropriate to the temperature of the scattering gas.

The correction arising from Equation 7.25 is fairly small if the most probable velocity in the chamber is less than a third that of the primary beam. An approximate relation for $\sigma(v)$ can then be used, the Mott and Massey based result:

$$\sigma(w)/\sigma(v_1) \approx (v_1/w)^{2/(s-1)} \tag{7.27}$$

usually being adequate. The correction factors calculated from Equations 7.25 and 7.27 for an unselected secondary beam and for a scattering chamber have been tabulated for a range of s values and target temperatures by K. Berkling et al., 1962.

Measurement of path length and target density

If the absolute total cross-section is to be measured, the number of scattering molecules in the target must be known. Absolute cross-sections are of particular value in determining C_6 coefficients but these depend on a high power of σ_{tot} so that accurate cross-section measurements are required. If a crossed-beam configuration is used, the absolute density cannot at present be obtained with sufficient accuracy because the absolute efficiency of beam detectors is not reliably known. Absolute cross-section measurements have therefore been made with the scattering chamber configuration despite the lower velocity resolution that results. The pressure in the target gas chamber is adjusted to yield about 10–20 per cent attenuation, a level at which multiple collisions are rare. Errors arising from molecules deflected by a small angle at their first collision but arriving at the detector by a second bounce are thus minimized. Unfortunately, pressure measurements in the necessary range ($\sim 10^{-4}$ Torr) are difficult. Indeed, in much of the early work total cross-sections ~ 30 per cent too high were reported due to a systematic error in measurements with McLeod gauges (E. W. Rothe, 1964, and with

R. H. Neynaber, 1965). More recently, diaphragm manometers have been used and appear to yield good accuracy.

In an alternative approach (R. J. Cross et al., 1966) a monitor molecular beam passing orthogonally through the scattering chamber has been used to measure the pressure. In this way a series of cross-sections can be measured relative to the monitor/target particle cross-section. Errors can also arise in measuring the path length through the target. Since target gas will flow out of the scattering chamber through the entrance and exit slots, the effective path length will be larger than the chamber dimension. These end effects can be compensated for by a series of measurements with differing chamber lengths.

7.4   Apparatus and results — total cross-sections

We now consider a few experiments which will exemplify the technique and the results obtainable. The apparatus used by E. W. Rothe and R. K. B. Helbing (1968) is shown in Fig. 7.7. This was designed to measure cross-sections as a function of velocity of alkali atoms scattered from a variety of partners. Since absolute cross-sections were not measured a crossed beam configuration was used to minimize the relative velocity spread. The apparatus used fairly conventional beam sources and a hot wire detector. The modulation and data collection was particularly interesting in the efforts made to minimize noise arising from fluctuations in the beam intensities. The primary velocity selected alkali beam was modulated at 10 Hz while the cross-beam was modulated at 17 Hz. Two lock-in amplifiers, one tuned to each frequency, then process the signal from the hot wire detector. The

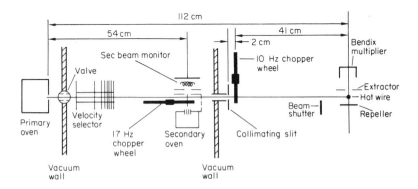

Fig. 7.7 Apparatus for total cross-section measurements with a primary alkali beam. Reproduced from E. W. Rothe and R. K. B. Helbing, 1968.

10 Hz signal I_{10} is proportional to the unattenuated primary beam and the 17 Hz signal (I_{17}) to the attenuated signal. Thus for small attenuations:

$$\frac{I}{I_0} = \frac{I_{17}}{I_{10}} \propto n_2 \sigma_{\text{tot}} l. \tag{7.28}$$

The ratio of the output of the two detectors is proportional to the cross-section. Fluctuations in the density of the target molecules were eliminated by cross-correlation using an ion gauge as a density detector to monitor the cross-beam. Potential parameters were obtained for a wide range of diatomics and hydro- and fluorocarbons. Typical atom impact spectra are shown in Fig. 7.8. (E. W. Rothe and R. K. B. Helbing, 1969). Particularly interesting was the apparent quenching of the glory undulations (a topic also investigated by P. R. LeBreton and H. L. Kramer (1967)). The explanation of these unexpectedly small (when compared with atom-atom impact spectra) oscillations in the cross-section has been sought in four directions; the shape of the potential, the effect of vibrational motion on the elastic scattering, the effect of angle dependent intermolecular forces on the elastic scattering or the effect of rotationally inelastic collisions. For most of the systems studied, a possible fifth cause – chemical reaction (see Section 8.4) – can be excluded.

In purely elastic scattering, the amplitude of the glory oscillations depends inversely on the curvature of the phase shift function $(\partial^2 \eta(l)/\partial l^2)$ at its maximum. This, in turn, is loosely related to the width of the potential bowl; potentials with broad minima give rise to large amplitude oscillations in the total cross-section. Weak oscillations may therefore arise directly from rather narrow potential wells. However, the data obtained by Rothe for a wide range of fluorocarbons (Fig. 7.9) that might be expected to have rather similar potentials suggests that in this case this is not the origin of the effect. Weak oscillations were found to correlate with anistropic targets. The explanation then, is that scattering takes place from a range of potentials, each with a slightly different glory spacing, which results in a blurring of the overall pattern. This hypothesis requires that the molecule remains essentially stationary during the collision. The third possible explanation is that low frequency vibration of the target (in particular the breathing modes of the more nearly spherical molecules) can lead to a change in polarisability and hence in C_6 during the collision. This, in turn, leads to a range of phase shifts of the forward scattered amplitude (if the vibrational period is appreciably longer than the lifetime of the collision) and hence to a partial quenching of the glory pattern. This process is now thought to be less important (P. R.

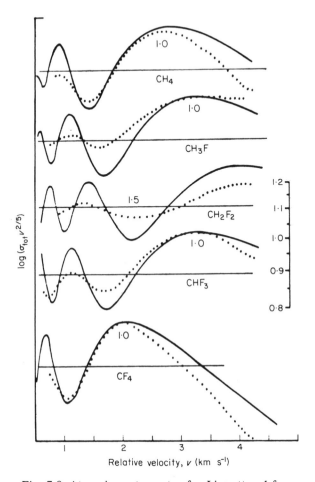

Fig. 7.8 Atom impact spectra for Li scattered from fluorinated methanes. The dotted lines represent mean experimental results, the solid curves are calculations based on a fitted LJ (12:6) potential. The apparent quenching at low velocities seems to increase with the dipole moment of the target; the molecular shape (i.e. the angular dependent part of the repulsive branch of the potential) remains almost unchanged in the series (E. W. Rothe and R. K. B. Helbing 1969.)

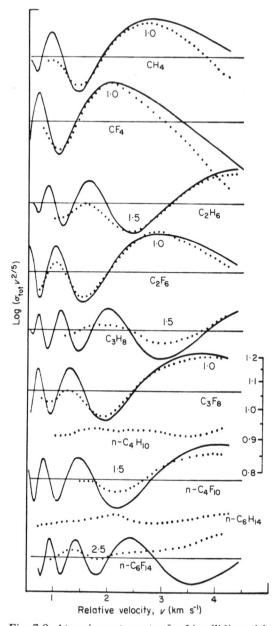

Fig. 7.9 Atom impact spectra for Li colliding with a series of hydro- and fluorocarbons. There is a correlation between the extent of damping of the glory undulations and the target asymmetry. Solid curves are predictions from a simple LJ (12:6) potential. The dipole moments of these molecules, in contrast to some of those in Fig. 7.8, are relatively small (E. W. Rothe and R. K. B. Helbing, 1969.)

LeBreton and H. L. Kramer, 1969 and R. K. B. Helbing, 1969) than the potential anisotropy. Rotationally inelastic collisions on the forward glory trajectory can also reduce the amplitude of $f(0)$ and hence damp its interference structure with the outer (entirely elastic) branch. This last effect is undoubtedly operating in some systems, but is difficult to disentangle from the effect of the anisotropy in the potential because the larger the anisotropy the more likely is rotational energy transfer.

Calculations by R. B. Bernstein and R. E. Olsen (1968) on the degree of damping of the glory structure to be expected from anisotropic potentials (target stationary during the collision) show that the observations in some cases can be completely accounted for. Thus, starting with a potential of the form

$$V(R, \theta) = C_{12}R^{-12}[1 + b_1 P_1(\cos\theta) + b_2 P_2(\cos\theta)]$$
$$- C_6 R^{-6}[1 + a_2 P_2(\cos\theta)], \quad (7.29)$$

and defining the anisotropy parameter a as:

$$a = 2a_2 - b_2, \quad (7.30)$$

they obtain as a first approximation (for $E^* > 1$)

$$1 - \frac{u}{u_0} \approx 4.45 \times 10^{-3} \left(\frac{2\mu\epsilon R_m}{\hbar^2 E^*}\right) a^2 \left[1 - \frac{1.54}{E^*}\right] f(j) \quad (7.31)$$

where u_0 is the amplitude of the undamped glory oscillations (i.e. calculated for the potential with a_2, b_1 and b_2 zero), u is the observed amplitude, $E^* = E/\epsilon$ and $f(j)$ depends on the rotational state of the target and approaches 1 rapidly as j increases. Applying Equation 7.31 to Rothe and Helbing's data on Li scattered from the hydrogen halides, values of $|a| \approx 1.1$ were found. This analysis is, of course, sensitive not only to the resolution of the experiment (and poor resolution can easily produce apparent quenching) but also to the values of ϵ and R_m used in calculating the unperturbed amplitude u_0. The quenching of total cross-section undulations is thus not a very reliable way of measuring anisotropy in the intermolecular potential.

Another apparatus for total cross-section measurement, this time for non-alkali species, is shown in Fig. 7.10 (M. G. Dondi, 1969) and has been used to measure the velocity dependence of σ_{tot} for He^4/He^4 scattering. The primary beam source is a nozzle operating at 77 K and a stagnation pressure of 3 torr. The primary beam is velocity selected with resolution $\Delta v/v = 5$ per

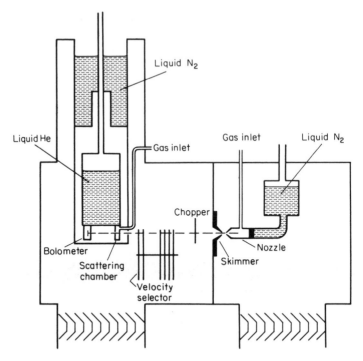

Fig. 7.10 Apparatus for total cross-section measurements used for He + He. Reproduced from M. G. Dondi, 1969.

cent. The scattering chamber is maintained at 2 K to minimize velocity averaging. The importance of this low ambient temperature can be seen from Fig. 7.11 where the effect of different scattering chamber temperatures on the resolution in σ_{tot} is shown; above 10 K the undulations are not resolved. The detector is a sensitive bolometer which responds to the kinetic energy of impinging beam molecules (M. Cavallini, 1967) and detects a minimum flux of 2×10^8 molecules s^{-1}. The results of this experiment are shown in Fig. 7.12.

The structure observed in $\sigma(v)$ is of particular interest since it does not arise from the normal glory region of stationary phase, but from the identical nature of the particles. Particles scattered through χ will be indistinguishable from those scattered through $(\pi-\chi)$ from the other beam and will therefore mutually interfere. The total cross-section has been found in Section 6.15 to be:

$$\sigma_{tot} = \frac{4\pi}{k^2} \left\{ \sum_l (2l+1)(1 - \cos 2\eta(l)) + \sum_l (2l+1)(-1)^l(1 - \cos 2\eta(l)) \right\}, \quad (7.3$$

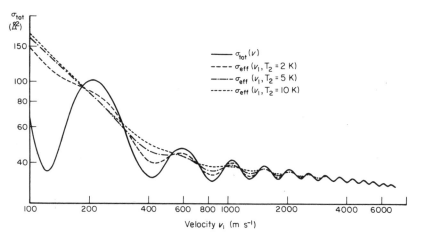

Fig. 7.11 Effect of scattering chamber temperature on observed total cross-section for $He^4 + He^4$ (calculated for LJ (12:6) potential $R_m = 3.0$ Å, $\epsilon = 1.4 \times 10^{-15}$ erg). Reproduced from M. G. Dondi, 1969.

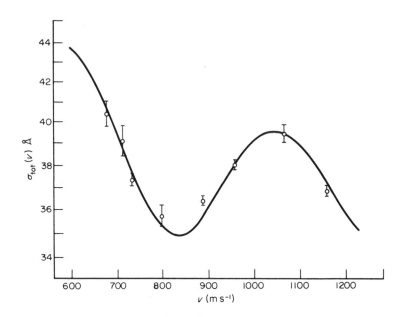

Fig. 7.12 $\sigma_{tot}(v)$ for $He^4 + He^4$. The very large amplitude glory oscillation is characteristic of identical boson scattering when only the S wave contributes. The full curve is calculated from a LJ (12:6) potential that gives the best fit. (M. G. Dondi, 1969.)

putting $(-1)^l = \cos l\pi$ yields:

$$\sigma_{tot} = \frac{4\pi}{k^2} \left\{ \sum_l (2l+1)(1 - \cos 2\eta(l)) \right.$$

$$\left. + \sum_l (2l+1) \cos l\pi - \sum_l (2l+1) \cos (2\eta(l) - l\pi) \right\} \quad (7.33)$$

Using the semi-classical approximation we may expect extrema in the total cross-section whenever any of the terms in Equation 7.33 are stationary. This occurs when

$$\text{(I)} \ \frac{\partial \eta(l)}{\partial l} = 0; \quad \text{(II)} \ \frac{\partial \eta(l)}{\partial l} = l\pi/2. \quad (7.34)$$

Of these, (I) arises from the first term in Equation 7.33 and gives rise to the normal glory oscillations in σ_{tot}; (II) arises from the third term in Equation 7.33 and represents back scattering of the main beam particle through π, and hence forward scattering of the second particle. If the negative deflection due to the attractive branch of the potential does not exceed $-\pi$, contribution (II) comes solely from the S-wave scattering (i.e. $b = 0$). The oscillations in σ_{tot} arising from this term thus correspond to η_0 passing through $\pi/2$, π etc. From this structure we thus obtain additional information compared with that from the normal glories in that not only is the velocity at which the phase of the forward scattered amplitude passes through multiples of $\pi/2$ known, but also that this refers to the $l = 0$ partial wave contribution. The authors also show that the S-wave phase shift is almost entirely dependent on the potential range parameter. Thus, for a L-J potential they determine R_m directly.

It is one of the advantages of the crossed beam technique that a very wide 'temperature' range is experimentally accessible. Measurements of total cross-sections at superthermal energies in excess of 10^4 K have been made by several groups. Both M. Hollstein and H. Pauly (1967) and R. J. Cross and C. J. Malerich (1968) have used charge exchange alkali atom sources to measure σ_{tot} for alkali atom/rare gas systems. In their energy range of 6 eV–1000 eV the transition occurs between attractive behaviour ($\sigma(v) \propto v^{-2/5}$) and the slower dependence characteristic of the repulsive potential. In the apparatus by Pauly, both the generation of the parent ion beam and the neutral alkali atom detection are by surface ionization on tungsten. The detector is run 'cold' to reduce noise without impairing efficiency at these high energies. Some typical results for K, Na/gas systems are shown in Fig. 7.13.

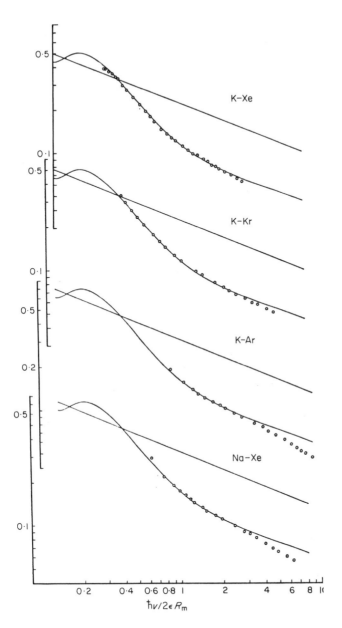

Fig. 7.13 Total cross-sections for alkali metals + rare gases in the superthermal collision range (M. Hollstein and H. Pauly, 1967). The transition between a total cross-section dominated by the attractive part of the potential and the repulsive part is seen at $\hbar v/2\epsilon R_m \sim 2$ (see Equation 7.7) and the first glory maximum ($N = 1$) is also visible.

By grafting results of experiments at this energy onto the thermal data, a potential valid over a much larger energy range can be established. It has become clear that the two parameter L-J form is not adequate to cover this energy range and that potentials with more parameters are required (C. Schlier et al., 1968).

7.5   Elastic differential cross-sections

(*i*) *Interpretation*

Fig. 7.2 gave some idea of the structure available in measurements of the differential cross-section. The calculation was, in fact, for potassium scattered from a heavy partner (I_2). The results were given in the laboratory reference system and ideal resolution was assumed. Clearly, considerable information about the intermolecular potential can be obtained from data with this amount of structure provided that the angular resolution is good enough — 0.2° (LAB) would be adequate for most potentials at thermal energies.

Once again interpretation follows the algorithm already suggested, namely estimation of parameters, identification and interpretation of key features, statistical fitting between observations and forward apparatus averaged calculations from a trial potential. These key features are, in order of increasing resolution necessary for their observation,

(i) The low resolution envelope of log $\sigma(\chi)$ versus χ plots, yielding some indication of the power law of the potential.

(ii) The location of the rainbow maximum, providing a good measure of the potential well depth.

(iii) Location and spacing of supernumerary rainbow maxima. The first of these yields information on the potential range and subsequent peaks give some evidence as to the curvature of the potential near its minimum.

(iv) The spacing of the high frequency interference oscillations, from which σ_{LJ} can be extracted with only an approximate knowledge of ϵ.

It has already been shown that, under classical (Equation 2.32) or semi-classical (Equation 6.132) conditions the major contribution to $\sigma(\chi)$ is given by:

$$\sigma(\chi) = s^{-1} \left(\frac{(s-1)}{E} C_s \right)^{2/s} \chi^{-(2s+2)/s}. \tag{7.35}$$

Thus a log plot of low resolution differential cross-section (in which the quantum interference structure is not resolved) against angle will yield a line with gradient $-(2s + 2)/s$ at angles smaller than the rainbow. In Fig. 7.2 a line drawn through the mean of the oscillations in the region $1°-8°$ of the plot $\sigma(\theta)$. $\theta^{7/3}$ versus θ is approximately horizontal in accord with these calculations and so verifies the 6 power attractive term used in the forward computations.

Quantum mechanically the maxim in the differential cross-section occurs at slightly narrower angles than the classical rainbow. To a good approximation

$$\chi \text{ rainbow} = \chi_{\max} + 0.772 \, (\chi_{\max} - \chi_{\text{first min}}), \qquad (7.36)$$

where $\chi_{\max}$ is the rainbow maximum in the differential cross-section and $\chi_{\min}$ is the minimum between $\chi_{\max}$ and the first supernumerary bow.

The semi-classical interpretation of the rainbow and of the supernumerary bows has already been discussed in Chapter 6. Their most important feature in determining elastic potentials is that the rainbow location is largely dependent only on the reduced energy and but weakly on the length parameter in the potential. This can be seen in Fig. 7.14 where the location of the rainbow maximum is plotted against the reduced collision energy. With no knowledge at all of Λ^* (which contains the length parameter σ) ϵ can be determined to ± 10 per cent. Calculations for a range of different potentials forms have shown that this is true for a wide range of potentials so that a measurement of $\chi_{\max}$ yields a value of the well depth to 10 per cent or 15 per cent directly irrespective of potential form or other parameters. If a supernumerary bow can be observed as well, information as to the potential range can be obtained. Similarly, additional bows can be interpreted to yield potential curvatures etc. With additional information of this kind an iterative process can be used to refine the initial estimate of ϵ. As an example consider the scattering in Fig. 7.2.

$$\theta \text{ max:} \qquad\qquad = 10.2° \text{ lab} = 11.9° \text{ centre of mass}$$
$$\theta \text{ 1st supernumerary bow} = 5.2° \text{ lab} = 6.04° \text{ centre of mass}$$
$$\text{Collision energy} \qquad = 1.9 \times 10^{-13} \text{ ergs.}$$

From Fig. 7.14, $\chi_{\max} = 11.9°$ yields a first estimate for E/ϵ of 7.2–9.2. From Fig. 7.15 we can relate the angular spacing Δ_χ between the two bows to Λ^* thus finding for $E/\epsilon = 8$ and $\Delta\chi = 5.9°$ that $\Lambda^* \approx 0.078$. Returning to

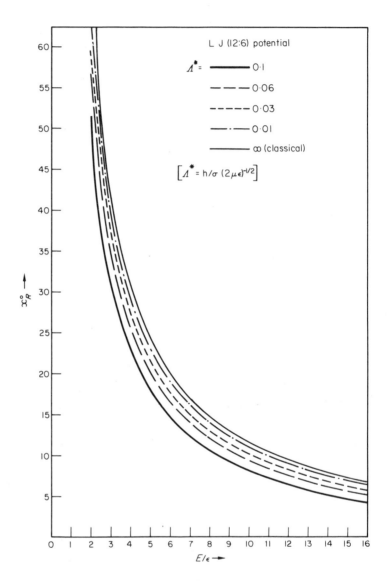

Fig. 7.14 Angle of rainbow maximum versus reduced impact energy for LJ (12:6) potential (R. J. Munn and F. J. Smith, 1966).

Fig. 7.14 with this value of Λ^* gives a revised value for E/ϵ of 7.8. Finally, Λ^* may be corrected using Fig. 7.16 where Λ^* and E/ϵ are related for various values of $\Delta\chi$. We finally obtain estimates for the potential parameters of $E/\epsilon = 7.8$ and $\Lambda^* = 0.083$, compared with the values 7.85 and 0.0855 used in the calculation of Fig. 7.2. Similar schemes can be set up to produce estimates of the potential function curvature from observations of additional

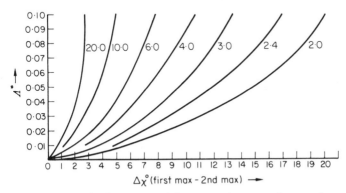

Fig. 7.15 Angle between rainbow maximum and secondary rainbow maximum versus Λ^*, Bohr parameter, for several reduced impact energies (LJ (12:6) potential). (R. J. Munn and F. J. Smith, 1966).

supernumerary bows. However, it is probably preferable to begin more detailed fitting computations at this stage together with the exploration of different potential forms.

The importance of operating in the optimum energy range can be appreciated from Fig. 7.14 or from the underlying relationship $\chi_r E^*$ = const. If there is an error $\Delta\chi$ in measuring the position of the rainbow and ΔE in the relative energy, there will be an error

$$\Delta\epsilon/\epsilon = \Delta\chi/\chi + \Delta E/E$$

in the derived well depth. For an apparatus of normal resolution, a rainbow in the region $15°-60°$ is perhaps optimum.

The spacing of the highest frequency structure is primarily dependent on the range a of the potential. If this can be precisely located, e.g. by a marked change in gradient of $V(R)$ at $R = a$, we can define a partial wave l^* such that

$$l^*\hbar = \mu v a$$

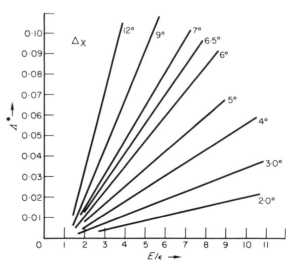

Fig. 7.16 Relation between Λ^* (and hence σ) and the reduced energy for several rainbow maxima to 1st supernumerary angular spacings.

The angular frequency for scattering from this edge (see Section 6.13) will then be:

$$\Delta\chi = \pi/l^*, \tag{7.37}$$

so that a can be determined directly. For smoothly varying potentials, e.g. of the L-J form, the parameter a is less easily defined, but will clearly be not too different from σ. For these potentials the high frequency structure arises from the interference between the inner two branches of $\chi(b)$ that lead to deflections of opposite sign. The interference spacing is given by (see Section 6.10)

$$\Delta\chi \approx 2\pi/[l_2 + l_3], \tag{7.38}$$

where l_2 and l_3 satisfy $|\chi(l_2)| \mu |\chi(l_3)| = \chi_{obs}$. l_2 and l_3 converge at $\chi = 0$ and for small angles

$$\Delta\chi \approx 2\pi/[k\sigma(b_2^* + b_3^*)] \approx \frac{\pi}{kb_0}, \tag{7.39}$$

where $b_0^*(= b_0/\sigma)$ is the reduced impact parameter leading to the forward glory. Then, using the fact that R_0^*, the reduced distance of closest approach on the forward glory trajectory is only a slowly varying function of E^* and also that $V(R_0) \approx 0.6\epsilon$ for an R^{-6} potential, we obtain:

$$\Delta\chi \approx \frac{\Lambda^*}{2.2} \left(\frac{1}{0.6 + E^*} \right)^{\frac{1}{2}}, \tag{7.40}$$

where Λ^* is the de Boer parameter. The basic dependence of $\Delta\chi$ on σ_{LJ} for $E^* > 1$ is apparent and Equation 7.40 enables a preliminary estimate of σ to be made.

A more rigorous analysis using the peak locations has been made by R. E. Olsen, 1968. Bernstein has shown that for $\chi < 30°$ and inside the rainbow the scattered intensity $I(\chi)$ can be written:

$$I(\chi) = I_1(\chi) \{ 1 + y(\chi)^2 + 2y(\chi) \cos \gamma(\chi) \}, \tag{7.41}$$

where I_1 is the scattered intensity contributed by the outermost branch of the deflection function. The peaks in $I(\chi)$ are then determined by the periodicities of $y(\chi)$ and $\cos \gamma(\chi)$:

$$y(\chi) = 2 \left[\frac{I_{2\,3}(\chi)}{I_1(\chi)} \right]^{\frac{1}{2}} \cos (l_{2\,3}\chi - \pi/4) \tag{7.42}$$

and

$$\gamma(\chi) = 2\eta(l_1) + l_1\chi - \pi/2 \tag{7.43}$$

$y(\chi)^2$ is associated with the forward glory contibution and the second term in Equation 7.41, $y(\chi).\cos \gamma(\chi)$, arises from the interference between the forward glory and the outermost branch centered at l_1. There are thus three wavelengths of oscillation possible in the combined scattered amplitude,

$$\Delta\chi_{1:23} = 2\pi/|l_{2\,3} \pm l_1| \tag{7.44}$$

resulting from the third term in Equation 7.41 and a structure of smaller amplitude having $\Delta\chi_{2\,3} = \pi/l_{2\,3}$ resulting from the second term in Equation 7.41 and already discussed in Equations 7.38–7.40. Olson (1968) and Bernstein have suggested that the finite apparatus resolution will erase the highest frequency structure, leaving the highest observed periodicity to be $\Delta\chi_{2\,3}$. For a typical potential and angles of deflection at thermal energies

$\leqslant 10°$, l_1 and $l_{2\,3}$ might be ~600 and 200 respectively so that $\Delta\chi_{1:23}/\Delta\chi_{23} \leqslant \frac{1}{2}$. These authors found that for the Li-Hg system a plot of χ_N^{-1} versus $(N + \frac{1}{4})^{-1}$, where N labels successive maxima and minima, gave a good linear plot and the slope was equated to $l_{2\,3}$. Hence from scans at several energies, a plot of $(l_{2\,3} + \frac{1}{2})/k$ versus E^{-1} can be constructed, in the same way that the BOB plots of $\eta_{2\,3}/k$ versus E^{-1} were used.

The curvature of these lines again analogously, can be written as:

$$(l_{2\,3} + \frac{1}{2})/kR_m = B_0(E^*) + B_1 E^{*-1} - B_2 E^{*-2} \qquad (7.45)$$

where B_0 depends upon the curvature of the potential and $B_1 = 0.3530$ and $B_2 = 0.1488$. Tables of B_0 for the Buckingham Corner potential have been given by R. E. Olsen, 1968, so that these oscillations may be interpreted directly in terms of this potential.

(ii) Measurement of differential cross-sections

The number of particles per second reaching a small detector a distance R away from the scattering centre in a direction (θ, ϕ) is (see Equation 3.4)

$$S(\theta,\Phi) = \frac{A_d}{R^2} J\left(\frac{\chi, \phi}{\theta, \Phi}\right) \frac{I_1 I_2}{v_1 v_2} \times \left(\begin{array}{c}\text{scattering}\\\text{volume}\end{array}\right) |v_1 - v_2| \sigma(\chi, \phi), \qquad (7.46)$$

where I_1 and I_2 are the fluxes of beam particles with velocities v_1 and v_2, $\sigma(\chi, \phi)$ is the CM differential cross-section and $J(\chi, \phi/\theta, \Phi)$ the Jacobian for the CM $\rightarrow$ LAB transformation.

In general, to make the transition $S(\theta, \Phi) \leftrightarrow \sigma(\chi, \phi)$ it is necessary to either average or unfold the results with respect to the distribution in magnitude and direction of the relative velocity $v_1 + v_2$, which is mainly felt through its influence on the co-ordinate transformation and on the Jacobian. The spread in velocity of the unselected cross-beam is usually the most important agent in blurring the scattering pattern, though the angular spread of v_2 can be important for slow heavy target molecules.

Some design criteria associated with apparatus resolution have already been discussed in Chapter 3. The ideal design procedure is to make a forward calculation from an assumed potential of roughly the right form through full apparatus averaging to $S(\theta,\Phi)$ via Equation 7.46 and to adjust the operating conditions so that enough structure is preserved in $S(\theta, \Phi)$ to allow a good fit to be made to the potential.

In practice, an experiment in which the supernumerary oscillations are resolved is always worthwhile and we can estimate the relative velocity resolution Δv needed to preserve this structure. In the CM system, if we require that Δv must be sufficiently small for the rainbow peak position to shift by less than one half the supernumerary spacing, we find from Fig. 7.14 that the reduced energy must range between 6.4 and 9.4, i.e. a 15 per cent spread in the relative velocity would just permit the resolution of the rainbow and first supernumerary.

The resolution of the higher frequency oscillations sets a much more severe limit on the velocity spread permissible. From Equation 7.39 we see that their period is inversely proportional to k and hence to the relative velocity. Thus the acceptable spread in velocity Δv if successive maxima and minima are not to overlap is:

$$\Delta v/v \sim (k\sigma\chi)^{-1}. \tag{7.47}$$

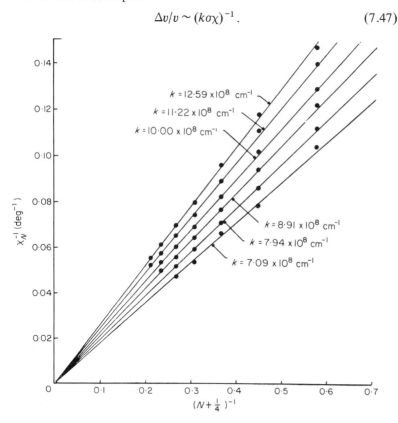

Fig. 7.17 Plot of reciprocal of interference extrema locations versus $(N + \frac{1}{4})^{-1}$ where N is the index number of extrema. The slope of the plot at each energy is αl_0 where l_0 is the l value of the forward glory. The example illustrated is for Li–Hg and for such a system with small reduced mass l_0 is typically $\sim$50, making the high frequency structure easy to resolve. (From R. E. Olson, 1968.)

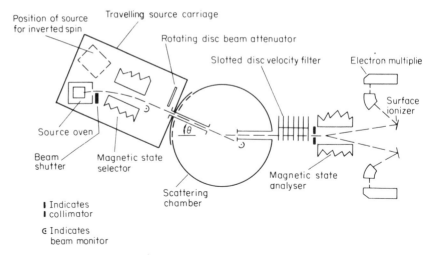

Fig. 7.18 Apparatus for studying spin dependence of alkali alkali collisions. (D. E. Pritchard et al., 1969.)

Typically a velocity resolution $\lesssim 10$ per cent is required, together with an angular resolution $\sim \Delta\chi/2$, i.e. $\sim 0.2°$. The resolution of this structure becomes easier at small angles.

Because of the important contribution to the resolution made by the cross-beam velocity spread, it is normal to use the heavier species in this beam and to operate the source at the lowest temperature possible. Besides minimising the velocity spread, the loss of angular resolution associated with the LAB $\rightarrow$ CM transformation (which generally results in χ being greater than θ) is also reduced. Even with the optimum configuration of masses, using a thermal effusive cross-beam can frequently result in an uncertainty of $0.5°$ in the CM angle of deflection. A further reduction in the effect of the cross-beam velocity spread especially at small angles of scattering can be achieved by firing the cross-beam in a plane perpendicular to the plane of the primary beam and detector motion (E. F. Greene et al., 1969).

7.6   Apparatus and results – differential cross-sections

Once again we propose to discuss only a few experiments to illustrate the technique and its present capabilities.

Because of the alleviated detection problem, alkali scattering experiments have seen the most ambitious applications of state and velocity filters to define the quantum channel of the collision. In the experiments of D. E. Pritchard and F. Y. Chu, 1970, the scattering of unlike alkali atoms was studied. Alkali atoms interact by two potentials depending upon their overall spin state, triplet or singlet, the two potentials being very different. In unpolarized beams, particles are incident in each pair state with a statistical weight of 3:1 ($^3\Sigma{:}^1\Sigma$). The particles may then scatter with or without an exchange of spin (see Section 6.17). To isolate the singlet and triplet potentials and to study the spin flipping process itself, two spin state selectors are required. The configuration used by Pritchard and Chu is shown in Fig. 7.18. The primary beam is spin selected by a two wire field magnet and then crosses a chopped unpolarized Na beam. The scattered K is velocity selected and finally spin selected again. The source and detector can be arranged to transmit and receive either spin state. The subsequent detection is of the modulated ion counting type. Differential cross-sections for spin exchange, $\sigma_{exch}(\chi)$ and for non-exchange (i.e. direct scattering), $\sigma_{direct}(\chi)$, were measured. These cross-sections are related to the scattered amplitudes due to the singlet, $f_1(\chi)$, and triplet, $f_3(\chi)$, potentials by

$$\sigma_{exch}(\chi) = \tfrac{1}{4}\,|\,f_1(\chi) - f_3(\chi)\,|^2, \tag{7.48}$$

and

$$\sigma_{exch}(\chi) + \sigma_{direct}(\chi) = \sigma_{sum}(\chi) = \tfrac{1}{4}\,|\,f_1(\chi)\,|^2 + \tfrac{3}{4}\,|\,f_3(\chi)\,|^2. \tag{7.49}$$

The two potentials can thus be determined from observations of $\sigma_{exch}(\chi)$ and $\sigma_{sum}(\chi)$ and in particular their difference can be found with good precision. Typical results obtained are shown in Figs. 7.19 and 7.20.

The alkali metals interact with the rare gases by only one potential in each case, and if the collision energy is below the threshold for any electronic excitation no state selectors are needed to specify the exit channel. The greater beam intensity then available permits much higher angular and velocity resolution to be used. The Bonn Group (P. Barwig et al., 1966) have studied these systems and have resolved the quantum interference structure out to wide angles. A typical example is the Na/Xe measurements shown in Fig. 7.21, in which the location of all the quantum peaks can easily be seen. With data of this quality, the functional dependence of $V(R)$ in the experimental energy range can be unambiguously determined. The usual forms of the Lennard-Jones potential (n, ϵ and σ as adjustable parameters) have proved inadequate under this searching examination and a series of potentials with five parameters have been fitted to the data (C. Schlier et al; U. Buck and H. Pauly, 1968). The apparatus used is shown in Figure 7.22. Data with the resolution of that shown in Fig. 7.21 can now be

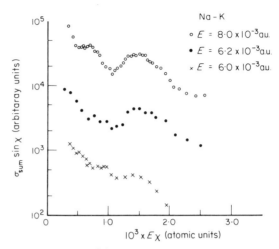

Fig. 7.19 $\sigma_{sum}(\chi)$ for Na−K scattering. Note the good scaling with respect to $E\chi$. The overall appearance is that of typical elastic scattering. (D. E. Pritchard et al., 1970a.)

subject to a two stage inversion procedure. The deflection function is first constructed, using any auxiliary information on R_m, χ_r and the phase shift of the forward glory branch; its functional form at this stage can still contain adjustable parameters equal in number to the number of resolved rainbow extrema and these are fixed by fitting the observed differential cross-section, a much speedier process than working with adjustable parameters in the potential. The deflection function is then inverted by Firsov's procedure to yield $V(R)$ pointwise, i.e. without making any assumptions about its analytical form. The potential for Na/Hg in Fig. 7.23 was obtained in this way and clearly illustrates the inadequacy of the Lennard-Jones potential in analyzing high resolution scattering. It is also observed in Li/Cs singlet state scattering (H. Kanes et al., 1971) that the actual potential minimum is broader than the Lennard-Jones form, but this may not turn out to be true of interatomic potentials in general (P. E. Siska, et al., 1971, or J. M. Parson et al., 1971, for the inert gases). If alkali atom scattering data is to be fitted with only a two parameter potential, then the (8:6) form rather than the (12:6) can be tried with its much smaller curvature ($\kappa = 20.2$) at the potential minimum.

Experiments with non-alkali partners are at a slightly less advanced stage due to the difficulties of detection. Advances in nozzle sources and vacuum

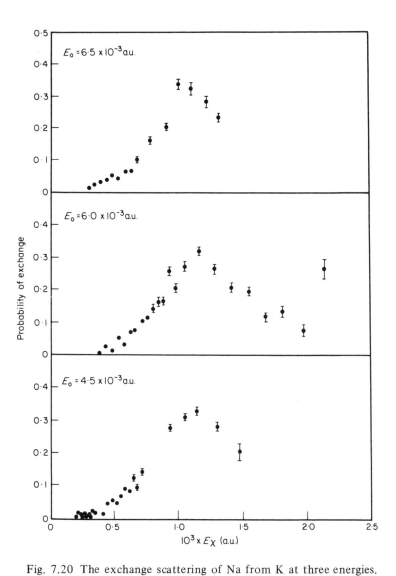

Fig. 7.20 The exchange scattering of Na from K at three energies. A maximum in $P_{ex}(\chi)$ is observed and occurs when the phase difference between the singlet and triplet scattered amplitudes at χ, $\arg(f_1(\chi)) - \arg(f_3(\chi))$, reaches an odd multiple of π. The first of these extrema is visible, with the suggestion of a higher order one in the run at $E_0 = 6 \times 10^{-3}$. The very good scaling of $P_{ex}(\chi)$ at different energies with respect to $E\chi$ indicates that the outermost branches of the triplet and singlet deflection functions are dominant. (D. E. Pritchard et al., 1970.)

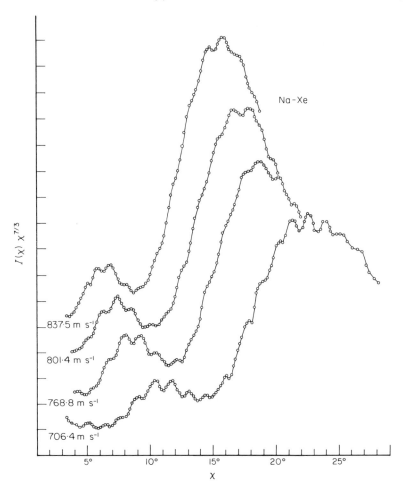

Fig. 7.21 Na–Xe scattering. The rainbow and one supernumerary bow are visible, together with high frequency structure of the type indexed in Fig. 7.17. (Taken from P. Barwig et al., 1966.)

techniques have, however, brought rapid progress. Recently the systems:

Ne + Ne, Ar, Kr, Xe	(J. M. Parson et al., 1970; P. E. Siska et al., 1970).
Ne + Ar	(W. Williams et al., 1969; M. Cavallini et al., 1970).
He + He	(M. Cavallini et al., 1970; P. E. Siska et al., 1970; P. Cantini et al., 1972; H. G. Bennewitz et al., 1971).
$D_2 + N_2$	(D. H. Winicur et al., 1970; V. Aquilanti et al., 1971).
Ar + N_2	(R. W. Bickes and R. B. Bernstein, 1970; K. G. Anlauf et al., 1971; p. Cantini et al., 1972).

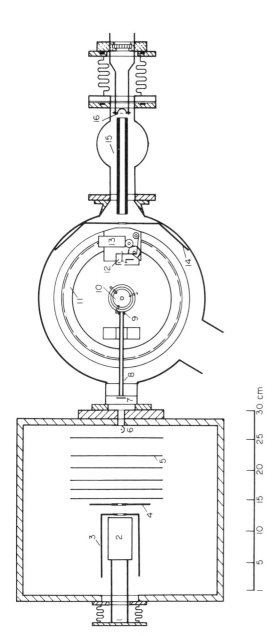

Fig. 7.22 Scale drawing of a cross-section through a molecular beam apparatus for measuring differential scattering cross-sections. The important parts of the apparatus are **2** oven, **5** velocity selector, **6** monitor detector, **10** secondary beam oven, **12** movable detector on the rotating platform **11**, **13** motor for raising and lowering the detector, **16** monitor detector, **4**, **8**, **14**, and **15** are liquid nitrogen cooled surfaces. (H. Pauly and J. P. Toennies, 1968.)

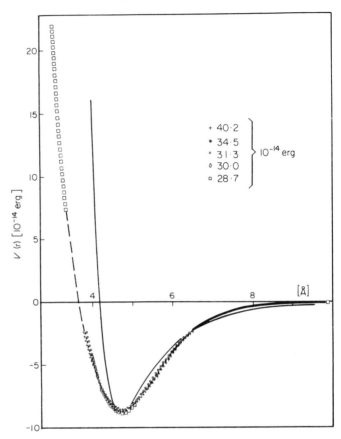

Fig. 7.23 Potential for the Na–Hg system determined by a two stage inversion of the differential cross-section. The various sets of points refer to $\sigma(\theta)$ data at different energies; the insensitivity of the derived potential to the energy of the scattering experiment is an important check of the validity of the procedure. The full line is the Lennard-Jones potential having the same value of ϵ and R_m. (U. Buck, 1971.)

CCl$_4$ + iso-octane	(M. J. Cardillo et al., 1971).
Ar + Ar	(J. M. Parson et al., 1972).
He + Ar, Ne, Kr	
Ne + Kr	(G. D. Lempert et al., 1971).
Ar + Kr	(J. W. Bredewout et al., 1971).
He + Ne	(F. G. Collins and F. C. Hurlburt, 1972).

have been the subject of initial reports. Rainbow angles and quantum interference structure have been observed and initial estimates of potential parameters have been made. The apparatus used by Y. T. Lee et al., 1969, employed two nozzle beams and an electron bombardment mass filter in a UHV chamber at $< 10^{-10}$ Torr which was separated by three stages of differential pumping from the scattering chamber. A modulated ion counting scheme was employed. The apparatus is shown in Figs. 7.24 and 7.25 and some data for inert gas scattering obtained with a similar machine is shown in Fig. 7.26. Clearly several research groups now have the capability of producing high resolution differential cross-section data for non alkali systems and continuing progress can be expected. Scattering measurements of this kind, extended over an even wider energy range, must now be our best source of intermolecular potentials.

Progress has also been made in determining potentials for excited species. The beam technique, in contrast to pressure broadening, is most suited to investigating metastable species rather than the short lived states that can decay by dipole radiation to the ground state. The crossed beam scattering of ^3S He (Grosser and H. Haberland, 1968) and of the $^3P_2$ and $^3P_0$ states of Hg (E. C. D. Darwall et al., 1971) have been reported. This, too, can be expected to be an area of growing interest.

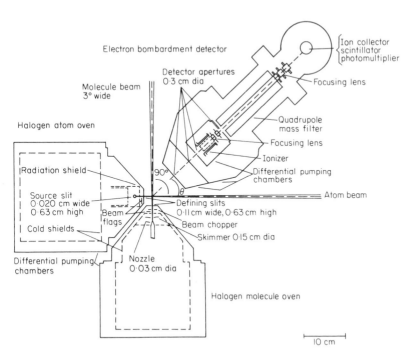

Fig. 7.24 Schematic of apparatus (top view). (Y. T. Lee et al., 1970.)

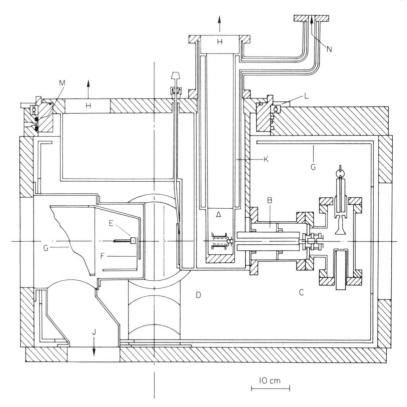

Fig. 7.25 Side view of apparatus. (**A**)–electron bombardment ionizer; (**B**)–quadrupole mass filter; (**C**)–ion counter; (**D**)–isolation valve; (**E**)–molecular beam source; (**F**)–beam flag; (**G**)–cold shields; (**H**)–to ion pumps; (**J**)–to oil diffusion pump; (**K**)–liquid nitrogen trap; (**L**)–ball bearing support of rotatable lid; (**M**)–rotatable vacuum seal; and (**N**)–to liquid nitrogen reservoir. (Y. T. Lee et al., 1970.)

7.7 Prospects

In this chapter we have only been able to discuss the results of a very few experiments. It is useful to close, therefore, with a rather broader view of the prospects in this field.

It now seems that beam production and detection techniques are sufficiently powerful to make experiments with almost any atomic or molecular system feasible. Limitations to further development now arise from the complexity of these systems when more than one potential operates and the inadequacy of current state selection methods that can resolve some of these cases. For the interaction of polyatomic molecules, the scattering without state or molecular orientation selection will tend to be rather

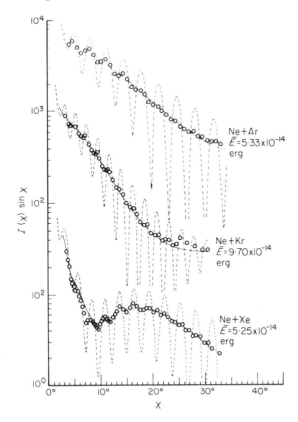

Fig. 7.26 Differential cross-sections for scattering of Ne from the heavier rare gases. Two lines are drawn through the experimental points; the full curve is the low resolution cross-section calculated from a LJ (20:6) potential and the dashed curves the high resolution cross-sections from the same potentials. The high frequency structure is just resolved experimentally. (J. M. Parson et al., 1970.)

structureless and at best only average potentials will be obtainable. In addition, in the case of non-central forces inelastic processes become important and again the state analysis methods are not sufficiently developed to explore these.

In contrast, for single central potential systems very accurate data should now be obtainable, although the experimental effort required to collect this information over a wide energy range will continue to be very great. Direct unfolding procedures will be improved and the development of accurate combining rules (H. L. Kramer and D. R. Herschbach, 1970) will be of especial value in extending this information to a wider range of systems.

CHAPTER EIGHT

Reactive Scattering

8.1 Scope of beam techniques in investigating chemical reaction

As already suggested in Chapter 1, the unique advantages of the scattering approach to studying chemical reaction arise from the ability to control the impact velocity (and, less easily the incident quantum state) and to measure the post-collision velocities, as well as the angular scattering pattern. Technical difficulties have limited the information obtainable about the internal state of the products, but this important information is in principle also accessible. The leverage that this very detailed information about reactive collisions brings to the understanding of chemical reaction is increased by the fact that the principle of microscopic reversibility can be applied to detailed cross-sections, thus extending the range of usefulness of the data into experimentally inaccessible regions.

Reactive scattering experiments have as their ultimate aim the mapping of the potential surfaces on which reaction occurs, but preliminary analysis and experiments of low resolution have the more modest aims of:

(1) Classifying the type of reactive encounter, largely from the angular scattering pattern.
(2) Estimating the reaction cross-section, sometimes as a function of incident energy.
(3) Estimating the partitioning of any energy released between relative translational energy of the products and their internal motion.

Current beam techniques are most powerful when applied to simple reactions in which only a few reactive channels are open. In these cases, if sufficiently intense beams are available, something approaching a complete kinematic analysis can be performed. Even relatively primitive observations of the angular dependence of the product flux, the minimal experiment, afford considerable chemical insight and permit correlation of properties (1–3) above with other properties of the reactants. In collisions where many reactive channels are open, such as those at high energies, the elementary beam technique is less useful. Some spectroscopic information of the products is then required and might be obtained in a separate bulb experiment, or perhaps eventually in a combined beam/spectroscopic system. These kinetic spectroscopy experiments are thus complementary to, rather than competitive with, scattering experiments; the interrelation of some of these techniques and their relations to current theoretical models is summarised in Fig. 8.1.

There are three main types of scattering measurement possible with reactive systems. The elastic differential cross-section, $\sigma(\theta, E)$ in which the distribution of unchanged reactant is measured; the reactive differential cross-section, $\sigma_R(\theta, E, \Delta E)$ in which some kinetic energy analysis of the scattered product is carried out and the total cross-section, $\sigma_{tot}(E)$ can also be measured. All of these can be accompanied by some internal state selection of reactant or product as appropriate.

The present state of the experimental front can be judged from Table 1, in which is listed the more definitive beam experiments performed since 1956. Not all of the work of the larger groups is included, but this can be traced from the references given. The evolution of the field is apparent; starting with alkali metal reactions at thermal energies without velocity selection, the techniques now in use cover universal detectors, velocity selection of reactants and products, beams of metastable species and beam energies that are limited only by the chemical interest of the results. The present limitations of the technique must not be disguised, however. Intensity problems are much more severe than in elastic scattering and have so far limited the applications of universal detectors to unselected beams. Until very recently velocity selectors have only been used on either reactant or product beams, not on both simultaneously. The range of materials that can be formed into a sufficiently intense beam for differential scattering is still small, though most organic compounds are suitable. In particular, it has proved difficult to build up sufficient densities of short lived ($< 10^{-6}$ s) excited species to carry out scattering experiments, although the high photon flux from lasers will doubtless provide a solution. There is still something of a gap in the beam energy available between 0.5 eV and 5 eV that is slowly being bridged by seeded beams. Finally, although vibrational excitation seems to be generally an important means of providing any activation energy necessary for reaction, very few scattering experiments have been carried out with vibrationally excited molecules. There is no reason to doubt, however, that all of these difficulties will be overcome, principally through the use of nozzle beams to increase source intensity and computerized data handling techniques at very low signal levels. The whole field of reactive scattering has most recently been surveyed by J. L. Kinsey (1972).

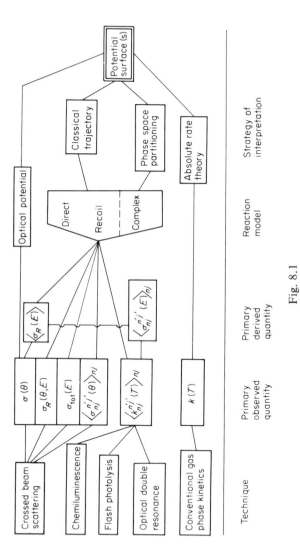

Fig. 8.1

290

(1) In the second column, the basic beam technique is taken to consist of two fixed effusive sources (or one replaced by a Laval nozzle), a movable hot wire detector (usually tungsten or Pt/W alloy) and no velocity selection or analysis. Only variants on this design are noted.

(2) In the second column, $\sigma_R(\theta, v')$ indicates that the angle of scattering and the product velocity have been measured. The velocity analysed elastic differential cross-section, $\sigma(\theta, v')$ in the presence of reaction has received very little attention so far.

(3) The angular resolution is rarely given in the earlier papers. Most of the experiments are of intermediate to poor angular resolution, with the detector subtending $0.5-1°$ (LAB) at the scattering centre.

(4) Some of the measurements of $\sigma_R(\theta)$ were obtained with a Pt–8%W alloy filament operated in a bimodal fashion. There is now considerable doubt (see Chapter 5) whether good discrimination is obtained in this way between highly vibrationally excited alkali halide molecules and alkali atoms, and also whether the presence of unreacted halogens can alter this relative sensitivity.

(5) An increasing number of ion/molecule beam experiments have been carried out in which $\sigma_R(\theta, E)$ is measured for the ionic product. In this way, the same detailed information is obtained as in neutral particle scattering, but with less severe intensity problems because of the higher detection efficiency. Some of these results are included in table 2.

System	Technique/measurements	Reference
K + HBr	$\sigma_R(\theta)$	E. H. Taylor and S. Datz, 1955
K + CH_3I, C_2H_5I	$\sigma_R(\theta)$	D. R. Herschbach et al., 1961
K + HBr	$\sigma(\theta)$ $\sigma_R(\theta)$	D. Beck, E. F. Greene, and J. Ross, 1962
D + H_2	$\sigma_R(\theta)$	S. Datz and E. H. Taylor, 1963
K + HCl, HI	$\sigma(\theta)$	M. Ackerman et al., 1964

HD velocity estimated by time of flight. Electron bombardment det.

Vel. selected K beam

Pt. detector for K

Vel. selected K. Optical potential analysis.

System	Technique/measurements	Reference
$Cs + Br_2$	$\sigma_R(\theta)$ Vel. selected Cs.	S. Datz and E. E. Minturn, 1964
$K + HBr$	$\sigma(\theta)$ Vel. analysis of KBr	A. E. Grosser et al., 1965
$K + \begin{cases} CH_3I \\ Br_2 \\ ICl \end{cases}$	$\sigma_R(\theta)$ Magnetic deflection analysis of KX	R. R. Herm, R. G. Gordon and D. R. Herschbach, 1964
$\left.\begin{matrix} K \\ Rb \\ Cs \end{matrix}\right\} + \begin{cases} Br_2 \\ I_2 \end{cases}$	$\sigma_R(\theta)$ Vel. analysis of KBr	J. H. Birely and D. R. Herschbach, 1965; A. E. Grosser and R. B. Bernstein, 1964
$K + Br_2$	$\sigma_R(\theta)$ Electric deflection analysis of KBr, CsBr	R. R. Herm and D. R. Herschbach, 1965
$Cs + HBr$	$T_{rot} \sim 1300$ K (see also C. Maltz and D. R. Herschbach, 1967)	
$K + Br_2$	$\sigma_R(\theta)$ Vel. analysis KBr. Differential surface det.	J. H. Birely and D. R. Herschbach, 1965
$K + CH_3I$	$\sigma_R(\theta)$ CH_3I orientated by 6-pole field	P. R. Brooks and E. M. Jones, 1966
$KBr\dagger + Na \rightarrow$ $K* + NaBr$	$\sigma_R(\theta)$ Chemiluminescence of K* product. A triple beam experiment. Angular distribution of resonance radiation measured	M. C. Moulton and D. R. Herschbach, 1966

System	Quantity	Notes	Reference
$\left.\begin{array}{l}\text{Cs}\\\text{K}\end{array}\right\}$ + RbCl	$\sigma_R(\theta,v')$	Bimodal surface det. + Mass spec. Velocity anal. products.	W. B. Miller et al., 1967
$\left.\begin{array}{l}\text{K}\\\text{Rb}\\\text{Cs}\end{array}\right\}$ + $\left\{\begin{array}{l}\text{Br}_2\\\text{I}_2\end{array}\right.$	$\sigma_R(\theta)$	Thermal energy range	J. H. Birely et al., 1967
Na + polyhalides	$\sigma_{R\,tot}(E)$	Quenching of glory undulations	E. A. Gislason and G. H. Kwei, 1967
$\left.\begin{array}{l}\text{K}\\\text{Cs}\end{array}\right\}$ + TBr	$\sigma_R(\theta)$	Radioisotope detection	L. R. Martin and J. L. Kinsey, 1967
CsCl + KI	$\sigma_R(\theta) + \sigma(\theta)$	Preliminary results. Velocity anal. products.	W. B. Miller et al., 1967
Cs + $\left\{\begin{array}{l}\text{TlCl}\\\text{TlI}\end{array}\right.$	$\sigma_R(\theta)$	Preliminary results.	G. A. Fisk et al., 1967
$\left.\begin{array}{l}\text{K}\\\text{Rb}\\\text{Cs}\end{array}\right\}$ + Cl$_2$	$\sigma_R(\theta)$	Thermal energy range	R. Grice and P. B. Empedocles, 1968
Li + $\left\{\begin{array}{l}\text{HHal}\\\text{MHal}_2\end{array}\right.$	$\sigma_{R\,tot}(E)$	Thermal energy range	R. K. B. Helbing and E. W. Rothe, 1968
K + CH$_3$I	$\sigma_{R\,tot}$	6–1,000 eV, static gas target	R. J. Cross and C. J. Malerich, 1968
N$_2^\dagger$ + Na		N$_2^\dagger$ vibrationally excited, $n \approx 8$. Total cross-section for energy transfer → N$_2$ + Na from emission of resonance radiation.	J. E. Mentall et al., 1967

System	Technique/measurements	Reference
$\left.\begin{array}{l}\text{Cs}\\\text{K}\\\text{Na}\end{array}\right\}$ + various halides	$\sigma_R(\theta)$ $\sigma(\theta)$	Inhomogeneous magnetic field in front of detector	R. J. Gordon et al., 1968
$\left.\begin{array}{l}\text{K}\\\text{Rb}\\\text{Cs}\end{array}\right\}$ + various organic and inorganic halides	$\sigma_R(\theta)$	Thermal energy range	K. R. Wilson and D. R. Herschbach, 1968
$\left.\begin{array}{l}\text{K}\\\text{Rb}\end{array}\right\}$ + CH_3I	$\sigma_R(\theta)$	At fixed θ. CH_3I velocity and orientation selected with 6-pole field	R. J. Beuhler and R. B. Bernstein, 1969
$Cl + Br_2$ etc.	$\sigma_R(\theta)$	Mass spec./electron bombardment detector	D. Beck et al., 1968; Y. T. Lee et al., 1968
$\text{K} + \left\{\begin{array}{l}Me_3CBr\\SiCl_4\\Hal_2\\ICl\end{array}\right.$	$\sigma(\theta)$	Pt. detector. Out of plane configuration. Velocity sel. K beam.	E. F. Greene et al., 1969
$Cs + Br_2$	$\sigma_{\text{ionsn}}(E)$	Velocity dependence of total ionisation cross-section in energy range $1.5-16.5$ eV	R. K. Helbing and E. W. Rothe, 1969
$\left.\begin{array}{l}\text{K}\\\text{Rb}\\\text{Cs}\end{array}\right\}$ + $\left\{\begin{array}{l}\text{ICl}\\\text{IBr}\end{array}\right.$	$\sigma_R(\theta)$	Thermal energy range	G. H. Kwei and D. R. Herschbach, 1969
$Na + O_2$	$\sigma_{\text{ionsn}}(\theta)$	Merging beams. Energy range $5-25$ eV. Retarding potential curves of Na^+ current	R. H. Neynaber et al., 1969

Reaction	Cross section	Notes	Reference
$Li + \begin{cases} Cl \\ ICl \\ SnCl_4 \\ PCl_3 \end{cases}$	σ_R	Inhomogeneous magnetic field in front of detector. Oxygenated W detector.	D. D. Parrish and R. R. Herm, 1969
$\begin{matrix} H_2^* \\ D_2^* \end{matrix} + M, RH_2$		Relative product ion abundancies. Low angular resolution. Electron bombardment source	H. Hotop, et al., 1969
$Na + \begin{cases} CH_3I \\ Br_2 \\ ICl \end{cases}$	$\sigma_R(\theta)$	Thermal energy range.	J. H. Birely et al., 1969
$\begin{matrix} K \\ Na \\ Li \end{matrix} + Br_2$	$\sigma_{R\,tot}(\theta)$	Static gas target. Sputter source of fast alkali.	A. P. M. Baede et al, 1969
$K + CF_3I$	$\sigma_R(\theta)$	Parallel and anti-parallel molecular alignment. KI product?	P. R. Brooks, 1969
$K + I_2$	$\sigma(\theta)$	Small angle scattering, high resolution. Velocity sel. K.	M. A. D. Fluendy et al., 1970
$Cl + Br_2$	$\sigma_R(\theta)$	Low resolution. Velocity analysis of product. Unselected beams. Mass spec. analysis.	N. C. Blais and J. B. Cross, 1970
$K + RI$	$\sigma_R(\theta)$	In and out-of-plane measurements. Bimodal surface detection.	G. H. Kwei et al., 1970
$D + H_2$	$\sigma_R(\theta)$	Product velocity anal. by time of flight. Mass. spec. det.	J. Geddes et al., 1970

System	Technique/measurements	Reference
K + $\begin{cases} C_6H_{12} \\ CCl_4 \\ SiCl_4 \\ SnCl_4 \\ Cl_2 \\ Br_2 \end{cases}$	$\sigma_R(\theta)$	Sputter source, 0.5–12 eV. Cool ribbon det. Pulsed K beam. Time of flight anal.	V. Kempter et al., 1970
F + D$_2$ → FD + D	$\sigma_R(\theta)$	Angular distribution of product in specific vibrational states.	T. P. Schafer et al., 1970
Rb + Br$_2$	$\sigma_R(\theta)$	Rotational state distribution of RbBr product by quadrupole analyser.	R. Grice et al., 1970
K + $\begin{cases} HBr \\ DBr \end{cases}$	$\sigma_R(\theta)$	Velocity analysis of scattered product.	K. T. Gillen et al., 1969
K + $\begin{cases} NO_2 \\ CH_3NO_2 \end{cases}$	$\sigma_R(\theta)$	Magnetic and electric deflection analysis of product in order to elucidate structure.	R. R. Herm and D. R. Herschbach, 1970
K + $\begin{cases} HCl \\ Cl_2 \\ N_2 \\ CO \\ NO \\ O_2 \end{cases}$	σ_{ionsn}	Cross sections for ionisation of K and excitation to 4^{2}P state. Charge transfer beam source	K. Lacmann and D. R. Herschbach, 1970
K + I$_2$	$\sigma_R(\theta,v')$ $\sigma(\theta,v')$	Thermal energy range. Differential surface detection of KI and K, coupled with velocity selection and analysis	K. T. Gillen et al., 1971

Reaction		Description	Reference
$\left.\begin{matrix}H\\D\end{matrix}\right\} + \left\{\begin{matrix}K_2\\Rb_2\\Cs_2\end{matrix}\right.$	$\sigma_R(\theta)$	M, M_2 and MH signals separated by kinematic arguments M_2 from nozzle source.	Y. T. Lee et al., 1971
$Cs + SF_6$		Vibrational temperature of CsF measured from vibrational fine structure of flop-in resonance spectrum. A fixed angle expt.	S. M. Freund et al., 1971
$Cl + \left\{\begin{matrix}Na_2\\K_2\end{matrix}\right.$		Fixed angle observation of Na and K resonance radiation. Estimation of total reaction cross-section.	W. S. Struve et al., 1971
$Li + \left\{\begin{matrix}NO_2\\CH_3NO_2\\SF_6\\CCl_4\\CH_3I\end{matrix}\right.$	$\sigma_R(\theta)$	Magnetic state deflection as in Parrish 1969	D. D. Parrish and R. R. Herm, 1971
$Cs + \left\{\begin{matrix}SF_6\\SF_4\end{matrix}\right.$		As in Freeman 1971. Vibrational temp. of CsF product.	H. G. Bennewitz et al., 1971
$K + HCl$	$\sigma_R(\theta)$	HCl vibrationally pumped with resonant laser radiation. Enhancement of reaction cross-section	T. J. Odirone et al., 1971
$\left.\begin{matrix}Na,\\Na^+\\K\\K^+\end{matrix}\right\} + H_2$		Inelastic back scattering, $\theta > 175°$ TOF analysis.	P. F. Dittner and S. Datz, 1971
$K + CH_3I$	$\sigma_R(E)$	Integration of $\sigma_R(\theta)$ in energy range 0.1–1 eV.	M. E. Gersh and R. B. Bernstein, 1971, 1972

System	Technique/measurements		Reference
K, Cs { RHal, RHal$_2$	$\sigma_R(\theta)$	As in Kwei, 1969. Unsaturated and aromatic halides	E. A. Entemann and G. H. Kwei, 1971
K, Rb, Cs { CCl$_4$, CH$_3$I, SnCl$_4$	$\sigma(\theta)$	Optical potential analysis	R. M. Harris and J. F. Wilson, 1971
Na + SO$_2$, NO$_2$	$\sigma_{excitn}(E)$	In 1–30 eV energy range for emission of the Na D-line. App. as in Kempter, 1970	P. R. LeBreton et al., 1971
Cl + I$_2$	$\sigma_R(\theta)$	Velocity selector in front of detector, keeps reactants from detector surface. Corrects Lee, 1968.	J. B. Cross and N. C. Blais, 1971
D + Cl$_2$, Br$_2$, I$_2$, ICl, IBr	$\sigma_R(\theta,v)$	Thermal dissociation and discharge source.	J. D. McDonald et al., 1972
Ba, Sr + NO$_2$		Polarization of visible emission from electronically excited MO. Single beam/scattering gas config, fixed energy.	C. D. Jonah et al., 1972
K$_2$ + Br$_2$, ICl, IBr, BrCN	$\sigma_R(\theta)$	Dimer source as in Lee, 1971. Differential detection of both K and KX products.	P. B. Foreman et al., 1972; J. C. Whitehead et al., 1972

8.2 Reactive differential cross-sections and the LAB→CM transformation

The procedure adopted in interpreting reactive scattering data depends upon the type of information e.g. $\sigma(\theta)$ $\sigma_R(\theta,E)$ etc. As in elastic scattering, the detail available in respect to resolution and range of experimental parameters explored will determine whether deductive argument based on gross features of the scattering is used or some more quantitative but laborious fitting process undertaken. In the latter case there is an important distinction between the reactive and elastic fields. In the latter it is now possible, in favourable circumstances, to deduce the potential by directly unfolding the data. No model potential is required. In interpreting reactive data, whether detailed rate constants or beam results, one must decide at the outset if detailed trajectory calculations with an assumed potential are appropriate, or whether a statistical approach is adopted. Ultimately, both approaches are governed by the same multi-dimensional potential surface, but at least in the present stage of development a model is needed, not only of the potential but of the type of collision. This preliminary classification into direct and complex collisions is of interest in itself. In one sense there is an analogy here with elastic scattering; if the reduced energy in an elastic scattering experiment is so low that orbiting and quasi-bound states are encountered, it is not yet possible to unfold the potential directly, however good the experimental information and in some energy domains the interpretation would be in terms of energy levels and widths (see Section 6.14) rather than the detailed shape of the potential.

The first step in interpreting $\sigma_R(\theta)$ is the transformation of the LAB scattering pattern into the CM system of co-ordinates. By so doing, the trivial dependence of the LAB results on the motion of the centre of mass of the colliding pair is removed and results obtained with different beam geometries (e.g. out of plane measurements or angles of intersection other than $90°$) should reduce to the same CM pattern (Fig. 8.2). The transformation depends upon the product velocity which, unlike the elastic case, cannot be deduced from the angle of scattering and the incident velocity. Ideally, a simultaneous measurement of either the product velocity or its internal energy together with the scattered intensity is needed. Until recently, beam intensities were not high enough to permit the product flux to be velocity analysed and two procedures were adopted to fix w'. In earlier work (G. H. Kwei and D. R. Herschbach, 1970) the extent of out of plane scattering was used in a rough estimate of w' (see Fig. 8.3); if w' is small the scattering is largely confined to the plane of the two incident beams. When possible, it is now customary to use an iterative procedure to build up an acceptable centre of mass

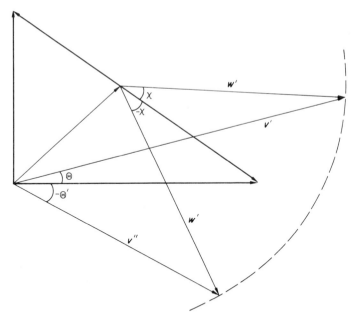

Fig. 8.2 Laboratory observations either side of the main beam must transform into a CM differential cross-section that is symmetrical about $\chi = 0$, even though $\sigma(\theta) \neq \sigma(-\theta)$. This serves to fix w', provided the scattered intensity at negative laboratory angles is not too small.

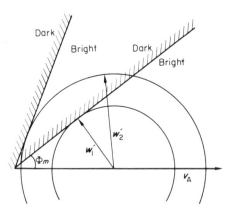

Fig. 8.3 Observation of out-of-plane scattering allows w' to be assigned once Φ_m is located. The larger w', the more extensive the out-of-plane scattering. The Newton diagram is viewed along v_B, with v_A forming the horizon.

distribution that is uniquely consistent with all the observed scattering. The reasoning behind the method is as follows; in favourable circumstances the laboratory angles corresponding to CM scattering through χ and $-\chi$ are well separated and w' can be adjusted until the scattering from one laboratory branch gives an identical CM differential cross-section to that deduced from the other branch, which is the required conclusion because we know that $\sigma_R(-\chi) = \sigma_R(\chi)$. Thus, in the case illustrated by Fig. 8.2, $w' > w$, scattering on either side of the main beam corresponds to scattering through positive and negative values of χ respectively. In the case $w' < v_{CM}$ a slow component in the scattered LAB signal is present due to scattering through some quite different CM angle, but it is usually found that $\sigma_R(\chi)$ is a fairly sharply peaked function and the slow component is much attenuated by the smallness of the associated differential cross-section. However, in Fig. 8.4, where $w' < w$, the two LAB angles corresponding to scattering through χ and $-\chi$ nearly overlap and laboratory measurements at any particular value of θ contain important contributions from both positive and negative values of χ. It would then be difficult to obtain an unambiguous choice of w'.

In principle, the observation of the angle of the edge effect can decide w'. However, in the cases most suited for observing this phenomenon ($w' \ll w$),

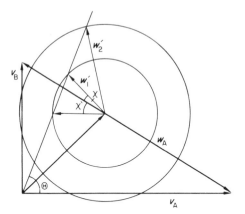

Fig. 8.4 Observation of scattering at θ does not allow w' or χ to be deduced. Two possible choices are shown. The observed scattering contains important contributions from particles scattered through the CM angles χ and χ' (assuming w'_1 to be the true CM final velocity). Contrast this with the situation in Fig. 8.2 where only one value of χ contributes at a given angle of observation.

one edge occurs near the cross-beam position. Furthermore, the strong angular dependence of $\sigma_R(\chi)$ can mask the effect by causing a rapid fall-off in intensity before the edge is reached.

For any guessed value of w', the LAB→CM transformation can be performed either on the scattered signal or on the differential cross-section; in the latter case,

$$\sigma_R(\chi, w') = \sigma_R(\theta, v') \, J\left(\frac{\theta, \Phi}{\chi, \phi}\right) \qquad (8.1)$$

where a primed velocity is that of a product. As for elastic scattering (Section 2.4), the Jacobian for a particular exit channel can be written* (K. T. Gillen et al, 1971)

$$J\left(\frac{\theta, \Phi}{\chi, \phi}\right) = \left(\frac{v'}{w'}\right)^2 \cos\alpha \qquad (8.2)$$

where α is the angle between v' and w'. For strongly exothermic reactions w', $v' > v_{CM}$ and α remains close to unity for a large range of scattering angles. v'/w' then tends to increase with increasing CM angle of scattering and the general effect of the Jacobian in Equation 8.1 is to enhance the ratio $\sigma(\chi)/\sigma(\theta)$ at larger CM scattering angles.

After the transformation (Equation 8.1) to CM co-ordinates, the results are best displayed in a polar diagram where $I(\chi)$ or $\sigma(\chi)$ is represented by the point (R,χ) and the radius R is proportional to the observed quantity. Ideally, a contour map can be built up, each contour corresponding to a quantum state of the product.

An important bonus from making the LAB→CM transformation is that the total reaction cross-section can then be estimated in favourable circumstances from laboratory observations confined to the plane of the two beams. The key step is recognizing that in the CM frame the scattered intensity has axial symmetry about the relative velocity vector w_{AB} (this is only true with unorientated target molecules). Exactly the same symmetry obtains in elastic scattering, with the difference that in reactive scattering the motion in individual collisions is not confined to a plane. This cylindrical symmetry of $\sigma(\chi,\phi)$ is in strong contrast to the asymmetry of $\sigma(\theta,\Phi)$ with respect to the plane defined by the two incident beams; the only symmetry possessed by

---

* See appendix A, Chapter 2, for situations in which the cos α factor is not appropriate

the scattering in the laboratory is that $\sigma(\theta,\Phi) = \sigma(\theta,-\Phi)$. Using the CM symmetry we can obtain the total cross-section from $\sigma_R(\chi, \phi = 0)$ by integrating immediately over ϕ and then over χ so that

$$\sigma_{R\,tot} = 2\pi \int_0^\pi \sigma_R(\chi) \sin \chi \, d\chi \qquad (8.3)$$

in which the scattered flux is integrated over the surface of a sphere surrounding the centre of mass of the colliding pair. Thus, we do not need to make any out-of-plane measurements in the laboratory if the transformation to CM is performed. As with elastic scattering, absolute measurements are difficult — even more so in view of the fact that the scattered product has to be detected with the same efficiency as the main beam reactant. However, the energy dependence of the total reaction cross-section can be obtained quite reliably from Equation 8.3 while the uncertainty in the absolute value may amount to a factor of 2. There are, unfortunately, few other methods of measuring absolute reaction cross-sections (but see Section 8.3), although methods for absolute rate constants abound.

It was found that when the limited data on reactive scattering of alkali metals available in the mid 1960's was examined in this way that two types of behaviour could be distinguished. In those designated class I, the product was predominantly back scattered in the centre of mass and in class II forward scattered (i.e. the MX emerged in the same general laboratory direction as the incident alkali metal, the Newton diagram being roughly that of Fig. 8.5). A somewhat idealized version of these cases is illustrated in Fig. 8.6. Work in

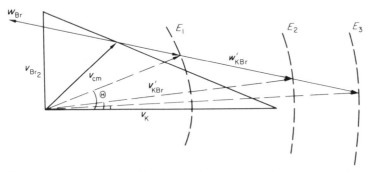

Fig. 8.5 Newton diagram for a stripping reaction, $K + Br_2 \rightarrow KBr + Br$. The product KBr appears at an angle Θ in the LAB which depends upon the energy partitioning, ΔE, the amount of energy transferred to translation of the products from the energy liberated. Three cases of increasing final relative kinetic energy are shown, leading to increased forward scattering.

Fig. 8.6(i) Typical CM polar diagram of the reactive differential cross-section of a class I reaction. The KI vector is drawn proportional to the KI signal at χ.

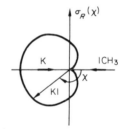

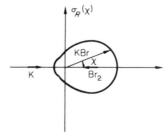

Fig. 8.6(ii) Typical CM polar diagram of the reactive differential cross-section of a type II reaction.

the last few years on a greater range of halogen containing compounds has produced evidence of a gradation in behaviour between these two classes even in the limited field of an alkali metal partner and in a sequence of reactions such as (R. J. Gordon et al, 1968)

$$Cs/Br_2 \ldots /CCl_4 \ldots /CHCl_3 \ldots /CH_3I$$

the peak in the scattered product intensity moves from $\sim 0°$ to $\sim 180°$ (CM).

A third and much less common type of scattering pattern (class III) has emerged from the work of Herschbach and his co-workers (W. B. Miller et al, 1967; G. A. Fisk et al, 1967; S. M. Freund et al, 1971) and is characterized by a CM product distribution symmetrical about $90°$, often with strong peaking at $0°$ and $180°$. This behaviour has been observed in the systems $Cs + SF_6$, $Cs + SF_4$ $Cs + RbCl$, $Rb + CsCl$, $K + RbCl$, $Rb + KCl$ and $Cs + TlCl$ (Fig. 8.7), though the LAB → CM transformation is not completely unambiguous yet. Inspite of the discovery of an increasing number of transitional cases that blurr this classification by means of the predominant angle of product scattering, the divisions remain useful ones because they have given rise to three important models of chemical reaction which would seem to have real validity as limiting cases. These are the recoil model associated with class I behaviour, stripping associated with class II and complex formation in class III. Estimates of total reaction cross-sections reinforce the division between class I and II behaviour in that, broadly, two groups of values are found coinciding with these classes. The reactions of class I have small reaction cross-sections, barely larger than the gas kinetic cross-section i.e. $\lesssim 30 \text{ Å}^2$, while reactions of class II exhibit large cross-sections, $\gtrsim 80 \text{ Å}^2$. Further work has produced a range of $\sigma_{R \, tot}$ values from 300 Å^2 downwards and a good correlation has emerged in alkali metal reactions between the magnitude of $\sigma_{R \, tot}$ and the shift from forward to backward product scattering.

As we have already seen, total reaction cross-sections are difficult to estimate accurately, but in the field of alkali metal reactions additional support at least for the relative reaction cross-sections in a series of reactions comes from the sodium flame experiments of M. Polanyi (1932) which indicated reaction cross-sections considerably larger than the gas kinetic diameter for the reaction Na/Hal_2 and of the order of the gas kinetic diameter for the reaction Na/CH_3I. By following spectroscopically the decay of flash generated caesium atoms in I_2 vapour Davidovits and his co-workers (C. C. Brodhead, et al., 1969) have found the reaction cross-section to be $195 \pm 40° \text{ Å}^2$, a value close to that estimated from beam studies. The attenuation of elastic scattering, to be discussed in Section 8.3, confirms that the total reaction cross-section for these reactions of the alkyl halides is $\lesssim 40 \text{ Å}^2$.

Some simple deductions follow from the facts so far presented. The reactions of class I, characterized by back-scattering of the alkali halide product largely along the relative velocity vector of the incoming alkali atom

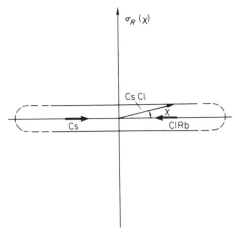

Fig. 8.7 Typical CM polar diagram of the reactive differential cross-section for a type III reaction. Note the symmetry about $\chi = 90°$ and compare with Fig. 8.6.

are of the simple recoil type. The alkali atom collides with the target in a nearly head-on fashion (hence the back-scattering) with an impact parameter not much greater than the equilibrium bond length of the K-X bond to be formed, the X-Y bond then breaks and the K-X bond forms as the products separate rapidly. The product back scattering is possibly accentuated by the mutual repulsion of the products.

The large cross-sections of class II reactions must be the result of the operation of either unusually strong intermolecular forces or of long range chemical forces. While the distinction is not a completely clear cut one, the two explanations might be as follows; in the first case the dispersion forces or other electrostatic forces draw in the approaching particles from large impact parameters to distances of closest approach comparable with equilibrium bond lengths, whereupon reaction follows. Alternatively, the intermolecular forces are of normal strength, but electron re-arrangement begins at distances much greater than normal bond lengths and so a larger bundle of trajectories than in class I lead to reaction. When the electron rearrangement begins, the inter-particle forces are no doubt much increased and the reaction proceeds to completion under their influence. For neutral-neutral reactions the second mechanism seems to be the more realistic for the simple reason that neither calculation nor total cross-section measurements indicate that C_6 values in class II reactants are uniformly greater than those in class I, or that the probable order of C_6 values (as estimated, for instance, from the molecular polarisability) parallels the order of reactivity within the class. For ion/molecule reactions, however, there is every indication that at low energies the dipole-induced dipole forces determine the often large reaction cross-sections which then approach the total cross-section in magnitude.

The picture that has emerged of class II reactions is based upon two simple models, the harpooning mechanism of J. L. Magee (1940), and the stripping model of nuclear reactions. As the two reactants approach, an electron is transferred from the alkali atom to the target molecule at distances R_c up to $\sim 9°$ A. Two ions are created by this harpooning and at thermal energies reaction follows with high probability, leading to a reaction cross-section equal to πR_c^2. At R_c the ionic potential surface crosses the atomic or covalent one, and the condition for this is to a first approximation given by

$$I - E_a - e^2/R_c = 0 \qquad (8.4)$$

where I is the ionization energy of the metal M, E_a is the electron affinity of the target molecule and e^2/R_c is the potential energy of the newly created dipole. In writing down this energy balance it is assumed that R_c is sufficiently large for dispersion and polarizability terms to be negligible (i.e. $R_c \gtrsim 5$ A). The target molecules of class II reactions are characterized by consistently larger electron affinities than those of class I and which are of the right order of magnitude to account for the large reaction cross-sections. A more detailed evaluation of Equation 8.4 is made difficult by the following uncertainty in the model. If the electron transfer is rapid compared with the target vibrational motion, E_a must be interpreted as the vertical electron affinity; if, however, the electron transfer is gradual and the target atoms have time to adjust their positions to the changing electronic environment, then something like the adiabatic (e.g. equilibrium) electron affinity is required, which is the energy liberated when a molecule is converted into the anion in its equilibrium configuration — assuming a stable anion exists. The difference is appreciable numerically, and is illustrated schematically in Fig. 8.8. There has been found to be a good correlation between the electron capture coefficient and the magnitude of the total reaction cross-section in a whole sequence of Na flame reactions $Na/I_2 \ldots Na/CH_3Cl$. It is not certain that all these species have stable anions and the electron capture coefficient is then a complicated ratio of rate constants, but one may assume that the larger the electron

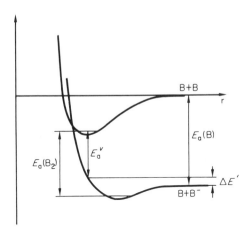

Fig. 8.8 The energetics of electron transfer. The equilibrium electron affinity of B_2 is $E_a(B_2)$ and that of B atom $E_a(B)$. The vertical electron affinity is E_a^v and if this value is used to determine the critical radius for harpooning, then an amount of energy $\Delta E'$ is released subsequent to electron transfer and can appear as either relative kinetic energy of the products or as internal excitation.

capture coefficient, the larger the cross-section for the process $\epsilon + AB \rightarrow A + B^-$, although no simple formula akin to Equation 8.4 can be written for R_c.

The harpooning model was originally developed to explain the larger cross-sections observed in the sodium flame experiments and without further elaboration it does not lead to the strong forward scattering revealed by beam experiments. The spectator stripping model was first applied to this phenomenon by Herschbach and, with some important modifications, still offers as good an interpretation as can be expected from a simple model. In essence, upon transferring the electron to the target molecule, the bond joining the reacting halogen atom to the rest of the molecule is severed and there is no further force acting between the detached halogen ion and the other fragment which looks on while the halogen atom is carried off. Although a strong Coulomb force operates between the newly formed anion and cation, the centre of mass of the MX product continues to move in the forward direction since the molecule experiences no repulsion by the spectator and predominantly forward scattering results. The model will be discussed in more detail when the experimental results on energy partitioning are discussed. At small impact parameters ($b \lesssim \sigma_{LJ}$) a collision between the newly formed products is unavoidable and will introduce some backscattering but the measure of these trajectories is small.

Type III reactions, in which $\sigma_R(\chi)$ is bipolar and symmetrically distributed about $\chi = \pi/2$ are thought to be due to the formation of a collision complex whose lifetime is greater than its rotational period ($\gtrsim 5 \times 10^{-12}$ s). That this will lead in some circumstances to strong peaking of the scattered intensity at $\chi = 0$ and $180°$ can be seen as follows. Suppose that the reaction is the transfer of excitation or charge between two structureless particles that do not possess intrinsic angular momentum. The conservation of angular momentum, in this case solely that arising from the relative motion, confines the motion to a plane (Fig. 8.9). The direction in which the products emerge is determined, at least classically, by the impact parameter and the relative kinetic energy. According to our definition of a long lived complex, at least one complete revolution has been performed and χ is greater than $360°$. The complete scattering pattern is built up by superimposing many trajectories covering the range of b and E represented in the beam; if, now, χ is a sensitive function of these parameters as it generally will be when large forces are involved the particles are released in effectively random directions even in a classically deterministic situation. Furthermore, if the completely random distribution of the plane of motion of successive collisions is taken into account by superimposing a number of circularly symmetrical distributions

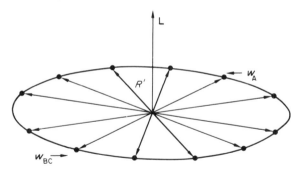

Fig. 8.9 A single long-lived collision. The reactants approach from left and right, form a collision complex from which the products are released in a direction indicated by the final relative position vector R'. The direction of R' is effectively random in the plane defined by constant relative angular momentum L.

about a common diameter that coincides with the initial relative velocity vector, we see a concentration of products emerging at the poles of the sphere generated by this rotation (Fig. 8.10). This uniform emission of product in the plane of motion has the results that the number of particles emerging between $\chi, \chi + d\chi$ and $\phi, \phi + d\phi$ per second is

$$dn = \frac{1}{2\pi^2} I_0 \sigma_{R\,tot} \, d\chi \, d\phi \tag{8.5}$$

where I_0 is the incident intensity. The differential cross-section is then found from

$$dn = I_0 \sigma_R(\chi,\phi) \sin \chi \, d\chi \, d\phi \tag{8.6}$$

to be

$$\sigma_R(\chi,\phi) = \sigma_{R\,tot}/(2\pi^2 \sin \chi) \tag{8.7}$$

If, now, the particles have an initial internal angular momentum j_i and a final j_f, the conservation of angular momentum J results in the asymptotic conditions (i.e. after the internal angular momentum has become frozen and is no longer coupled to L)

$$J = j_i + L_i = j_f + L_f, \tag{8.8}$$

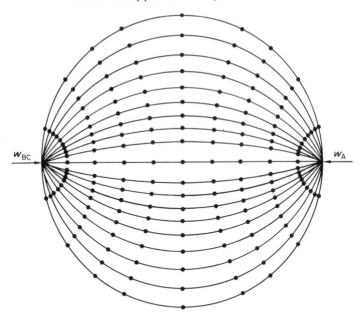

Fig. 8.10 The cumulative result of many collisions of the type
shown in (i) is to superimpose all possible planes of motion of the
complex consistent with L perpendicular to w. The product flux
is thereby concentrated at the poles defined by the initial
direction of approach.

so that $L_i \neq L_f$ and the exit plane of motion no longer co-incides with the
incident plane. In processes with fairly large cross-sections at thermal energies
and above, J_i is generally small compared with L_i so that

$$J \approx L_i = L_f + j_f$$

a range of j_f values in the product will thus produce a related distribution of
L_f (Fig. 8.11). Superimposed upon this is the additional distribution arising
from the undefined plane of the motion so that all orientations of the vector
J in a plane perpendicular to the relative motion are equally probable in the
sample. We might try to approximate the system at the point of break-up as
either a diatomic molecule, the interparticle axis of which gives the direction
of departure of the products (w'), or as a symmetric top in which w' lies
along the principal axis. From either model, we can ask for the probability
distribution of the orientation of the molecular axis and hence, if the
disintegration rate is constant, of the angular distribution of the scattered
products. Quantum mechanically, the diatomic system is characterized by a

Fig. 8.11 (1) The final orbital angular momentum, L_f is the resultant of j_f and J. The plane of motion (shaded) of the two departing fragments is $\perp$ to L_f and χ is the polar angle between the axis of the diatomic and the initial direction of approach which defines the z-axis. In a sequence of collisions all directions of J in a plane perpendicular to z are equally likely and so the resultant L_f lie on the surface of a cone with constant z−component M_f.

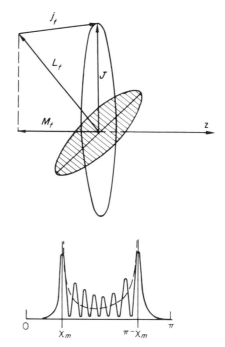

(2) Quantum mechanically, this distribution of the plane of motion with constant M_f of the relative motion results in an angular distribution described by the spherical harmonic $Y_{L_fM_f}$, the envelope of which (dashed line) approximates the classical distribution, with χ ranging between χ_m and $\pi - \chi_m$.

total angular momentum quantum number L_f with a range of projection quantum numbers ranging from $-M_f$ to M_f as discussed above. The diatomic complex wave functions will be spherical harmonics so that the probability of product scattering at angle χ from a diatomic complex with quantum number L_f and M_f is $\mathscr{P}(\chi) = |\, Y_{L_fM_f}(\chi, \phi)\,|^2$. More usefully, this probability can be expressed in terms of the state of the scattered product j_f and m_j. From Fig. 11 it is clear that $M_f = m_j$, while if $j_f \ll L_f$ then $L_f \sim L_i$ (or more generally $L_f = (J^2 + j_f^2 - 2Jj_f \cos \beta)^{1/2}$). The distribution of product in this state is thus $|\, Y_{L_f,\, m_j}(\chi \phi)\,|^2$. A typical distribution is sketched in Fig. 8.11. In general the transition state is formed in a range of angular momentum and orientation states. The observed intensity (without state analysis) will then be the superposition of many such distributions, those with low m_j values peaking at angles near 0 and π while product with high m_j scatters near the equator, $\chi \sim \pi/2$. The net effect of such averaging is, in the limit of $j_f \sim L_f$, to wash out the bipolar form and produce a spherically isotropic distribution of product. A possible ansatz to describe this range of possibilities might be:

$$\mathscr{P}(\chi) = \sum_{L_f} \sum_{m_f} \mathscr{W}(L_f, M_f)\, |\, Y_{L_fM_f}(\chi, \phi)\,|^2 \qquad (8.9)$$

where $\mathcal{W}$ (L_f, M_f) is the probability of finding the state (L_fM_f) in the ensemble. This formulation does not give us $\mathcal{W}(L_f M_f)$, which must come from some further assumption about the distribution of j_f. If, for instance, in the rather artificial case that j_f is isotropically distributed in direction and all values of M_f from $-j_f$ to j_f are equally probable, then if j_f is appreciably less than L_i we may neglect the correlation between L_f and M_f and write

$$\mathcal{W}(L_fM_f) = \frac{1}{2j_f + 1}; \quad L_f \sim L_i. \tag{8.10}$$

Taking these equations to define the model, and regarding M_f as continuously distributed and replacing $Y_{L_fM_f}$ by its asymptotic approximation (from Equation 8.18) with $K = 0$

$$\mathcal{P}(\chi) = \frac{1}{4\pi^2} \int_{-L_i\sin\chi}^{L_i\sin\chi} (L_i^2 \sin^2 \chi - M_f^2)^{-\frac{1}{2}} dM_f$$

$$= \frac{1}{4\pi^2}; \quad L_i \sin \chi < j_f$$

$$= \frac{1}{4\pi^2} \int_{-j_f}^{j_f} (L_i^2 \sin^2 \chi - M_f^2)^{-\frac{1}{2}} dM_f$$

$$= \frac{1}{2\pi^2} \sin^{-1}(j_f/L_i \sin \chi); \quad L_i \sin \chi > j_f \tag{8.11}$$

where the two ranges of the integral are caused by the restriction $M_f \leqslant j_f$. The result (Equation 8.11) is plotted in Fig. 8.12. The object of this simple model is to illustrate the smoothing out of the poles at $\chi = 0$ and π that occurs when product angular momentum is introduced. In the limit $j_f \gg L_i$ $(L_f \approx j_f)$ and again with all values of M_f equally likely, we can use the completeness relationship

$$\sum_{M_f=-L_f}^{L_f} |Y_{L_fM_f} (\chi, \phi)|^2 = (2L_f + 1)/4\pi \tag{8.12}$$

to show from Equation 8.9 that the distribution $\mathcal{P}(\chi)$ becomes independent of χ (i.e. the contribution of the second integral in Equation 8.11 vanishes).

A more realistic model would allow us to include some correlation between the direction of j_f and L_f, and more progress can be made if the

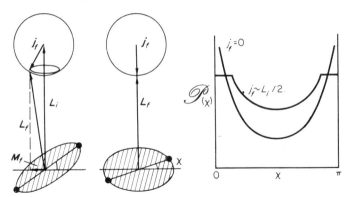

Fig. 8.12 The effect of various orientations of j_f with respect to L_i is to introduce a spread of M_f values. The superposition of the angular distribution $Y_{L_f M_f}(\chi)$ with a range of M_f values then destroys the poles in the probability distribution $\mathscr{P}(\chi)$.

complex on the point of break-up is regarded as a symmetric top. Quantum mechanically, a symmetric top is characterized by its total angular momentum J and the components of J on a space fixed axis, M and on the body fixed symmetry axis, K (see Fig. 8.13). If we know the distribution of J, of M and of K, the probability distribution of the symmetry axis orientation can be found from:

$$\mathscr{P}(\chi) = \sum_J \sum_{|M} \sum_K \mathscr{W}(J, M, K) \frac{(2J+1)}{8\pi^2} |\mathscr{D}_{MK}^J (\phi, \chi, \alpha)|^2 \qquad (8.13)$$

where the $\mathscr{D}_{MK}^J$ are the Wigner functions.

Once again, if the weights $\mathscr{W}(J_f M_f K)$ are independent of either M or K we can use the sum rule

$$\sum_{m \text{ or } m'=-j}^{j} |\mathscr{D}_{mm'}^j|^2 = 1 \qquad (8.14)$$

to show that the distribution of χ is isotropic, provided that $j_f \gg L_f$ so that a sufficient range of M_f states are available to complete the summation.

In the case $j_i = 0$ (and hence $J = L_i, M = 0$) the result:

$$\mathscr{D}_{OK}^J (\chi, \alpha) = \frac{4\pi}{2J+1} e^{-iK\alpha} Y_{LK}(\chi) \qquad (8.15)$$

yields

$$\mathscr{P}(\chi) = \sum_L \sum_K \mathscr{W}(L, K) |Y_{LK}(\chi)|^2. \qquad (8.16)$$

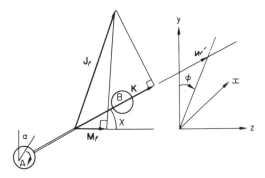

Fig. 8.13 The two product fragments, A and B, of a collision complex regarded as a symmetric top. The projection, K, of J_f on the symmetry axis AB is a constant of the motion and the orientation of AB is described by three angles (α, χ, ϕ). The direction of the symmetry axis at break-up (when K is frozen) coincides with the final relative velocity vector, w'.

A typical simple model of complex formation that would then enable $\mathscr{W}(L,K)$ to be extracted consists of two parts;

(i) All impact parameters up to b^* lead to complex formation and hence to a reactive channel. The upper limit to L in Equation 8.16 is thus given by $L^* = \mu v b^*$.

(ii) The distribution of K values for a given value of J is of the form

$$\mathscr{W}(K) = e^{-K^2/2K^{*2}}, \quad K \leqslant J \sin \chi. \tag{8.17}$$

($J \sin \chi$ being the maximum value of the component of J on w'). There are thus two parameters in the model, L^* and K^*. These may be fitted empirically to the observed $I(\chi)$, or deduced from a statistical mechanical analysis of the collision complex in its 'saddle point' configuration i.e. in the transition state of absolute reaction rate theory. The analysis is completed by substituting integration for the summations in Equations 8.16, with the asymptotic replacement for the smoothed $\mathscr{D}$ functions

$$|\mathscr{D}_{MK}^{J}(\phi, \chi, \alpha)|^2 \xrightarrow[J \gg 1]{} \pi^{-1} [J^2 \sin^2 \chi - M^2 - K^2 + 2MK \cos \chi]^{-\frac{1}{2}} \tag{8.18}$$

to yield the scattered intensity distribution

$$I(\chi) = 2\pi \int_0^{L^*} \mathscr{P}(\chi, L) L \, d L. \tag{8.19}$$

The broad features of the model are summarized in Fig. 8.14 where $\sigma(\chi)$ is plotted for various values of the parameter $(L^*/2K^*)^2$. For $K^* = 0$, the problem reduces to that of the reaction of two point masses and Equation 8.7 holds; for $K^* \to \infty$ (i.e. all allowed values of K equally probable) the scattering is isotropic as required by Equation 8.14. Essentially the same angular plots are obtained from this crude statistical model when it is applied to rotationally inelastic scattering of atoms from diatomics (W. H. Miller, 1970).

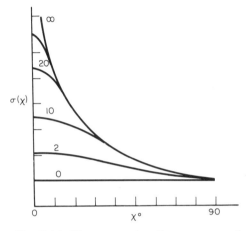

Fig. 8.14 The progressive disappearance of the poles in the product scattered intensity with increasing angular momentum of the products about the final interparticle vector. The various $\sigma(\chi)$ are scaled to unity at $90°$, and are labelled with the value of $L^{*2}/2K^{*2}$. (From I. Halpern and V. M. Strutunskii, 1958.)

Besides the final partitioning of the angular momentum between internal and relative motion, another basic parameter of the problem of complex formation is the lifetime τ_c of the complex. So far, we have assumed that τ_c comfortably exceeds a rotational period of the complex, τ_r; but as τ_c diminishes, the symmetry between forward ($\chi = 0$) and back ($\chi = \pi$) scattering is destroyed. The attenuation of the back scattering is already pronounced for $\tau_c = \tau_r$ and finally when $\tau_c \ll \tau_r$, the very anisotropic distributions characteristic of direct reactions are obtained. This effect has probably been observed in the scattering of Cs from thallium halides where the results can be interpreted by $\tau_c/\tau_r \sim 0.8$ (G. A. Fisk et al., 1967).

The whole subject of the angular distribution of products from the breakup of complexes is of interest in nuclear fission theory and a development of some of the ideas of this section can be found in L. Wilets, 1964.

8.3 Elastic scattering in the presence of reaction

Because of the strength of the elastically scattered signal compared with that
of the reaction products, measurement of the elastic differential cross-section
in the presence of reaction is an attractive, if indirect method of investigating
some parts of the potential surface governing reaction. The basic limitation of
the technique is, of course, that it cannot probe the interaction of the
products in the reactive exit channels; a separate elastic scattering experiment
starting with the products would be necessary for this.

Even in the presence of reaction, elastic scattering is determined solely by
the diagonal S-matrix elements. In the absence of inelastic or reactive exit
channels, we found in Chapter 6 that, for the lth partial wave associated with
the nth internal state of the system, the diagonal elements were:

$$S_{nl:nl} = e^{2\,i\eta_l} \tag{8.20}$$

and so the probability of emerging after the collision in the (n,l) exit channel
is unity:

$$\mathscr{P}_{nl:nl} = |\,S_{nl:nl}\,|^2 = 1. \tag{8.21}$$

In the presence of new exit channels, the $\mathscr{P}_{nl:nl}$ will be less than unity so that
probability can be conserved and in general we can write for the elastic
channel

$$S_{nl:nl} = e^{-2\,\epsilon_l}\, e^{2i\eta_l}$$

so

$$\mathscr{P}_{nl:nl} = e^{-4\epsilon_l}. \tag{8.22}$$

From $\epsilon(l)$ and $\eta(l)$, the elastic scattered amplitude can be constructed:

$$f_n(\chi) = \frac{1}{2ik}\sum (2l + 1)\,(S_{nl:nl} - 1)\,P_l(\cos\chi). \tag{8.23}$$

Just as a knowledge of the potential energy function in the elastic case
enables the phase shift function to be calculated, so a complex or *optical*
potential,

$$V_{\text{opt}}(R) = V(R) + iW(R) \tag{8.24}$$

yields a complex phase shift function and hence S matrix elements of the type (Equation 8.22). The solution of the radial wave equation with a complex potential splits it into coupled real and imaginary parts and is not straightforward; however, as might be hoped, it can be shown that the attenuation factor $\epsilon(l)$ is given to a good approximation by a Born type expression (R. E. Roberts and J. Ross, 1970):

$$\epsilon(l) = \left(\frac{\mu}{2}\right)^{\frac{1}{2}} \hbar^{-1} \int_R^\infty \frac{W(R)dR}{\{E - V(R) - \hbar^2(l + \frac{1}{2})^2/2\mu R^2\}^{\frac{1}{2}}}. \tag{8.25}$$

Although a knowledge of the optical potential that reproduces the observed elastic scattering could conveniently summarize a large body of scattering data and enable some of the transport properties in the presence of reaction to be calculated, it is hard to ascribe any physical reality to the details of $W(R)$. Instead, interest has so far centered on the absorption function $\epsilon(l)$ and this is extracted from the scattering data and interpreted in a semi-classical fashion parallel to that of $\eta(l)$. Thus, if the concept of a classical path is valid in the presence of reaction, i.e. if Equation 8.23 can be evaluated by the method of stationary phase in which $\epsilon(l)$ plays no part, then Equation 8.21 means that along the classical path with angular momentum l^{th} the probability of reaction is, from Equation 8.22, $\exp(-4\epsilon(l))$. The interpretation of $\sigma(\chi)$ is now as follows; the potential parameters of $V(R)$ are deduced from $\sigma(\chi)$ in the angular regions assumed to be unaffected by inelastic events. The unattenuated differential cross-section over the whole angular range is then deduced from this potential, and deviations from the observed scattering at any angle are ascribed to reaction on the classical trajectory leading to the observed deflection. More precisely, defining $\mathscr{P}(b)$ as the reaction probability on a trajectory with impact parameter b, we have

$$\mathscr{P}(b) = \frac{\sigma_{calc}(\chi(b)) - \sigma_{obs}(\chi(b))}{\sigma_{calc}(\chi(b))} \tag{8.26}$$

The reactions that respond well to this analysis are those of small reaction cross-section in which the rainbow structure is intact (class I) and where $\mathscr{P}(b)$ is appreciable only where $\chi(b)$ is single valued. The observed $\sigma(\theta)$ for the K/HX reactions are of the form sketched in Fig. 8.15 and are characterized by a rainbow structure of apparently normal amplitude and a fairly pronounced step in the scattered intensity beyond the rainbow. It is typical of these reactions that $\sigma(\chi)$ vs. $E\chi$ plots at different energies are nearly super-imposable, indicating that the step in $\sigma(\chi)$ at χ_c occurs on trajectories with

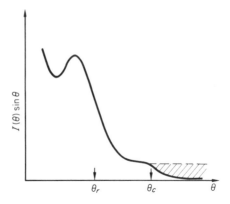

Fig. 8.15 Typical elastic scattering pattern in the presence of reaction confined to small impact parameters (Class I). The dashed line is the predicted behaviour from the rainbow structure and there is evidence for the onset of reaction at θ_c. The shaded area represents the number of particles lost per second by reaction.

the same value of the turning point R_c. Using Equation 8.22 and the deflection function $\chi(b)$ deduced from the Lennard-Jones parameters obtained from the rainbow angle, the reaction probability function, either $\mathscr{P}(b)$ or $\mathscr{P}(b/\sigma)$ if the estimation of σ is felt to be unreliable, is deduced. The general form is given in Figs. 8.16 and 8.17. Although the experimental and deductive uncertainty in $\mathscr{P}(b)$ is high, it seems clear that the reaction probability does not rise to unity even for head-on collisions, probably showing that the reaction cross-section has some orientation dependence, a conclusion in keeping with the classical trajectory calculations described in Section 8.7. Some additional weight is given to this method of interpretation of the elastic scattering from the observation that the potential energy at the distance of closest approach at the reaction threshold, $V(R_c)$, deduced from runs at different energies, is approximately constant. Similarly, the $\mathscr{P}(b)$ curves are nearly independent of the initial energy, at least over the rather limited velocity range so far explored.

There are at least two weaknesses in this analysis. The first is the uncertainty in the extrapolation of the hypothetical elastic scattering curve into regions of large deflections. The simple rainbow phenomenon is a poor guide to σ_{LJ} or any length parameter of the potential and extrapolation of

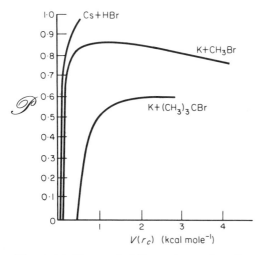

Fig. 8.16 The probability of reaction $\mathscr{P}$ vs potential energy at the distance of closest approach for various reactive systems. The relative initial kinetic energy in all cases is ~6 Kcal mole^{-1}. (Taken from E. F. Greene et al., 1969.)

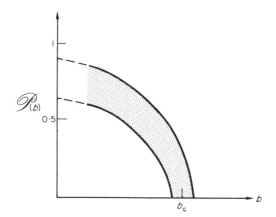

Fig. 8.17 The probability of reaction as a function of impact parameter for K + HX. The uncertainty in $\mathscr{P}(b)$ is indicated and the function has to be extrapolated to zero impact parameter because of the difficulty of measurement near $\chi = \pi$. The area under the curve, weighted by b is the total reaction cross-section (Equation 8.23).

$\sigma(\chi)$ beyond the rainbow is increasingly sensitive to the short range part of the potential. If the absolute total cross-section can be measured, $V(R)$ can be extrapolated more accurately (though only for some assumed form of the potential) but possibly the best procedure is to measure the supernumerary rainbow spacing from which the range of the potential can be deduced more accurately, (see Chapter 7 and below). A second objection to the above analysis is that inelastic events, mainly vibrational/rotational energy transfer near the reaction threshold, might smooth or distort the shape of the threshold step in $\sigma(\chi)$. This effect is probably present, but the range of trajectories affected, or the measure of the effect in influencing deduced values of $\sigma_{R\,tot}$ is likely to be small unless the reaction cross-section itself becomes small, e.g. at higher energies.

When the elastic scattering in the presence of type II reactions is investigated, an entirely different pattern emerges. The rainbow is no longer seen and the scattered alkali atom intensity falls monotonically with increasing angle. The significance of this can best be appreciated by following the effect on the observed scattering pattern of an increasing value of the critical impact parameter for reaction, b_c. A typical deflection plot is shown in Fig. 8.18 and the 'black sphere' model assumes that all partial waves with an impact parameter less than b_c are absent from the scattered wave and so any interference structure in $\sigma(\chi)$ involving branches of the deflection function with $b \leqslant b_c$ will also be absent. Thus, for $b_c = b_1$ (case I, Fig. 8.18) the corresponding angle of deflection lies on the dark side of the rainbow and there are no semi-classical interfering branches at that angle; a simple step in $\sigma(\chi)$ is thus observed. As b_c increases such that, on the positive branch of the deflection function, $\chi_c < \chi_r$, the high frequency interference structure in $\sigma(\chi)$ is progressively attenuated until, when $b_c \approx b_0$, the forward glory is destroyed and with it the interference structure in the total cross-section. At this stage, (I), the supernumerary structure to the rainbow is still intact but as b_c increases still further this structure is damped out until, when $b_c \approx b_r$, it has disappeared (case II). Superimposed on all these cases is the small amplitude diffraction structure (not shown in Fig. 8.18) due to diffraction at the surface of the black sphere and thus of periodicity π/l_c (see Equation 6.13). This latter structure has not, so far, been observed and is easily suppressed by substituting a more gradual absorption function for the step function characteristic of the black sphere model. The relation between the absorption as a function of $\chi, \mathscr{P}(\chi)$ and the probability of reaction as a function of distance of closest approach can be computed with the aid of Fig. 8.19 where $\chi(R^*)$ is plotted for several values of the reduced energy. It is generally at this point that the analysis stops.

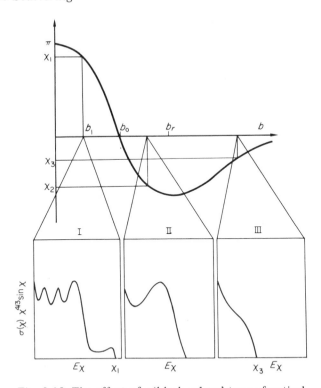

Fig. 8.18 The effect of a 'black sphere' type of optical potential on the elastic scattering pattern arising from a typical molecular deflection function. In case I, the rainbow and supernumerary structure is intact; in case II the rainbow only is present; in III $(b_c > b_r)$ the scattered intensity falls monotonically to zero.

Since the total reaction cross-section is approximately πb_c^2, we expect reactions of large cross-section (class II) to exhibit a weakened or absent rainbow structure. This is borne out in practice by such systems as K/Br_2, K/CBr_4, K/Cl_2, $K/SnCl_4$ in which the rainbow is absent. Also in contrast to class I reactions, it has been observed (V. Kempter et al, 1970) that for systems K/Br_2, K/Cl_2 and $K/SnCl_4$ the $I(\chi) \cdot \sin \chi$ *vs* $E\chi$ plots at different energies are not superimposable but show a definite trend towards increased elastic scattering with energy in the range $1.5 - 6$ eV (Fig. 8.20). This interesting behaviour, which is not observed for K/CCl_4 or $K/SiCl_4$, is tentatively ascribed to non-adiabatic electron behaviour. Thus, at the lowest energies, less than ~ 1.5 eV, the lower or ionic potential surface is exclusively followed. As the energy increases, the electron fails to jump on trajectories that take the system over the crossing point with sufficient speed – i.e. those

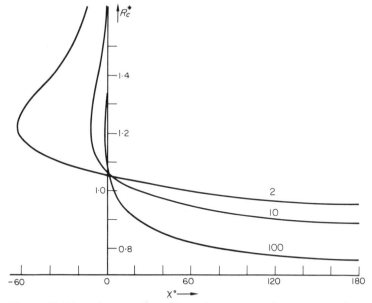

Fig. 8.19 Plot of reduced turning point versus deflection angle for a LJ (12:6) potential at various values of the reduced kinetic energy, E/ϵ.

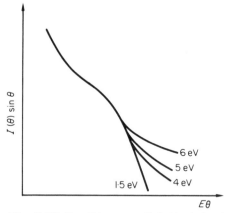

Fig. 8.20 Possible non-adiabatic behaviour in the scattering of superthermal potassium from a variety of halogen containing compounds in class II. The plots would be expected to be superimposable if only one potential (real or complex) were operating. Each curve is labelled with the energy of the alkali atom. (Adapted from V. Kempter et al., 1970.)

of smallest impact parameter – and elastic or possibly inelastic scattering from the upper potential surface is substituted for some of the reactive scattering. This new motion is sometimes described as *diabatic* and has been invoked to explain some of the small angle scattering of potassium from I_2 at 100 eV (B. Duchart et al, 1971) where it is probably quite widespread. At these high energies elastic scattering can also take place from the Coulomb potential because the relative velocity of the incoming K atom is now so high that, even though the electron may jump, the K atom may fail to pull away an I atom before the second crossing is reached. The electron will then return to the K atom and elastic scattering results. The probability of this happening is largely dependent on the mass ratio of M and X, the lighter X the more chemical reaction persists at high energies.

The whole question of non-adiabatic effects in reactive scattering has hardly been investigated. One of the most direct examples of the operation of the effect is in the phenomenon of auto-ionization. When a beam of alkali atoms collides with a halogen molecule or atom target, a considerable ionic flux is observed when the collision energy rises above the threshold for the process:

$$M + X_2 \longrightarrow M^+ + X_2^- + \Delta E_1$$

or

$$MX + A \longrightarrow M^+ + X^- + A + \Delta E_2.$$

We will not discuss these experiments (see, for example A. P. M. Baede et al 1969, and F. P. Tully et al, 1971) except to remark that, ultimately, a unified description of high energy elastic scattering, reactive scattering and collisional ionization must be found, probably in terms of two potentials.

A useful bonus from the optical model of elastic scattering is that the total reaction cross-section can, in some cases, be obtained without recourse to absolute measurements. Thus, in terms of the reaction probability function $\mathscr{P}(b)$, the total reaction cross-section is given by

$$\sigma_R = 2\pi \int \mathscr{P}(b) b \, db. \tag{8.27}$$

Once again, if the estimate of σ_{LJ} is felt to be unreliable, Equation 8.23 can be expressed in the reduced form

$$\sigma_R / \sigma_{LJ}^2 = 2\pi \int \mathscr{P}(b^*) b^* \, db^*. \tag{8.28}$$

Values obtained in this way agree to within at least an order of magnitude with the directly integrated product flux (Section 8.2) and relative values in a sequence e.g. K/HCl, K/HBr, K/HI are sensible. Furthermore, in this route to σ_R the relative sensitivity of the detector to the product and to one of the reactants does not appear as a factor. Altogether, this is the most satisfactory route at present to σ_R for reactions of small cross-section.

8.4 Energy dependence of the total cross-section

As we have seen, elastic scattering in the presence of reaction can be described by an optical potential which results in S-matrix elements of the form $S = e^{2i\eta_l}e^{-2\epsilon_l}$. The imaginary part of the phase shift, ϵ_l, represents the absorption of flux from the lth incident channel. The total cross-section, as measured in the standard experiment described in Chapter 7, is found to be:

$$\sigma_{tot}(E) = \frac{2\pi}{k^2} \sum_l (1 - e^{-2\epsilon_l})(2l + 1) + \frac{4\pi}{k^2} \sum_l (2l + 1) e^{-2\epsilon_l} \sin^2 \eta_l$$

(8.29)

by applying the optical theorem to Equation 8.23. An elastic total cross-section can be defined in operational terms as the integrated elastic differential cross-section and so, integrating Equation 8.23,

$$\sigma_{el}(E) = \frac{4\pi}{k^2} \sum_l (2l + 1) e^{-2\epsilon_l} \sin^2 \eta_l + \frac{\pi}{k^2} \sum_l (2l + 1)(1 - e^{-2\epsilon_l})^2.$$

(8.30)

The total reaction cross-section is the difference between Equations 8.29 and 8.30:

$$\sigma_R(E) = \frac{\pi}{k^2} \sum_l (2l + 1)(1 - e^{-4\epsilon_l})$$

(8.31)

and so the largest possible ratio of σ_R to σ_{tot} is ½. Note that Equation 8.31 does not contain an l-dependent phase factor in the summation which is not, therefore, susceptible to the normal methods of stationary phase evaluation and the concept of interfering branches does not apply. For most functional forms of $\epsilon_l(E)$, then, $\sigma_R(E)$ will be a smooth function of E, perhaps exhibiting a single maximum, rather than an oscillatory function – in contrast to the behaviour of $\sigma_{tot}(E)$ and $\sigma_{el}(E)$. This does not, of course, mean that the *differential* reaction cross-section is structureless; angular structure has, for instance, been observed in the ion production from $K + Hal_2$.

The l dependence of ϵ_l cannot at present be deduced from measurements of $\sigma(\chi)$ or $\sigma_{tot}(E)$ and is usually obtained from an assumed model of reaction in which an adjustable parameter is retained. The simplest such model, the black sphere, can readily be recast in terms of an optical potential or an absorption function. Thus, ϵ_l for a black sphere radius R_d is:

$$\begin{matrix} \epsilon_l = \infty, & l \leqslant l_d \\ \epsilon_l = 0, & l > l_d \end{matrix} ; \quad l_d = \mu v R_d / \hbar \qquad (8.32)$$

which represents the situation in which all particles approaching with an impact parameter R_d or less are absorbed. Referring to Equation 8.29, there are two types of behaviour that can arise according to whether l_d is greater or less than the value for the onset of random phase, l^*. We identify l^* by a Massey-Mohr criterion and so, if

$$l_d \leqslant l^* = k \left(\frac{2C_s f(s)}{\hbar v} \right)^{1/(s-1)}, \qquad (8.33)$$

the random phase region encompasses the whole range of the partial wave summation in which ϵ_l is non-zero. In this random phase region, the $\sin^2 \eta_l$ factor in Equation 8.29 averages to ½ and the contribution of partial waves with $l < l^*$ to $\sigma_{tot}(E)$ is independent of ϵ_l. $\sigma_{tot}(E)$ is therefore unchanged from the elastic case. However, the energy dependence of the two critical l values is different in the presence of intermolecular forces and they become equal at a velocity v_t given by:

$$v_t \approx 2C_s f(s)/(\hbar R_d^{s-1}). \qquad (8.34)$$

At velocities higher than this value, reactive processes begin to increase the total cross-section above the purely elastic value. Finally, when $v \gg v_t$ and $e^{-2\epsilon_l}$ is still ~ 0, each partial wave contributes $2\pi\lambda^2(2l+1)$ to the total cross-section — the maximum possible value. The velocity dependence of σ_{tot} changes from the Massey-Mohr value of $-2/(s-1)$ for the energy exponent at low energies to become independent of velocity in the high energy limit.

The fate of the fine structure in $\sigma_{tot}(E)$ as the reactive part of the potential energy surface changes is more difficult to trace analytically since all regions of stationary phase must be included in the partial wave summation. Qualitatively, the main features are as follows. For normal potentials we have seen that there are at least two contributions to the forward scattered amplitude in the incident channel, $f_i(0)$ and under semi-classical conditions we write

$$f_i(0) = f_i^{(1)}(0) + \sum_{\substack{\text{inner} \\ \text{branches}}} f_i^{(n)}(0). \tag{8.35}$$

The first and largest contribution comes from those partial waves of large l value associated with phase shifts $\lesssim \pi/2$. The inner branch contributions come from those trajectories of smaller impact parameter with nearly zero deflection or multiples of 2π. In the elastic case these additional branches are responsible for the undulations in the energy dependence of the total cross-section. Reverting to classical language, molecules that contribute to the forward glory can be said to have penetrated to a distance of closest approach $R_0 \approx 1.05\sigma$ and constitute the leading inner branch, $f^{(2)}$. As we have seen, just as the rainbow is associated with a distance of closest approach that is almost independent of energy, so also is the inner trajectory of zero deflection (see Figs. 18.19 and 18.21). If any reactive or inelastic channels are open to these more penetrating collisions, the magnitude of the scattered elastic amplitude $f^{(2)}$ will be diminished and with it the amplitude of the undulations it causes in the total cross-section. This amplitude ranges between

$$\{|f^{(1)}| + |f^{(2)}|\}^2 \quad \text{and} \quad \{|f^{(1)}| - |f^{(2)}|\}^2.$$

Finally, when $f^{(2)}$ vanishes, the undulations disappear. If throughout the energy range only two branches contribute, the effect of a slowly increasing black sphere radius R_d can be followed from Fig. 8.21; note that we have slightly modified the primitive black sphere model from the discussion above to one in which the criterion for reaction depends upon the distance of closest approach rather than the impact parameter. The values of the reduced turning point on the zero deflection trajectory, R_0^*, slowly increase from 1 to 1.07 as the relative kinetic energy rises from 0 to ∞. Thus, a value of R_d^* less than unity will leave the undulatory structure of $\sigma_{\text{tot}}(E)$ intact. As R_d^* increases beyond unity, the undulations at low energies are first suppressed until with R_d^* somewhat less than 1.07 (the precise value depends upon the parameters) the highest energy undulation disappears, leaving $\sigma_{\text{tot}}(E)$ structureless across the whole energy range. In terms of the classification of the previous section (e.g. Fig. 8.18), the structure disappears across the whole energy range at the borderline between classes I and II of reactive systems.

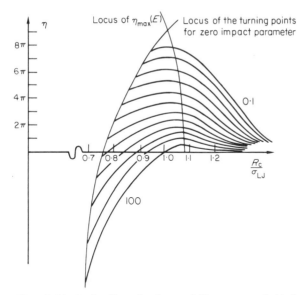

Fig. 8.21 A family of phase shift curves plotted against the reduced distance of closest approach and labelled with the reduced energy E/ϵ. The maximum in $\eta(R_c^*)$ for a given value of E^*, η_{max}, occurs on the forward glory trajectory. A maximum in the total cross-section occurs at the energies for which $\eta_{max}(E)$ passes through a multiple of π.

Because the range of R_d^* that separates the onset from the completion of quenching is so small it is likely in practice that cases of partial quenching due to reaction will be very rare.

There are several weaknesses in this primitive model, the major one being the neglect of inelastic events. We return to this later and discuss briefly the less important question of whether the introduction of a sharp cut-off in the partial wave summation, as in the black sphere model, will itself induce observable structure in the total cross-section of an interference nature. From Equation 8.29, the diffraction oscillatory structure can only come from the second term; as l_d changes, the magnitude of this term passes through a maximum every time $\eta(l_d)$ is equal to a multiple of $\pi/2$. Assuming for the purposes of an order of magnitude calculation that the phase shift varies linearly with l near $l = l_d$, we readily find that the difference between the maximum and minimum contributions of the $\sin^2 \eta_l$ term in Equation 8.29 is given by

$$\Delta\sigma_{\text{tot}} \approx \frac{4\pi^2}{\eta'(l_d)} \frac{l_d}{k^2} \tag{8.36}$$

where $\eta'(l)$ is the gradient of the phase shift function. The ratio $\sigma_{tot}/\Delta\sigma_{tot}$ is thus of order $(1/\eta'(l)$ and is small unless $\eta'(l)$ is nearly zero, i.e. unless the critical impact parameter b_d is close to the glory value. This type of structure has not yet been observed.

Both chemical reaction and inelastic events can remove terms from the partial wave summation and the latter, especially rotational energy transfer, will probably have a rather less step-like dependence on the impact parameter than chemical reaction (a 'grey sphere' model) and could lead to a dampening of the structure of σ_{tot} across the complete energy range. The experimental $\mathcal{P}(b)$ functions, available from an optical analysis of the elastic scattering in the presence of reaction (Section 8.3), are found to be somewhat rounded by the imperfect angular resolution of the apparatus, but for some systems this function does approach step-like behaviour (e.g. for K + HX, Fig. 8.17, see also K/CCl$_4$, R. M. Harris and J. F. Wilson, 1971). In these systems, consistent application of the optical model would lead to almost complete or zero quenching respectively. However, partial quenching of the glory structure, especially at the low velocity end of the spectrum, is a common feature of molecular scattering, even in non-reactive systems. The favoured explanation here (W. D. Held et al., 1970 and Section 7.3) is an orientation dependent potential that effectively introduces a range of ϵ values into the collision dynamics. Experimentally, a small amount of quenching might well escape detection since the amplitude of the undulations in $\sigma_{tot}(E)$ depends upon the shape of the potential (in particular on the curvature of the potential near the minimum) and on the velocity and angular resolution.

Against this background, we now review the experimental data on $\sigma_{tot}(E)$ for reactive systems and this is summarized in Table 8.2 in which two relatively unreactive systems, Na/SF$_6$ and Li/SO$_2$, have also been included.

Total cross-section measurements are carried out with the lighter atoms Na and Li in order to improve resolution and the 'rainbow observed?' entry usually refers to the corresponding K/X system. There is a fairly clear cut division between complete and partial quenching that follows the division between class I and II reactions. Thus, for collisions involving the halogens, the Lennard-Jones parameter σ_{LJ} is estimated to be 4–5 Å, which is considerably smaller than the harpooning radius that is deduced from the magnitude of σ_R. It is thus entirely to be expected that the forward glory should be suppressed by reaction in class II. None of the molecules listed departs very much from spherical symmetry and thus should show only partial quenching of the glory structure due to shape effects, although the case of Na/C(CH$_3$)$_4$ (H. L. Kramer and P. R. Le Breton, 1967) which exhibits complete quenching may not be the sole exception to this rule. This partial

Table 8.2

System	Rainbow Observed?	Quenching	Reference
Na/CBr$_4$	no	complete	
/Br$_2$	no	complete	E. A. Gislason and
/CCl$_4$	yes	complete	G. H. Kwei, 1967
/CH$_3$I	yes	complete	
/SiCl$_4$	(yes)	complete	
/SF$_6$	yes	none	
Li/Br$_2$	no	complete	
/Cl$_2$	no	complete	R. K. B. Helbing and
/ICl	no	complete	E. W. Rothe, 1968
/HI,HBr	yes	partial	
/DCl,HF	yes	partial	
/CH$_3$I	yes	complete	
/CH$_3$Br	yes	complete	E. W. Rothe et al.,
/SO$_2$		complete	1970
/CCl$_4$	yes	almost none	

quenching is probably exhibited by the hydrogen halide reactions in class I where, because of the angular term of P_2 symmetry in the atom/molecule potential, rotational transitions may be responsible for the quenching. In the system Na/CCl$_4$, the critical distance of closest approach is estimated to be $\sim 0.90\sigma_{LJ}$ and thus no quenching through reaction or through asymmetry in the potential would be expected. The pairs methyl iodide/Li and methyl bromide/Li are borderline cases. The opacity function $\mathscr{P}(b)$ (R. M. Harris and J. F. Wilson, 1971) for the methyl halides are 'greyer' than for the hydrogen halides in the sense that some elastic scattering occurs at all impact parameters (probably due to steric factors). The transition region of the grey sphere extends from values of the reduced distance of closest approach of ~ 0.8 to ~ 1.2. Energy analysis of the elastic scattering in the presence of reaction is just beginning to reveal the importance of inelastic events in fairly hard collisions with $R_c^* \sim 1$ and it is probable that the virtually complete quenching of the structure in $\sigma_{tot}(E)$ that is observed for the alkali halide systems is due to both reactive and inelastic events. The case of Li/SO$_2$ is interesting in relation to the role of complex formation as a quenching mechanism. Release from a complex takes place through many inelastic channels and as far as elastic scattering is concerned, the target is essentially a black sphere with a cross-section equal to that for complex formation. For K/SO$_2$ this cross-section is estimated to be ~ 350 A^2 and although the potential parameters are uncertain, 'normal' values would lead to a glory impact parameter of between 3 and 5 Å — well below the radius for complex formation and so leading to the suppression of the glory undulations.

It follows from the above interpretation of the results for the hydrogen and methyl halides that inelastic events can quench the glory branch of the deflection function and yet have died out at larger impact parameters associated with the rainbow angle, for this feature is observed to be intact in all these systems.

The fairly common observation that the highest energy undulations in $\sigma_{tot}(E)$ for both reactive and non-reactive systems are the least quenched is possibly indicative of an orientation dependent well depth of the potential. Thus, for a given change in σ_{LJ}, the lower velocity peaks in $\sigma_{tot}(E)$ are more displaced relative to the local spacing than the higher energy ones, essentially through the operation of Equation 7.11. In a standard scattering experiment the observed beam attenuation is the average over all molecular orientations and so there is a progressive destruction of the lower energy peaks. Total cross-section measurements from orientated target molecules might be helpful here.

To summarise, the observation of glory quenching in the total cross-section only indicates that those particles that would have been elastically scattered in the forward direction on the inner branch of the deflection function have been removed by some process or that a rather anisotropic potential is operating. Since an anisotropic potential implies rotational energy transfer, the two effects are linked. The operation of chemical reaction is only unambiguous in reactions of type II where both the glory structure and the rainbow are absent.

8.5 Energy partitioning among reaction products

In direct reactions, i.e. those not proceeding through a long-lived complex, the energy and angular momentum partitioning between relative and internal motion of the products is very sensitive to the nature of the potential energy surface. In contrast, reactions involving an intermediate complex tend to conform, subject to angular momentum constraints, to the equipartition rule with the exoergicity shared equally among all the active degrees of freedom of the complex.

Experimentally, the program is a formidable one. For the simplest class of reaction, $A + BC \rightarrow AB + C$, a velocity analysis of one of the products together with a vibrational or rotational analysis of the diatomic product is required for a complete assignment of the energy liberated. In practice there are three levels of sophistication in beam experiments:

(I) *'Kinematic' analysis*: no velocity or state analysis of the products is carried out, but a final CM velocity and angular distribution of assumed analytical form is derived that fits the observed LAB scattering.

(II) *Product velocity analysis only.* $\sigma_R(\theta, v)$ is measured over as wide an angular range as possible, generally $\lesssim 120°$ in the LAB. Sometimes, for reasons of intensity, the velocity profile at a fixed angle of observation is scanned and this velocity distribution assumed to hold at all angles. That is, recalling the definition in the CM co-ordinate system:

$\sigma_R^{(i)}(\chi, v_i)$ = number of product particles i scattered between $\chi, \chi + d\chi$ and with velocity between $w, w + dw$ per second per unit reactant flux

the reaction cross-section is assumed to be factorisable thus:

$$\sigma_R^{(i)}(\chi, v_i) = \sigma_R^{(i)}(\chi) f^{(i)}(v). \tag{8.37}$$

The number of particles transported in to $d\chi$ with energy between E and $E + dE$ is related to the above cross-section by:

$$\sigma_R^{(i)}(\chi, E_i) dE_i = \sigma_R^{(i)}(\chi, v_i) dv_i$$

and so

$$\sigma_R^{(i)}(\chi, E_i) = \frac{1}{m v_i}\, \sigma_R^{(i)}(\chi, v_i). \tag{8.38}$$

This latter formula transforms between the differential cross-sections measured by energy analysis and those obtained by velocity analysis. The transformation is also a useful one when comparing beam measurements with the results of chemiluminescence studies which yield information about the distribution of products among energy levels.

(III) *Complete energy analysis.* In thermal energy scattering, the electronic state of the products is generally certain, leaving the translation and vibration/rotation energy assignment to be made. If the product is highly polar, inhomogeneous electric fields (see Chapter 4) can be used to focus or deflect low rotational states so that the relative population of specific rotational states can be obtained; more usually, for highly rotationally excited states, a rotational temperature can be obtained.

The vibrational-rotation distribution of the CsF formed in the reaction

$$Cs + SF_6 \longrightarrow CsF + SF_5$$

has also been measured (S. M. Freund et al., 1971). The CsF was analysed by a flop-in molecular beam resonance technique in which transitions of the type $njm \rightarrow njm'$ (Stark splitting) were observed. Since the moment of inertia and hence the resonant frequency for the transition varies with the vibrational quantum number n, the relative population of several vibrational states could be measured. The method is so far only applicable to highly polar diatomic products.

Beam data with state analysis of a product is still so meagre that it is best augmented for interpretative purposes by results on energy partitioning obtained by other techniques. These are basically spectroscopic and comprise:

(i) *Flash photolysis*, yielding the vibration rotation distribution of the molecular product but no angular information. A very versatile technique with regard to the number of reactions that can be studied, especially those involving very short lived species.

(ii) *Infra-red chemiluminescence*, again yielding the vibration-rotation state distribution of the product without angular information.

In neither of these methods is there selection of the initial translational or internal energy. With care, an average of absolute rate constants for the processes

$$AB(n,j) + C \longrightarrow A + BC(n',j')$$

can be obtained in which the true detailed rate constants $k_{nj}^{n'j'}(T)$ are appropriately weighted by the initial distribution of n and j. Then, if the functional form of $k(T)$ can be measured or assumed (S. H. Lin and H. Eyring, 1971), absolute reaction cross-sections with the same initial state averaging can in principle be obtained from the Laplace transform of $k(T)$:

$$E \langle \sigma_{nj}^{n'j'}(E) \rangle_j = \frac{1}{2\pi i} \int_{\gamma - i\infty}^{\gamma + i\infty} \langle k_{nj}^{n'j'}(\beta) \rangle_j \, e^{\beta E} \sqrt{\pi\mu/8} \, \beta^{-3/2} \, d\beta$$

where $\beta = 1/kT$ and Maxwell-Boltzmann translational energy distribution is assumed to hold during the measurement of $k(T)$. The integration of reactive differential cross-sections with energy analysis yields a total cross-section for scattering into a final relative kinetic energy range dE. If both the energy density of final internal states and the partitioning of the energy between n and j is known, $\sigma_R(E)$ can be transformed into the total cross-section for scattering into a range $dndj$ of internal states (see Fig. 8.1). As yet, this complete tie up between the results of kinetic spectroscopy and reactive scattering with translational energy analysis remains to be made.

Rather than review the results from neutral beam work in isolation, the energy partitioning for a sample of reactions of the type $A + BC \rightarrow AB + C$, $A + BCD \rightarrow AB + CD$ and $A + BCD \rightarrow ABC + D$, whether or not investigated by beam techniques, will be discussed together. Collisionally induced dissociation reactions, $A + BC \rightarrow A + B + C$ are not included, though they have been observed in ion/neutral beam work. The results to be discussed are summarized in Table 8.3, which includes all the neutral beam work utilizing energy analysis of the scattered products up till 1972.

In all cases at least 25 per cent of the total available energy (exoergicity + collision energy) is converted into internal energy of the products. In stripping reactions involving the alkali metals and the halogens most of the available energy appears as vibrational excitation of the product, their effective rotational and translational temperatures being relatively cool. In contrast, reactions with recoil dynamics, e.g. $K + CH_3 I$, appear to display the reverse behaviour with a large fraction of the available energy appearing in the final translational energy. Whether these two types of behaviour are characteristic of these two classes of reaction in general, or peculiar to alkali atom reactions is not yet clear.

Continuing our survey of direct reactions, the ion/molecule reactions in which $\sigma_R(\theta, E)$ has been measured are all characterised by strong forward scattering, i.e. on this basis alone they would be characterized as stripping reactions. They differ from the alkali reactions with regard to reaction parameters only in that the collision energy is greater than the exoergicity and that some of the reactions are endothermic.

The spectator stripping model allows the energy partitioning between reaction products to be calculated easily. In a collision in which the target molecule BC is at rest and A approaches in the z-direction, the initial and final momenta are related by the conservation of momentum thus;

$$P_z^A = P_z^{AB'} + P_z^{C'} \quad ; \quad \tag{8.39}$$
$$P_y^{AB'} = -P_y^{C'} \qquad P_x^{AB'} = -P_x^{C'}$$

Table 8.3

System	Technique and energy partitioning	Model and reference
$N_2^+ + D_2 \rightarrow N_2 D^+ + D$ $Ar^+ + D_2 \rightarrow ArD^+ + D$	Between 55 per cent and 90 per cent into internal energy, depending on E_t^i in the range 0.1–3 eV Strong forward scattering.	Direct. (Z. Herman et al., 1967). Modified spectator stripping, Some recoil above 40 eV.
$H + Hal_2 \rightarrow HHal + Hal$ $H + HHal \rightarrow HHal^* + H$ $Hal + HHal \rightarrow HHal^* + Hal$	I. R. chemiluminescence. Between 45 per cent and 65 per cent into internal energy, rising to 80 per cent for Cl + HI.	Direct. Repulsive energy surface. (K. G. Anlauf et al., 1967; M. J. Mok and J. C. Polanyi, 1969).
$O(^3P) + CS_2 \rightarrow SO + CS$	Flash photolysis. 8 per cent to internal motion of CS 18 per cent to internal motion of SO	Direct. Linear encounters on a repulsive P.E. surface. (I. W. M. Smith, 1967).
$K + CH_3I \rightarrow KI + CH_3$	Thermal X-beam. Early results gave too high a value for product excitation. Direct energy analysis gives ~60 per cent to internal motion.	Direct, recoil. (R. B. Bernstein, M. E. Gersh and A. M. Rulis, 1971).
$K + Br_2 \rightarrow KBr + Br$	Thermal X-beam. Correlation of product velocity with angle of scattering. 90 per cent available energy to internal motion depending on angle.	Spectator stripping. (T. T. Warnock et al., 1967). Trajectory calculations (P. J. Kuntz et al., 1969).
$H + Hal_2, SCl_2 \rightarrow HHal + Hal, SCl$	I. R. chemiluminescence. > 37 per cent to internal motion of HCl.	(R. L. Johnson et al., 1970)
$N_2^+ + CH_4 \rightarrow N_2 H^+ + CH_3$	Ion energy analysis at 25 eV. All the exoergicity into internal motion for forward scattered products.	Ideal stripping (E. A. Gislason et al., 1969).
$N_2^+ + H_2 \rightarrow N_2 H^+ + H$	Ion energy analysis, 3–11 eV	Stripping, changing to knockout. (W. R. Gentry et al., 1968).

Reaction	Method	Reference
$CO^+ + H_2 \rightarrow HCO^+ + H$	Ion energy analysis	Stripping. (K. Lacmann and A. Henglein, 1965).
$CH_3^+ + CH_4 \rightarrow C_2H_5^+ + H_2$	Ion energy analysis, differential scattering	Pure stripping above 3 eV. (R. R. Herm and D. R. Herschbach, 1969). Complex formation. RRK theory for lifetime.
$C_2H_4^+ + C_2H_4 \rightarrow CH_3 + C_3H_5^+$ $\searrow CH_3 + C_3H_3^+ + H_2$		
$K + I_2 \rightarrow KI + I$	Thermal X-beam. $\sim$ 97 per cent transfer to internal motion. Coupling between angular and recoil energy distributions.	Stripping (K. T. Gillen et al., 1971). Trajectory calculations, (P. J. Kuntz et al., 1969).
$Cs + SF_6 \rightarrow CsF + SF_5$	Thermal X-beam. Results correspond to equipartition.	Complex formation (S. M. Freund et al., 1971). (H. G. Bennewitz et al., 1971).
$Rb + Br_2 \rightarrow RbBr + Br$	Thermal X-beam Velocity and rotational analysis. $\sim$ 5 Kcal mole^{-1} into rotation and $\sim$ 37 Kcal mole^{-1} into vibration	Stripping (R. Grice et al., 1970).
$F + D_2 \rightarrow FD + D$	Thermal X-beam, Newton diagram analysis under favourable conditions.	(T. P. Schafer et al., 1970).
$D+ \left\{ \begin{array}{l} Cl_2 \\ \ldots \\ ICl \end{array} \right.$	Thermal X-beam, velocity analysis of DX. Between 55 per cent and 76 per cent of total available energy into internal motion.	Direct (recoil) Comparison of energy release with photo-dissociation spectra (J. D. McDonald et al., 1972)
$K + HBr, DBr$	Kinematics unfavourable for detailed analyses. Broad product velocity distribution peaked near 100 per cent transfer of available energy to internal motion	(K. T. Gillen et al., 1969).

where post-collision values are primed. In a pure stripping reaction the velocity of the spectator atom C is unchanged and so

$$\boldsymbol{p}^{C'} = 0, \quad P_z^{AB'} = P_z^A; \quad P_y^{AB'} = 0, \quad P_x^{AB'} = 0 \tag{8.40}$$

The amount of energy transferred to internal motion of AB is thus

$$E_{int} = \frac{m_P}{m_A + m_B} \times (\text{collision energy}) \tag{8.41}$$

but how this energy is partitioned between rotation and vibration depends upon the impact parameter. In Fig. 8.22 both the detailed post collision relative velocity vector diagram and the Newton diagram are given, the former constructed on the principle that immediately after reaction all particles continue to move with the same velocities that they had before the collision. From the Newton diagram for the more general case in which v_{BC} is non-zero it follows that the centre of mass velocity of the new diatomic AB is

$$w_{AB} = \frac{m_A m_C}{M(m_A + m_B)} w \tag{8.42}$$

where $w_r = w_A - w_{BC}$ is the relative velocity of the reactants and M is the mass of the whole system. In terms of LAB velocities with a stationary target, the final product velocity is given simply by

$$v_{AB} = \frac{m_A}{(m_A + m_B)} v_A. \tag{8.43}$$

These results are independent of the orientation of the target molecule at the moment of collision, of the force acting between the newly paired atoms and of the impact parameter. However, if C is to continue to move with unchanged velocity it is necessary that AB and C do not collide.

The partitioning of internal energy of the product diatomic is found by first calculating the angular momentum of AB with the aid of Fig. 8.22;

$$J_{AB} = \mu_{AB} w (b - [m_C/(m_B + m_C)] r_{BC} \sin \theta) \tag{8.44}$$

where θ is the orientation of BC with respect to the z-axis. If $b \gg r_{BC}$ (as is

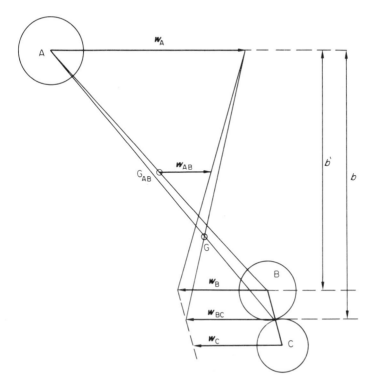

Fig. 8.22 A stripping collision between an atom A and a diatomic BC. The relative velocities, w_i, are drawn assuming a non-rotating target and are unchanged when the bond BC is broken. The atoms continue to move in their pre-collision directions until the force between A and B begins to take effect. The initial angular momentum (which is also the final value) can be calculated from this diagram (Equation 8.44). G is the centre of mass of the three particles and G_{AB} that of A and B.

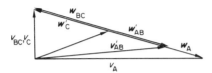

Fig. 8.22a Newton diagram for stripping, constructed on the basis that $v_c = v_{BC}$.

the case for thermal energy class II reactions) the rotational energy of AB is

$$E_{rot}^{AB} \cong \frac{1}{2}\mu_{AB}w_r^2 \, b^2/r_{AB}^2. \tag{8.45}$$

This leaves, by difference,

$$E_{vib}^{AB} \cong \frac{1}{2}\mu_{AB}w_A^2 \, (1 - b^2/r_{AB}^2) \tag{8.46}$$

as the final vibration energy of AB in the limit $w_A \gg w_{BC}$ appropriate to laboratory ion/molecule reactions.

These relations for the internal energy of the product in the stripping model impose constraints on the magnitude of the reaction cross-section which reduce the value πb_s^2 expected from the stripping impact parameter b_s. Thus, if the product is to survive, the vibrational energy E_{vib}^{AB} must be less than the bond dissociation energy; this imposes a lower limit on b. In the limit of large impact parameters, $b \approx r_{AB}$, the rotational energy E_{rot}^{AB} may be sufficient to dissociate the molecule if the relative velocity is large enough. Hence, from Equation 8.45, we see that at high energies both these constraints lead to a $1/E$ dependence of the stripping cross-section.

In the above discussion of stripping we have made three assumptions (1) the target BC has no internal energy, (2) there is no interaction between B and C after stripping and (3) all three atoms lie in a plane. If BC is not at rest but possesses internal momentum due to rotation or vibration, the product AB will no longer appear solely along the relative velocity vector but will be smeared out over a cone of half angle $\tan^{-1}(P^A/P^B)$. All three limitations are unimportant at high energies but distort the model for thermal scattering.

We now turn to the experimental results for stripping reactions to see how closely the ideal case is obeyed in practice. Results of velocity or energy analysed reactive scattering are best displayed as a polar contour map (Figs. 8.23, 8.24) in which the distance R from the origin is proportional to the velocity of the scattered particle and θ the angle of observation. Contours are then drawn through observational points (R, θ) of the same signal strength. From the reactions in Table 8.3 we consider first a thoroughly investigated group that illustrate the operation of a predominantly stripping mechanism:

$$N_2^+ + CH_4 \longrightarrow N_2H^+ + CH_3 \quad \text{(at 25 eV)}$$
$$CH_3^+ + CH_4 \longrightarrow C_2H_5^+ + H_2 \quad \text{(at 3 eV)}$$
$$K + I_2 \longrightarrow KI + I \quad \text{(thermal)}$$

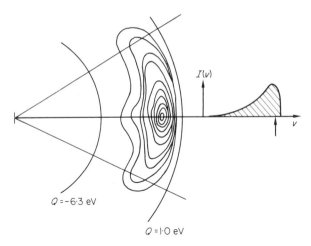

Fig. 8.23 A velocity contour map of the intensity of N_2H^+ from 25 eV N_2^+ colliding with CH_4. The beam velocity profile at $\theta = 0$ is shown on the right, in which the value of the stripping velocity is arrowed. Velocities for two values of Q, the energy transferred from the collision energy to internal motion of the products are shown and a $30°$ cone, into which almost all the reactive scattering is directed, is superimposed. (Taken from E. A. Gislason, et al., 1969.)

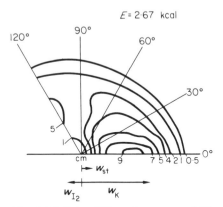

Fig. 8.24 Polar CM contour map of KI scattered in the reaction $K + I_2$. The relative velocities of the two reagents are shown beneath. The intensities labelling the contours are arbitrarily scaled with 10 as the maximum.

Also shown is the CM product velocity for pure stripping, w_{st}. (K. T. Gillen et al., 1971.)

All three of these reactions are characterized by strong forward peaking of the product intensity in the CM. For $N_2^+ + CH_4$ and $CH_3^+ + CH_3$, the peak product velocity corresponds closely to the stripping value of Equation 8.42, although as the impact energy falls below 1 eV the product velocity distribution shows increasing back scattering and the peak forward velocity is several times the stripping value.

The system $K + I_2$ shows evidence of fairly strong interaction between the newly formed products as they separate. Thus, the KI, although largely forward scattered, appears with a most probable velocity at least six times the stripping value and, although the experiments do not extend into the backward hemisphere, there is a hint of a second peak in the scattered intensity at $\chi \sim \pi$. In each case there is considerable sideways scattering, even after allowing for the angular and velocity distribution of the parent beams. In this system, there is no reason to doubt that a harpooning mechanism operates (Section 8.2), but in the two ion/molecule reactions electronic re-arrangement probably does not begin until separations only slightly greater than ordinary bond distances. Departure from the stripping predictions have perhaps rather different causes in the K/I_2 case and in the two ion/molecule reactions. Early energy release, before stripping, is unlikely in the K/I_2 reaction because the critical radius for stripping is so large, and post-stripping interactions are probably important. They can operate to transfer energy to either the internal modes of the newly formed product or to the relative kinetic energy of the departing fragments. A detailed analysis of these effects is best done by trajectory calculations (Section 8.7), but qualitatively the key factor is the nature of the interaction between the fragments of the ruptured bond in the target. This is most clearly illustrated in the case of harpooning by electron transfer. There are two possibilities in general

$$A + BC \longrightarrow A^+ + BC^-$$
$$A + BC \longrightarrow A^- + BC^+$$

with the former illustrated by $K + I_2$ and the latter by $H + K_2$. The potential energy curves of I_2^- and I_2 were given in Fig. 8.8 and should be contrasted with Fig. 8.25 for K_2^+ and K_2. Electron transfer is rapid compared with the motion of the target atoms and the transition will therefore be vertical. In the case of I_2 this transition is to a repulsive part of the negative ion potential and the two fragments are initially forced apart but at larger separations experience an attractive force. There is a net energy release and, according to the various reduced masses, this is partitioned between translation and internal motion of the products; in the case of $K + I_2$ it appears mainly as

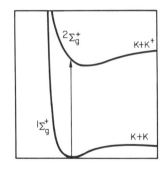

Fig. 8.25 The potential energy curves for the lowest Σ states of K_2 and K_2^+. Adiabatic ionisation would result in the transition shown.

enhanced kinetic energy. In contrast, the process $K_2 \rightarrow K_2^+ + e$ is followed by a slight repulsion of K^+ and K, but the K_2^+ cannot dissociate without further energy being supplied. This must come from the relative kinetic energy of the K_2^+ and H^- ions. Partly because of the increased bond strength of K_2^+ compared with K_2, the triatomic molecule K_2H is thought to have considerable stability (Y. T. Lee et al., 1971) and this leads to quasi-complex formation (as seen in the bimodal product distribution, Y. T. Lee et al., 1972) in contrast to the modified stripping behaviour of $K + I_2$. At higher energies this reaction might well move towards the stripping mechanism, except that the light mass of the hydrogen atom means that the duration of the collision is short compared to the time required to separate the two target K atoms. This is a point that has not been stressed in the discussion of stripping so far. If the atom A is very light, most of the motion in the newly formed AB molecule is the drawing in of A with relatively little motion of B. Under these conditions A may well begin to recede again before B and C have separated and the electron can then be transferred back from BC to A at the crossing point of the ionic and covalent surfaces appropriate to the current value of the BC separation leaving BC vibrationally excited. There is now direct evidence that this happens in K/I_2 scattering (see Section 8.3). Alternatively, the electron may fail to return and ionisation occurs.

The two ion/molecule examples in this section, involving the removal of an H atom from methane correspond to almost pure stripping over a range of a few eV. This is in part due to the fact that, compared with the K/I_2 thermal reaction, the exothermicity is now a much smaller fraction of the collision energy so its disposal is only a small perturbation on the initial motion. On these grounds we can expect $K + I_2$ to assume more stripping character as the energy increases above ~ 1 eV, with the same proviso about reverse electron transfer at high relative velocities.

The energy range in which the stripping model is adequate is bounded at the lower end by orbiting and complex formation and at the higher energy limit by the increasing importance of recoil or knock-on reactions, in which the particles behave as almost elastic billiard balls. Furthermore, as the energy increases beyond ~ 10 eV, the direct dissociation channel $(A + BC \rightarrow A + B + C)$ assumes greater importance. Finally, at still higher energies the electronic motion may cease to be adiabatic and more than one potential surface is needed.

In the case of the reaction $Cl + Br_2 \rightarrow BrCl + Br$, although the product is strongly forward scattered, the velocity analysis results indicate extensive sideways scattering and very little change in the peak LAB product velocity with angle. An important difference between this reaction and $K + I_2$ is that the total reaction cross-section is much smaller, suggesting the greater importance of small impact parameter collisions and hence to secondary encounters between the newly formed products. Thus, despite the forward scattering, this reaction may be much more comparable to the recoil type involving strong impulsive coupling of all three particles. Considerable energy transfer to the third particle is now possible and the division between stripping and recoil reactions is no longer useful. Recoil reactions do not produce any distinctive partitioning of the available energy into product excitation and translation in contrast to the high internal excitation characteristic of stripping. Experimentally it now seems that at least in some cases (e.g. $K + CH_3 I$) a considerable fraction can appear as translation energy.

In the long lived complex type of reaction, class III, in which electron rearrangement results in a relatively stable transition state, the scattering is almost symmetrical in the forward and backward hemispheres and this is illustrated by the reactions

$$C_2H_4^+ + C_2H_4 \longrightarrow C_3H_5^+ + CH_3$$
$$Cs + SF_6 \longrightarrow CsF + SF_5.$$

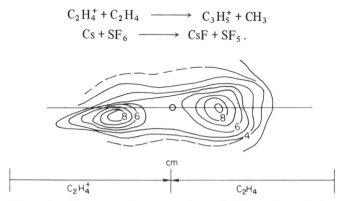

Fig. 8.26. The polar flux map of the $C_3H_5^+$ product of the reaction $C_2H_4 + C_2H_4^+$. The contours are arbitrarily scaled to 10 at the peak intensity. $E_r = 3.25$ eV. (From Z. Herman et al., 1969.)

In comparing the very different behaviour of $C_2H_4^+ + C_2H_4$ with $CH_3^+ + CH_4$, Wolfgang (Z. Herman et al., 1969) has used an RRKM model to account for the differences in lifetime of the respective molecular complexes resulting in the two systems. The fact that there is no evidence of complex formation in $CH_3^+ + CH_4$ is at first sight surprising in view of the stability of the well known molecular ion $C_2H_7^+$, but the essential result of the RRKM theory of unimolecular decay is that

$$\tau \approx 10^{-13} \left(\frac{E - E^*}{E} \right)^{1-s} \quad \text{s,} \qquad (8.47)$$

where τ is the lifetime of the transition state, s the number of active modes and E^* the dissociation energy of the complex. In going from $(C_2H_7^+)^*$ to $(C_4H_8^+)^*$, the increase in the number of vibrational modes increases τ beyond $\sim 10^{-12}$ s and forward/backward symmetry in all the exit channels is found. More generally, there is a tendency in many ion/molecule reactions for stripping behaviour to emerge from complex formation as the relative energy increases, a direct result of the operation of Equation 8.47.

The neutral/neutral reaction $Cs + SF_6$ (S. M. Freund et al., 1971) also exhibits symmetrical scattering in the CM and here added evidence for complex formation comes from the observation that the rotational temperature and the vibrational temperature of the CsF product are almost equal and correspond to sharing of the total energy available by all the degrees of freedom except one – identified by the authors as the rotation needed to fulfill angular momentum conservation requirements. This equipartition result is for a fixed angle of scattering (near the forward peak) and deviations might be expected if a direct mechanism is superimposed upon that of complex formation.

Further analysis of the polar flux/velocity plots illustrated in this section must await trajectory calculations over various trial potential surfaces, but it is worth emphasising again that, experimentally, we have probed only a relatively narrow energy region and relatively few types of potential energy surface. The beam studies described in this section, particularly the ion/molecule ones, also underline how rapidly the nature of a reactive collision can change with energy – the sequence of complex formation → stripping → recoil can be passed through in a few eV.

8.6 Steric factors in reactive-scattering

A cross-section diminishing in a series of chemically related reactions all without energy of activation might be due either to a decreasing distance of approach necessary for reaction or to an increasingly stringent orientation requirement for reaction (an 'entropy of activation'). Orientation factors are certainly present and operate in a rather predictable fashion. There are two direct experiments that are relevant. In the first, the total cross-section for a series of reactions $K + RI(R=CH_3 \ldots C_7H_{15})$ (G. H. Kwei et al., 1970) was measured and relatively little variation was found with the size of the alkyl group σ_R varying by less than a factor of 2 down the group. In the second type of experiment, a beam of CH_3I was prepared in either parallel or antiparallel alignment to the direction of approach of the potassium in the CM frame (i.e. $\cos \phi = \pm 1$) by passing through a hexapole filter (see Chapter 4) into a uniform electric field in the required direction (R. J. Beuhler and R. B. Bernstein, 1969) (Fig. 8.27). By this means either the halogen or the methyl end of the molecule was brought into the path of alkali atom. Even with the imperfect orientation of the molecule due to its residual precession ($\theta \approx 133°$ rather than $180°$) it was deduced that the reactive cross-section in the favourable orientation exceeded that in the reverse orientation by at least 3:1. Expressed somewhat differently, if the CH_3I is regarded as a spherical target with its surface divided into reactive and non-reactive portions, then

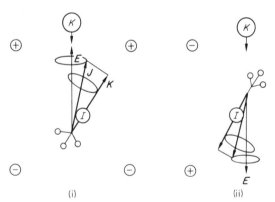

Fig. 8.27 Methyl iodide molecules with a selected range of orientations precess around the direction of E, which is reversed by reversing the polarity of the electrodes $(i) \to (ii)$. If E is aligned along the relative velocity vector, the two ends of the molecule are then presented in turn to the incoming potassium atom.

the reactive surface comprises ~70 per cent of the total (this is probably somewhat less than the admittedly imprecise fractional solid angle subtended by the iodine atom at the centre of the mass of the molecule). Another simple model has also been used to interpret these orientation experiments (P. R. Brooks and E. M. Jones, 1966). If the methyl iodide is pictured as two spheres of equal radius, then the fraction of the total hard sphere cross-section due to the iodine atom, averaged over the rotational motion of the molecule appropriate to the (jm) state, is readily calculated. From this may be directly calculated the experimental quantity

$$F = \frac{\text{signal in favourable orientation} - \text{signal in reverse orientation}}{\text{signal in favourable orientation}}$$

In this way a value $F = 0.4$ is calculated compared with an observed value of 0.6.

In a similar experiment in which methyl iodide was replaced by CF_3I, P. R. Brooks and E. M. Jones (1969) found, unexpectedly, that a larger reaction cross-section was obtained with the CF_3 group pointing towards the potassium atom than with the reverse orientation (the orientations are based on the assumption that the CF_3 group forms the negative end of the molecular dipole) but that the product was probably KI rather than KCF_3. The anisotropy factor **F** was again 0.6. It is very hard to account for this result if the mechanism is a recoil one (the total reaction cross-section is not known), but if a harpooning mechanism is invoked, it is possible that the critical radius for electron transfer, R_c, may be considerably larger if the CF_3 group points towards the incoming alkali atom. The simple formula for R_c (Equation 8.4) does not show any dependence of R_c on the target orientation, but as R_c decreases the location of the excess charge on the target becomes important in that the anion can no longer be regarded as a point charge but higher moments must be taken into account in evaluating R_c. The asymmetry of the charge distribution is then determined by the polarizability of the anion and the relative electronegativity of the two ends. A larger value of R_c is obtained when the more electronegative end (CF_3) is in the region of higher field strength, i.e. pointing towards the K^+ ion; subsequent reaction is accompanied by charge migration.

Also relevant to the question of steric factors are the elastic scattering experiments described in Section 8.3. In the sequence of recoil reactions (E. F. Greene et al., 1969) K + HBr, CH_3Br, $(CH_3)_3CBr$, σ_R/R_m^2 is found to be 1.75, 1.7 and 0.95, in approximate agreement with the changes in the again rather imprecise angle subtended by the bromine atom at the centre of mass.

One further deduction that can be made from all these experiments is that re-orientation of the target molecule as the alkali atom approaches is not pronounced. That is, both the conservation of angular momentum and the shortness of the collision lifetime make any large alteration in j difficult and the target axis does not readily follow the direction of the incoming atom.

8.7 Classical trajectory calculations

We have seen that reactive collisions can be characterized by the predominant directions of scattering of the products, by the total reaction cross-section and by the partitioning of the energy released between internal and translational modes of the products. All these, together with the notion of a critical distance of approach for reaction are classical concepts. So far, the only observations with a uniquely quantum origin are the relative probability of scattering into different vibrational channels (even these results are sometimes best reported as a vibrational or rotational temperature) and perhaps some undulations in the differential cross-section for ion production. Doubtless both elastic and reactive scattering experiments with better resolution will reveal quantum effects and systems will no doubt be discovered in which two electronic states of the molecular pair play an important part, with consequent interference between them. It is likely, though, that a model based on classical mechanics and a single potential surface will be successful in interpreting low resolution data over a significant energy range. The reactive scattering situation is similar to, and perhaps more favourable than, that of vibrational energy transfer where at least for collinear collisions there is good agreement (10–20 per cent), even quite close to threshold, between quantum and classical calculations (D. Secrest and B. R. Johnson, 1966). Classical calculations have also been surprisingly successful in treating charge transfer and ionization problems involving highly excited atoms where the electronic motion is almost classical (A. Norcliffe and I. C. Percival, 1968). It seems likely that for some time to come uncertainties in the potential surface will outweigh the errors arising from a classical approximation.

Classical models have ranged in complexity from very approximate two body models that can yield analytical results, three body systems constrained in some way (e.g. to collinear collisions) to be mathematically tractable, to the full complexity of many body (usually no larger than four) simulation models. The impetus to work with detailed models has largely come from beam work. The use of simplified three body potentials in which the potential energy is constrained to be a function of only two relative co-ordinates (i.e. fixed symmetry during collision) has a relatively long history in chemical kinetics in the form of London-Eyring-Polanyi surfaces. Through the well known device of skewing the axes, the effect of changing the reduced masses of the particles on the amount of reflection back into the incident channel was convincingly demonstrated, together with the coupling of this mass effect with the effectiveness of initial vibrational energy in promoting chemical reaction. The same effects are discernible in the more sophisticated modern calculations to be described (D. L. Bunker, 1970).

Typical of the simplest models is that of R. D. Present (1958). Here the prescription is that reaction occurs in all collisions whenever potential energy at the distance of closest approach reaches a critical value E_c. The total reaction cross-section is then readily found, in the absence of intermolecular forces, to be:

$$\sigma(E) = \sigma(E = \infty) \ (1 - E_c/E); \ \ E > E_c$$

$$\sigma(E) = 0; \qquad\qquad\qquad E \leqslant E_c.$$

(8.48)

Recently, modifications to include additional steric and energy dependent factors have been made to improve agreement with more detailed calculations (R. Grice et al., 1970).

A more specialised model has been developed for stripping reactions. In this *spectator* model, discussed in Section 8.6, simplicity is bought at the price of entirely neglecting the motion of the spectator group after stripping and the effect of intermolecular forces beforehand. Models of this type are important because they represent limiting cases to which a variety of reactions tend, if only over a limited energy range. Models in which angular momentum effects are neglected would also fall into this class. Thus, it has been pointed out (J. D. McDonald et al., 1972) that in the series of reactions $H, D + X_2$, the very light mass of the hydrogen isotopes considerably simplifies the inter-relation of the potential surface and angular scattering pattern of the products. Both the linear and angular momentum of the initial motion provide severe kinematic restraints on the scattering pattern, but in this series of reactions ($X = Cl \ldots I$) the reduced mass of the reactants is almost constant and the relative initial momentum very small; changes in reactive scattering among the systems are thus largely due to changes in the potential surface. Particularly in the case of reactions with late energy release, we can picture the following sequence of events; the H atom reaches the transition state by a virtually straight line trajectory and the X_2 bond then breaks with repulsion of the products which move away along the line of centres of the two heavy X atoms. This mechanism focuses attention on the geometry of the transition state, for which one can picture two extreme models:

(i) The three atoms, H–X–X must be collinear to within some specified small solid angle $\Delta\Omega$ for reaction to occur.
(ii) There is no restriction on the geometry of the transition state.

It is now a simple exercise to calculate the two product scattering patterns, $\sigma_R(\chi)$. From (i) we calculate the deflection function of the product, $\chi_{pr}(b)$ (where b is the impact parameter of the *reactants*) to be (see Fig. 8.28)

$$\chi_{pr}(b) = \sin^{-1} b/R_c \qquad (8.49)$$

where R_c is the critical distance of approach for reaction. The differential cross-section for reaction is then:

$$\sigma_R(\chi) = \frac{b\mathscr{P}(b)}{\sin\chi \left|\dfrac{d\chi}{db}\right|} = R_C^2 \cos\chi \frac{\Delta\Omega}{4\pi} \qquad (8.50)$$

where $P(b)$ is the probability that, when the H atom strikes the sphere radius R_c it finds the X_2 molecule in a suitable orientation for reaction. The total cross-section is clearly $\Delta\Omega R_c^2/4$. Alternatively (see again Fig. 8.28 where this is emphasized), we can regard the $\cos\chi$ factor as coming from the angle dependent illumination of the reactant sphere by the incident H beam.

The consequences of model (ii) are very simple; since the X–X axis is isotropically distributed at the time of impact, the product departs isotropically.

In practice, the observed pattern is peaked at between $35°$ and $90°$ from the direction of approach of the H atom. We will not pursue the implications of this, but merely remark that some other ingredient, perhaps depending on the relative velocity at the turning point, must be put into the model.

There is no doubt that in the description of reaction by classical models the most important developments have been provided by the computer simulation method for studying many body collisions. A Monte Carlo algorithm is used to choose the starting configurations and the coupled equations of motion are integrated by any one of several stepwise procedures. Properties such as $\sigma_R(\chi)$ and energy partitioning are then determined as an average over an ensemble of trajectories. Consideration of these methods falls naturally into three parts; the choice of the initial conditions, the solution of the equations of motion and the adjustment of the potential hypersurface

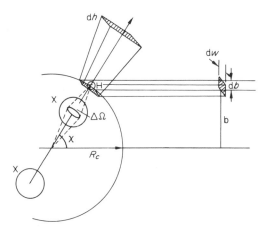

Fig. 8.28 A simple model for impulsive reactive scattering. H atoms incident in a plane wave from the right illuminate the reactant sphere with an intensity proportional to cos χ. If an X_2 molecule is encountered in the solid angle $d\Omega$ about χ, reaction ensues and the HX product departs along the line of centres of X_2. The detector, width dh, subtends an area $R_c d\chi dW$ on the reactant sphere. Thus, for an H atom to reach the detector as HX, it must be incident through an area dwdb, where $db = R_c d\chi \cos \chi$. Hence the differential cross-section is proportional to cos χ, Equation 8.50.

over which the reaction proceeds. The starting values that must be specified in a classical calculation are quite different from those of a quantum calculation. In the former, position, velocity and phase of motion replace the quantum state of the wave mechanical prescription. Luckily, the phase factors usually have little effect on final outcome so that a fairly coarse scan can be used for this parameter. The initial impact parameters must, however, be chosen from a uniform distribution between 0 and b_{max}^2, where b_{max} is taken as the limiting value of b above which the trajectories cannot influence the reactive scattering. Selection of the velocities of the particles (which determine the initial rotational and vibrational energy) will depend on the purposes of the calculation, which may either be to mimic a particular incident quantum channel or to represent the conditions in an experiment with less perfect resolution. In the latter case the velocities must be drawn from the correct Boltzmann distribution. The orientation angles of the colliding molecules (the phase of the rotation) are then selected (in the ensemble average case) to provide a uniform probability for collision with respect to orientation.

The most convenient formulation of the classical equations of motion is Hamilton's which, for an N-particle system, takes the form of 6N-6 coupled first order differential equations for the relative motion of the particles:

$$\frac{\partial H}{\partial p_i} = \dot{q}_i; \quad \frac{\partial H}{\partial q_i} = -\dot{p}_i \tag{8.51}$$

where the p_i's and q_i's are the conjugate momenta and displacements. The Hamiltonian is of the usual form,

$$H = \frac{1}{2} \sum_{i=1}^{N-1} m_i(\dot{q}_{ix}^2 + \dot{q}_{zy}^2 + \dot{q}_{iy}^2 + \dot{q}_{iz}^2) + \sum_{i \neq j}^{N-1} \sum^{N-1} V(R_{ij}). \tag{8.52}$$

For a potential $V(R_{ij})$ defined in terms of all the interparticle distances (Equation 8.51) is solved by stepwise integration, such as the method of Runge and Kutta or by a predictor-corrector routine. The procedure is quite standard, though since a trajectory may take a second or more to compute, an efficient process is required. The stability of the calculation with regard to round-off error etc., is usually monitored by observing the conservation of energy (in the form of the Hamiltonian) and angular momentum during the collision.

In analysing the results of these computed trajectories, the final angle emergence (irrespective of the out-of-plane angle) from the collision together with the final relative velocity are noted. A histogram is then built up of the number of trajectories emerging in equal angular intervals $\Delta\chi$. This histogram is the classical numerical approximation to the differential cross-section and approaches statistically a smooth function as the number of trajectories is increased. With so many parameters to scan, the convergence is slow; Fig. 8.29 illustrates a typical histogram after 400 trajectories have been run and although the distribution clearly denotes strong back scattering of atom C (i.e. the diatomic product is forward scattered and the mechanism is a stripping one), it is far from smooth.

The relationship between the differential cross-section as computed, $q(\chi)$ and the true cross-section $\sigma_R(\chi)$, is simply

$$q(\chi)\Delta\chi = 2\pi \int_{\chi}^{\chi+\Delta\chi} \sigma_R(\chi) \sin \chi d\chi \tag{8.53}$$

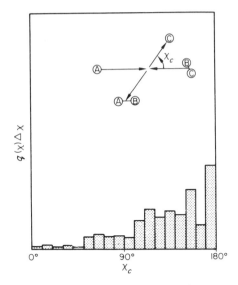

Fig. 8.29 A typical histogram after 400 trajectories compiled from ten initial values of χ_{BC}, ten of ϕ_{BC} and four values of the impact parameter. The reaction is a typical recoil one.

and so the total reaction cross-section is:

$$\sigma_{R\,tot} \simeq \int_0^{\pi} q(\chi)\mathrm{d}\chi. \qquad (8.54)$$

From a physical point of view, the most interesting feature of these model calculations is in the effect of the form of the potential on the type of scattering pattern. Before any detailed comparisons are made, a body of such calculations serves to 'educate' the intuition in this field. For this purpose we need an analytic form for the many body potential that is flexible enough to describe the variety of interactions encountered in reactive scattering and in which each adjustable parameter is as nearly as possible uniquely related to a key topographical feature of the surface.

Taking an example from elastic scattering, we might wish to test if a certain scattering phenomenon is a sensitive function of the well depth; for this purpose it would be unsuitable to take an intermolecular potential of the form:

$$V(R) = C_n R^{-n} - C_6 R^{-6} \qquad (8.55)$$

because varying either C_n or C_6 alters the well depth. The natural choice in this case is:

$$V(R) = \frac{6\epsilon}{n-6} \left\{ \left(\frac{R_{AB}^0}{R} \right)^n - \frac{n}{6} \left(\frac{R_{AB}^0}{R} \right)^6 \right\} \tag{8.56}$$

where altering R_{AB}^0 does not influence the well depth ϵ. If, however, the effect to be investigated were changes in the long range part of the potential, the form (Equation 8.55) would be adopted. When we come to consider the potential energy of a group of three atoms A, B and C, of which A and B and B and C are known to form stable diatomic molecules, the simplest analytical expression for the potential would seem to be the sum of the two separate diatomic potentials. If we represent these by Morse functions (thereby introducing the approximation that will be implicit throughout this section that the long range part of the potential plays no part in the reactive scattering) the result is:

$$V = D_{AB} \{1 - e^{-\beta_{AB}(R_{AB} - R_{AB}^0)}\}^2 + D_{BC} \{1 - e^{-\beta_{BC}(R_{BC} - R_{BC}^0)}\}^2 \tag{8.57}$$

where D_{AB} and D_{BC} are the dissociation energies of Ab and BC respectively and R^0 is the relevant equilibrium diatomic separation. This potential is mapped in Fig. 8.30 for a collinear configuration in the familiar form of a contour diagram. Inspection of the surface shows that it is characterized by a deep potential minimum corresponding to a stable triatomic molecule ABC without preference for a bent or linear configuration. Although a potential of this form would be a possible choice for a system such as $O(^1S) + CO$, there is no reason to suppose that it is suitable for the systems so far examined by beam methods that fall into class I or II. This is confirmed by trajectory calculations using potentials of the form Equation 8.57 from which it is found that for those impact parameters that permit the system to enter the well, a long lived complex is almost invariably formed and the atoms execute several vibrations before dissociating. This, in turn, leads to an almost isotropic distribution of products in the centre of mass frame (see the more detailed discussion in Section 8.2).

Two improvements suggest themselves; the introduction of repulsion between non-bonded atoms and the progressive attenuation of existing bonds as another atom approaches. These changes are incorporated in the N. C. Blais

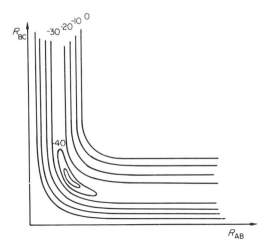

Fig. 8.30 Contour diagram of the potential
$V = D_{AB} \{1 - \exp \ (-\beta(R_{AB} - R_{AB}^{\circ}))\}^2 +$
$D_{BC} \{1 - \exp (-\beta(R_{BC} - R_{BC}^{\circ}))\}^2$ for a collinear configuration. Arbitrary energy units.

and D. L. Bunker (1962) potential:

$$V = D_{AB} \{1 - e^{-\beta_{AB}(R_{AB} - R_{AB}^{\circ})}\}^2$$
$$+ D_{BC} \{1 - e^{-\beta_{BC}(R_{BC} - R_{BC}^{\circ})}\}^2$$
$$+ D_{BC} \{1 - \tanh (aR_{AB} + c) \, e^{-\beta_{BC}(R_{BC} - R_{BC}^{\circ})}\}$$
$$+ D_{AC} \, e^{-\beta_{AC}(R_{AC} - R_{AC}^{\circ})} \qquad (8.58)$$

where the third term introduces a tanh cut-off in the attractive part of the AB
potential and the fourth term is an exponential repulsion between the
non-bonded atoms. The adjustable parameters are now four − a, c, β and
R_{AC}°. The tanh attenuation factor reaches a value of 0.5 at a value of the
argument roughly equal to 0.55 and the steepness of the cut-off is determined
by a. According to the value of c, such a potential can either be of the early
or the late downhill type, illustrated in Fig. 8.31. In the former, the major
energy release (potential drop) occurs when R_{AB} is still appreciably greater
than its equilibrium value and in the latter case the energy release
accompanies the repulsion of C which does not begin until the A−B bond is
nearly complete. These two types of surface differ sharply in the distribution
of the reaction exoergicity that they yield in the products. The early downhill
type produces much more internal excitation than the late downhill surface.

The results from this surface with the parameters set to model the $K + CH_3I$ reaction were not in accord with experiment. The computed differential cross-section for CH_3 scattering peaked at somewhat less than $90°$ and the total reaction cross-section was ~ 400 Å^2.

In the failure of potential (Equation 8.58), one weakness is clear. The force between the approaching A and B atoms is that of the full bonding force of the AB molecule, even though atom C is still present. The introduction of a second tanh function to switch between a bonded and a non-bonded force between A and B is clearly necessary:

$$V = D_{AB}\{1 - \exp(-\beta_1(R_{AB} - R_{AB}^0))\}^2$$
$$+ D_{BC}\{1 - \exp(-\beta_2(R_{BC} - R_{BC}^0))\}^2$$
$$+ D_{BC}\{1 - \tanh(a_1 R_{AB} + c_1)\}\exp(-\beta_2(R_{BC} - R_{BC}^0))$$
$$+ D_{AB}\{1 - \tanh(a_2 R_{BC} + c_2)\}\exp(-\beta_1(R_{AB} - R_{AB}^0))$$
$$+ D_{AC}\exp(-\beta_3(R_{AC} - R_{AC}^0)) \tag{8.59}$$

With this type of surface, Fig. 8.32, the total reaction cross-section for CH_3I/K was ≈ 25 Å^2 with strong backward peaking of the KI in good agreement with experiment (L. M. Raff and M. Karplus, 1966). In a further application of this surface, Raff has investigated the effect of replacing the methyl group in CH_3I by an ethyl group, treating C_2H_5 as a diatomic group held together throughout the reaction by an unattenuated Morse function. In order that both the CH_3 and CH_2 groups participate in the reaction, a repulsion term between the K atom and the CH_3 centre of mass was introduced. In spite of the omission of several terms from this potential that a chemist would intuitively consider important, such as the changing properties of the C–C bond in passing from C_2H_5I to the ethyl radical, the conclusion that the ethyl radical carries away between 10 per cent and 20 per cent of the energy released as internal motion is probably qualitatively correct. This type of calculation should stimulate the study of such reactions by I. R. chemiluminescence and by crossed-beam product velocity analysis so the energy partitioning can be pinned down.

In a series of calculations using idealised surfaces, Polanyi and his co-workers (M. H. Mok and J. C. Polanyi, 1969) have explored the effect of early and late energy release on the energy partitioning and the effectiveness of vibrational compared with translational energy in providing the energy of activation.

These simulation calculations have now been made for quite a range of molecular systems including those of the stripping and recoil types. In all

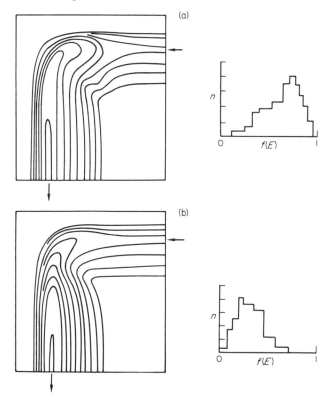

Fig. 8.31 Two surfaces illustrating early (i) and late (ii) release of the energy of reaction. The particles enter in the top valley and exit at the bottom. The corresponding fraction of the total available energy $f(E)$ that appears as internal motion of the products is plotted on the left, where n is the number of trajectories. (D. L. Bunker and N. C. Blais, 1964)

cases potentials capable of reproducing the angular scattering have been found, though the uniqueness of such surfaces is doubtful. An example of two rather different potentials that can give a similar scattering pattern introduces the concept of charge migration. In the reactions of the alkalis with the halogens, the electron transferred must take up a final position on one or other of the two halogen atoms as the products depart, but whether this electron can migrate from one halogen atom to the other during the collision according to the prevailing electric field arising from the cation is a question that, although not susceptible to direct experiment, must be settled before the potential can be written down. The work of Polanyi's school (P. J. Kuntz et al., 1969; M. Godfrey and M. Karplus, 1968) showed that, with only

Fig. 8.32 The co-linear potential energy surface for K + CH$_3$I, with the CH$_3$ group treated as a point mass. (From L. M. Raff and M. Karplus, 1966), surface (8.59).

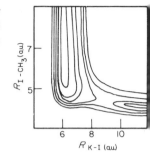

Typical trajectories over the modified Bunker and Blais surface used by Raff and Karplus for the K + CH$_3$I reaction. A direct reactive collision is shown, for which the time while all the particle separations are small is 5 x 10^{-13} s.

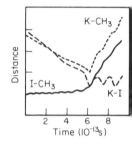

a weakly repulsive potential between the atom and ion of the newly formed X$_2^-$ charge migration, if allowed, frequently occurred and was found necessary to achieve the forward scattering found in practice. However, if an X$_2^-$ potential is adopted that is strongly repulsive (see Fig. 8.8), then the required forward scattering can be obtained without invoking charge migration, (N. C. Blaise, 1968). This sort of question is best settled by a direct investigation of the kinematics of electron/halogen dissociative attachment collisions.

The broader question of the uniqueness of the potential surfaces that fit reactive scattering data turns on the amount of experimental detail available and the energy range over which $\sigma_R(\theta), v$) is measured. At the present time, the spread in initial energy and angular momentum, together with the operation of simple reduced mass effects, often obscures the changes in the potential energy surface in a related series of reactions. There is currently a need for a parallel development in ab initio calculations of these surfaces; with increasing refinement of the scattering data they will both hopefully converge on the 'true' many body potential.

8.8   Summary of observations and reaction models

Most of the reactions so far investigated by crossed-beam techniques are of the direct type in which the product is scattered into a relatively narrow angular range. These reactions comprise the thermal energy reactions of the alkali metals with halogen containing compounds and some reactions of halogen atoms and of hydrogen atoms. A much smaller class of reactions, notably those of the alkali metals with their halides, exhibit a symmetrical bipolar CM distribution. These reactions are thought to proceed through the formation of a complex that survives for several rotational periods, i.e. that has a lifetime τ greater than $\sim 10^{-13}$ sec. All bimolecular collisions can be assigned a place on the lifetime scale but, even for a given pair of molecules, τ is a function of the relative angular momentum and energy. It so happens that under current experimental conditions the reactions so far investigated fall into the short and long-lived groups with respect to τ, but examples will undoubtedly be found of an intermediate character. Furthermore, as the colliding energy increases it is probable that the lifetime of collisions that lead to reaction decreases and those proceeding via complex formation become direct, though probably with a change in the nature of the reaction products.

In the field of direct reactions, a fairly good correlation is observed in the following properties; dominant CM scattering angle, magnitude of the total reaction cross-section and the angular position of the onset of attenuation in the elastic scattering. The ranges of behaviour in these observables can be displayed in the following table in which the correlations are vertical:

Property	Trend		
$\sigma_R(\chi)$	forward peaked $\longrightarrow$	sideways $\longrightarrow$	backward peaked
σ_R	large ($\gtrsim 100$ Å^2) $\longrightarrow$	medium $\longrightarrow$	small ($\lesssim 30$ Å^2)
$\sigma_{el}(\chi)$	Monotonic fall in intensity with angle $\longrightarrow$	rainbow appears $\longrightarrow$	full rainbow and supernumerary structure
$\sigma_{tot}(E)$	Monotonic energy dependence $\longrightarrow$	undulations appear $\longrightarrow$	full undulatory behaviour
$\sigma_R(\chi, v)$	Very high product excitation $\longrightarrow$	lower product excitation	

The behaviour of a reaction with respect to the last two properties, energy dependence of the total cross-section and energy partitioning in the products, is less predictable from the position of the reaction with respect to the first three properties.

The existence of these correlations points to the operation of a single potential energy surface (i.e. to the absence of non-adiabatic effects) in each reaction and these surfaces, though differing widely in chemical nature, are all characterized by a potential that falls monotonically along the reaction path (i.e. zero activation energy). If a reaction fails to conform to the above trends, strong inelastic scattering may be the cause which can destroy the structure in $\sigma(E)$ and $\sigma(\chi)$, or a complex may be formed. In the latter case, with τ approximately equal to the rotational period of the complex, the product could still be thrown forwards or sideways but the total reaction cross-section need not be large.

The bunching of examples at either end of the various scales listed above suggests the use of simple models, two of which have achieved considerable importance – spectator stripping for reactions of large cross-section and recoil for those of small cross-section. Of these the stripping mechanism is capable of simple quantitative development and deviations from it serve as a measure of spectator participation both in neutral/neutral and ion/neutral reactions. Deficiencies in the model are numerous at thermal energies and the spectator generally plays a part in carrying off some of the energy liberated. Peculiar to reactions involving atoms of low ionization potential is the harpooning mechanism which leads to reactions of large cross-section and also suggests a convenient form for the initial part of the potential energy surface. Some of these surfaces have been described in Section 8.7 and have been quite successful in accounting for our knowledge of stripping reactions at thermal energies. The recoil mechanism is not so precise in its predictions or in formulating the nature of the potential surface and simply states that the pronounced back scattering found in these reactions is due (i) to the predominance of small impact parameter collisions in causing reaction and (ii) to the essentially binary rather than multiple nature of the reactive collision. Product back scattering, as in elastic scattering, is due to repulsion in this case of the newly formed products. Qualitative factors of interest are firstly the early or late release of the energy of reaction and secondly the directionality of the incident channel. The latter factor is related to the degree of linearity of the transition state and affects both orientation dependence of the reaction cross-section and the extent of sideways scattering.

Reactions proceeding via long lived complexes (lifetimes greater than their rotational period) are comparatively poorly represented in the beam literature in contrast to their important role in very low energy ion/molecule reactions and in unimolecular reactions. The reasons for this are probably (i) that neutral aggregates of a few atoms of which one is an alkali metal do not usually exhibit a pronounced potential minimum in the transition state configuration, (ii) most of the vibrational modes of the reactant molecules are inactive during the collision, (iii) the reactions studied are all exothermic. The only examples of the alkali metals participating in these reactions so far encountered are their reactions with the alkali halides, SF_6 and, possibly, $H + K_2$, $H + Na_2$. As non-alkali systems become increasingly explored, especially those involving free radicals, this type of mechanism will no doubt become more common.

Theory is well prepared to deal with them through conventional transition state methods for the lifetime and energy partitioning, by angular momentum analysis for the angular scattering and perhaps by the prediction and observation of resonances.

The energy partitioning between translational and internal motion is an important additional observable that helps to define the potential energy surface. In neutral **beam** experiments to date, this has been achieved most usually by velocity analysis of one of the scattered products. These results, taken in conjunction with the mean energy partitioning from infra-red chemiluminescence and flash photolysis studies, show that a wide range of the total available energy may be found in the rotation and vibration of the products, from $\leqslant 25$ per cent to virtually 100 per cent. The most detailed results in this area promise to come from a marriage of I.R. luminescence or fluorescence and crossed-beam techniques by which the angular distribution of product excitation can be measured.

In almost all the reactions so far studied in beams, there has only been a single reactive exit channel open. As the relative kinetic energy or the complexity of the molecules increases, new reactive channels open up and the dimensionality of the potential energy surface increases. The amount of data needed to make a choice between various many-body potentials then escalates so that detailed analysis of only one of the scattered products becomes rapidly less useful. The exploration of these more complicated reactions has in the past been confined to bulb kinetic measurements of the reaction rates into the various product channels. There is now the possibility with existing beam techniques of measuring the relative cross-sections for the formation of the various products as a function of the angle and energy of scattering. Even under these more complicated conditions, an optical analysis of the true elastic scattering remains a simple way of summarizing the effects that remove incident particles from the beam. Some of the most exciting prospects in beam work are in the field of chemical reaction between simple molecules under unfamiliar conditions. New correlations and new models will surely be needed as an increasing range of reaction parameters such as activation energy and initial electronic state are explored.

CHAPTER NINE

Inelastic Scattering

Although the molecular beam technique has illuminated a whole area of chemical reaction and revolutionized the determination of intermolecular forces, its impact in understanding inelastic collisions has been much less dramatic. There are two reasons for this. The more important is that detection of single quantum state changes or the transfer of small amounts of internal energy is much more difficult than the detection of the gross effects of chemical change. This has the secondary effect that the theory needed to interpret such results must be correspondingly detailed. Although for a given system both reaction and inelastic processes may occur on the same potential surface, it is not yet clear how far the methods of classical mechanics that were central to the interpretation of reactive scattering can take us in discussing quantum changes. Nevertheless, although not ideally suited to the task, it is probable that classical mechanics will not be grossly in error when applied to vibrational and rotational energy transfer.

In this section the reader will not find tables of potential anisotropies or coefficients giving the dependence of the intermolecular potential on the internal co-ordinates of the system. As with relating chemical reaction to a potential surface, one is up against the problem of uniqueness. The terms in an intermolecular potential responsible for inelastic effects can rarely be reduced to a single parameter and in order to unravel a multiparameter situation detailed cross-sections (i.e. those between single quantum channels) over a wide angular or energy range are needed. These are not yet available. It is only in curve crossing problems – which result in electronic excitation – that one is possibly dealing with an effect governed by two quite different parameters (Section 9.4.iii) whose effects can be separated.

360

The extension of the quantum theory of scattering to more complicated systems in which chemical reaction and energy transfer can take place is possible in a formal sense and is currently the subject of investigation (R. D. Levine, 1969). The required formalism based on the S matrix has already been developed in the elementary particle and nuclear physics fields (T. Y. Wu and T. Ohmura, 1962). However, methods useful at high energies or where only a very few partial waves are involved are less useful in molecular systems and there is a great need for approximate methods. In this book we discuss these approximations in relation to energy transfer processes since theory and experiment can march more closely here and some systems may be sufficiently simple to permit comparison of theory and experiment at several levels of sophistication. The discussion of the theory given here is very much in outline and is intended to illuminate general principles and to show what is needed from experiment rather than to provide a working knowledge for the theorist. Excellent and more detailed accounts for the latter purpose can be found in R. D. Levine, 1969; N. F. Mott and H. S. W. Massey, 1965; D. R. Bates, 1961; M. L. Goldberger and K. Watson, 1964.

Experimental information on these processes is available from a number of sources including spectral line broadening, relaxation measurements of various types and shock tube data (R. G. Gordon et al., 1968) but we restrict the present discussion to scattering methods. Once again we shall see that the beam technique promises unique detail in providing not only probability but also phase information.

Beam measurements on inelastic processes can be divided into three classes according to the exact technique employed. There is the 'velocity change' method in which the pre and post collisions velocities are measured and the corresponding translational to internal energy change inferred. The 'state change' method in which state filters (usually operating on rotation or spin state properties) are used to select the incident beam and then to analyze the scattered particles. Finally, photon, ion or excited atom emission from the collision zone may be monitored.

9.1 The S matrix

The elements comprising the S matrix have already been defined in Chapter 6 as the ratio of the amplitude of the outgoing partial wave in one channel to the incident amplitude in some other channel. For the central force elastic problem only the diagonal elements were non-zero; in inelastic collisions the off-diagonal terms will play an essential role. Of course, as shown in the discussion on singlet-triplet scattering, Section 6.16, transformation of the S matrix to a new description based on a more convenient set of quantum states may diagonalize a matrix that would otherwise appear to involve inelastic effects. In this section we assume that such simplifying transformations as are possible have already been made. (See also Section 9.3iii.)

Consider collisions of the type:

$$A_i + B_j \longrightarrow A_k + B_l \tag{9.1}$$

where particles in specific states i and j collide with a velocity corresponding to a wave number k_α. The wave function for a particular partial wave, relative angular momentum l, in the entrance channel $A_i + B_j$, which we label α, is:

$$\psi_{\alpha l 0} = R^{-1} \, Y_{l0} \, (\chi, \phi) \, u_{\alpha l 0}(R) \phi_\alpha \tag{9.2}$$

where ϕ_α is the total wave function of the two isolated species A_i and B_j appropriately symmetrised. $U_{\alpha l m}(r)$ is the translational wave function and Y_{lm} is a spherical harmonic. As usual only the asymptotic behaviour of $u_{\alpha l m}(r)$ is of importance and we can write:

$$u_{\alpha l 0} \xrightarrow[R \to \infty]{} k_\alpha^{-\frac{1}{2}} \, [\mathscr{B}_{\alpha l 0} \, e^{-i(k_\alpha R - l\pi/2)} - \mathscr{A}_{\alpha l 0} \, e^{i(k_\alpha R - l\pi/2)}] \quad \text{(a)}$$

$$u_{\alpha' l' m'} \xrightarrow[R \to \infty]{} k_{\alpha'}^{-\frac{1}{2}} \, \mathscr{A}_{\alpha' l' m'} \, e^{i(k'_\alpha R - l\pi/2)} \quad \text{(b)}$$

$$\tag{9.3}$$

where in distinction to the case of purely elastic scattering, Equation 6.56, the ingoing and outgoing amplitudes are no longer equal and the inelastic channels α' have only outgoing waves. The amplitudes of the outgoing partial waves follow from the definition of the S matrix as:

$$\mathscr{A}_{\alpha' l' m'} = S_{\alpha l 0 : \alpha' l' m'} \, \mathscr{B}_{\alpha l 0} \tag{9.4}$$

for transitions between the entrance partial wave $\alpha l 0$ and the exit channel $\alpha' l' m'$. The range of states available is of course limited by the requirement that the total angular momentum and energy be conserved during the collision.

The boundary conditions of interest in the calculation of cross-sections, i.e. an incident plane wave associated only with state α, can be achieved by correct choice of the incident amplitudes $\mathscr{B}_{\alpha l 0}$, so that (comparing Equation 6.61):

$$2i\,\mathcal{B}_{\alpha l0} = -i^l(4\pi)^{1/2}\,k_\alpha^{-1/2}\,(2l+1)^{1/2} \tag{9.5}$$

and

$$2i\,\mathcal{A}_{\alpha'l'm'} = -S_{\alpha l0:\alpha'l'm'}\,i^l\left(\frac{4\pi}{k_\alpha'}\right)^{1/2}(2l+1)^{1/2}. \tag{9.6}$$

Since all partial waves are populated in the incident wave the amplitude in any exit channel α' must sum all their different contributions, i.e. the matrix relation

$$\mathcal{A} = S\mathcal{B} \tag{9.7}$$

must be used so that the differential cross-section for scattering in the inelastic channel α' from an incident plane wave in the channel α is:

$$|f_\alpha^{\alpha'}(\chi,\phi)|^2 = \frac{4\pi}{k_\alpha k_\alpha'}\left|\frac{1}{2i}\sum_l i^l(2l+1)^{1/2}\sum_{l'm'} i^{-l'}S_{\alpha l0:\alpha'l'm'}\,Y_{l'm'}(\chi,\phi)\right|^2. \tag{9.8}$$

The summation over $l'm'$ calculates the scattering resulting from a single incident partial wave, l, and the first summation over l, accounts for all the partial waves in the incident flux.

In the usual way the total cross-section for the processes $\alpha \to \alpha'$ is:

$$\sigma_\alpha^{\alpha'} = \frac{\pi}{k_\alpha^2}\sum_{l'm'}\left|\sum_l (2l+1)^{1/2}\,i^l\,S_{\alpha l0:\alpha'l'm'}\right|^2. \tag{9.9}$$

The summation over l' and m' is formally over all the accessible states satisfying the energy and angular momentum constraints.

As already discussed in Section 6.16 the S matrix calculated in one representation may be transformed to alternative descriptions if required.

9.2 Wave equation for inelastic scattering

The formalism of the S matrix just described is a convenient 'store' for all possible experimental information about the molecular collision. The calculation of the elements in the matrix, however, must involve the solution of the total wave function for the system. As an example of the formulation of the required wave equation and to provide a basis for discussion of the several approximate methods useful in its solution, we consider (as a special case of Equation 9.1):

$$A + B_i \longrightarrow A + B_n \qquad (9.10)$$

where A is a structureless particle and B has a Hamiltonian $H_B(r_B)$ for its internal motion (the coordinate r_B represents all the internal coordinates of B). After an encounter at a relative wave number k_i the particle B may be excited to any of its states which are accessible. The exit wave number k_n will then be:

$$k_n^2 = \frac{2\mu}{\hbar^2} \Delta E + k_i^2. \qquad (9.11)$$

Energetically closed channels will have an imaginary wave number since they cannot result in unbounded solutions, but only in exponentially decaying ones.

The unperturbed states of the target B are given in the usual way by:

$$H_B(r_B)\phi_n = E_n\phi_n, \qquad (9.12)$$

where E_n and ϕ_n are the eigen-values and functions appropriate to B. The Hamiltonian for the complete collision system will be:

$$H = -\frac{\hbar^2}{2\mu}\nabla_R^2 + H_B(r_B) + V(R, r_B) \qquad (9.13)$$

and $V(R, r_B)$ is the interaction potential between A and B. This must be a function of the internal coordinates of B if inelastic effects are to occur. The system wave function ϕ can be expanded in terms of the complete set ϕ_n as:

$$\Psi(R, r_B) = (\sum_n + \int) \phi_n(r_B) F_n(R) \qquad (9.14)$$

where both the continuum and discrete states of ϕ are included. $F_n(R)$ is the translational wave function in the exit channel n and asymptotically at large R will have the form:

$$F_i(R) = e^{ik_i z} + R^{-1} e^{ik_i R} f_i(\chi, \phi) \qquad (9.15)$$

$$F_n(R) = R^{-1} e^{ik_n R} f_n(\chi, \phi) \qquad (9.16)$$

for the elastic and inelastic channels respectively. With the expansion

(Equation 9.14) and the Hamiltonian (Equation 9.13) the total system wave equation is:

$$\left(\sum_n + \int \right) \phi_n(\mathbf{r_B}) \left[\frac{\hbar^2}{2\mu} \nabla_{\mathbf{R}}^2 + E + \frac{k_i^2 \hbar^2}{2\mu} - E_n \right] F_n(\mathbf{R}) = V(\mathbf{R},\mathbf{r_B})\Psi(\mathbf{R},\mathbf{r_B}) \quad (9.17)$$

where the result $H_B(\mathbf{r_B})\phi_n = \phi_n E_n$ has been used. To proceed further we multiply Equation 9.17 by $\phi_n^*(\mathbf{r_B})$ and integrate over $\mathbf{r_B}$, i.e. all the internal coordinates of B, to obtain:

$$\left\{ \frac{\hbar^2}{2\mu} \nabla_{\mathbf{R}}^2 + E - E_n \right\} F_n(\mathbf{R}) = \sum_m F_m(\mathbf{R}) \int \phi_n^*(\mathbf{r_B})V(\mathbf{R},\mathbf{r_B})\phi_m(\mathbf{r_B})d\mathbf{r_B}. \quad (9.18)$$

where there is a term on the R.H.S. for each state of the target. This still exact result can be written more succinctly by defining a matrix element $\mathscr{V}_{nm}$ of the intermolecular potential:

$$\mathscr{V}_{nm}(\mathbf{R}) = \frac{2\mu}{\hbar^2} \int \phi_n^*(\mathbf{r_B}) V(\mathbf{R},\mathbf{r_B})\phi_m(\mathbf{r_B})d\mathbf{r_B} \quad (9.19)$$

so producing the set:

$$[\nabla_{\mathbf{R}}^2 + k_0^2] F_0(\mathbf{R}) = \sum_m F_m(\mathbf{R}) \mathscr{V}_{0m}(\mathbf{R}),$$
$$\cdots \cdots \cdots \cdots$$
$$[\nabla_{\mathbf{R}}^2 + k_n^2] F_n(\mathbf{R}) = \sum_m F_m(\mathbf{R}) \mathscr{V}_{nm}(\mathbf{R}) \quad (9.20)$$

We can see from Equation 9.19 that the perturbation must be of the correct symmetry with respect to $\mathbf{r_B}$ if $\mathscr{V}_{mn}$ is to be non-zero. In practice this does not yield any useful collisional selection rules except in the limit of weak coupling.

The Equations 9.20 are hardly directly useful as they stand since not only is there an infinite number of them but also most computational schemes would be carried out after a partial wave expansion thus multiplying the number of equations still further. After applying the partial wave expansion to the $F_n(\mathbf{R})$ and solving the set of Equations 9.20, the S matrix elements $S_{nlo:n'l'm'}$ would in principle be obtained from the lth translational wave function once it had settled down to its asymptotic form:

$$F_{n'l'm'}(R) \longrightarrow |F_{n'l'm'}| e^{i(k_n'R - l\pi/2 - \eta_{n'l'm'})}. \quad (9.21)$$

If the calculation were started with a wave of unit amplitude in the incident channel (*nlo*) we obtain from Equation 9.4:

$$S_{nl0:n'l'm'} = \left(\frac{k_n'}{k_n}\right)^{1/2} \left| F_{n'l'm'} \right| e^{i\eta_{n'l'm'}} \tag{9.22}$$

These S matrix elements may then be used in Equations 9.8 and 9.9 to compute differential cross-sections. Note that while there will be interference between partial waves of different l' values in a given inelastic exit channel, this will not occur between different exit channels since $k_n \neq k_n'$, i.e. the wavelengths are different.

9.3   Approximation methods

Further simplifications must be made if anything but a formal solution to the basic Equations 9.20 is required. A large number of different schemes have been proposed. Almost inevitably it is necessary to close the infinite set of coupled equations by selecting only a few channels for calculation, equivalent to representing ϕ by a limited number of terms in the expansion of Equation 9.14. In electronic excitation problems this is not a high price to pay because the conservation of energy severely limits the number of open exit channels and at most one or two virtual states might be required; but for rotational energy transfer where a quantum of energy is a small fraction of the incident kinetic energy at least ten rotational states might have to be included and classical mechanics is strongly indicated. Approximate quantum methods can be broadly classified into those that treat both the internal and relative motion quantum mechanically and those that introduce the concept of a classical path for the relative motion. Each of these classes can then be subdivided by the number of internal states that is included in the quantum description of the target (D. R. Bates, 1961).

(i) The close coupling approximation

In this, the most rigorous method, a limited number of channels are selected and the resulting set of coupled equations of the form of Equation 9.20 solved numerically. The effect of including additional channels can only be explored by repeating the calculations with an expanded basis set. In this method the prime requirement is for a fast and accurate numerical technique and a use of a polynomial approximation to the potential (rather than to the wave function) as discussed in Section 6.8 is particularly attractive. The incorporation of the special boundary conditions into the numerical problem has been discussed by W. A. Lester and R. B. Bernstien (1968) for the particular case of the rotational excitation of a diatomic molecule by an atom.

(ii) The Born approximation

If the coupling and spherically symmetric part of the intermolecular potential are weak enough to produce only small changes in the incident wave, i.e. both small momentum changes and small transition probabilities, the inelastic Born approximation is appropriate. In the spirit of its application to elastic scattering, Section 6.5, we retain only a single term on the right hand side of the leading equation in Equation 9.20 and replace $F_m(\mathbf{R})$ by the incident plane wave. The amplitude in any channel is then considered separately as arising directly from the incident channel and we obtain the completely uncoupled equations

$$\{\nabla_{\mathbf{R}}^2 + k_n^2\}\, F_n(\mathbf{R}) = \mathscr{V}_{ni}(\mathbf{R})\, e^{i\mathbf{k}_i \cdot \mathbf{R}} \tag{9.23}$$

which clearly give the *first order* contribution of the coupling potential to the scattered amplitudes. In the case of the interaction of a homonuclear diatomic molecule with an S state atom, for which the coupling potential would contain the factor $P_2(\cos\beta)$ where β is the angle between $\mathbf{r}$ and $\mathbf{R}$, Equation 9.23 indicates that only $\Delta j = \pm 2$ transitions are allowed (even assuming both odd and even j states to be populated). As in elastic scattering, however, the Born approximation in this form is not really applicable to molecular problems because of the distortion of the plane wave by the diagonal term $\{\mathscr{V}_{ii}\}$. It is, however, an important method for transitions induced by electron/molecule collisions.

Proceeding in the same way as in the elastic case we can go on to obtain the scattering amplitude in the nth channel (using vector notation again) as:

$$f_n(\chi, \phi) = -\frac{\mu}{2\pi\hbar^2} \int e^{i(\mathbf{k}_i - \mathbf{k}_n) \cdot \mathbf{R}}\, \mathscr{V}_{ni}(\mathbf{R})\, d\mathbf{R}. \tag{9.24}$$

(iii) Distorted wave approximation

The D.W.A. is a natural development of the Born method in which we use a better approximation to the wave function in the incident channel. In place of the incident plane wave we now use the wave function calculated assuming that $F_i(\mathbf{R})$ is governed solely by the potential $\mathscr{V}_{ii}(\mathbf{R})$, i.e. solving the equation

$$\{\nabla_{\mathbf{R}}^2 + \mathscr{V}_{ii}(\mathbf{R}) + k_i^2\}\, F_i^{(0)}(\mathbf{R}) = F_i^{(0)}(\mathbf{R}). \tag{9.25}$$

As in the Born approximation the excitation is assumed to be direct from the elastic channel and as an improvement on Equation 9.23 we have:

$$\{ \nabla_{\mathbf{R}}^2 + k_n^2 \} \, F_n(\mathbf{R}) = V_{in}(\mathbf{R}) F_i^{(0)}(\mathbf{R}) \qquad (9.26)$$

where $F_i^{(0)}(\mathbf{R})$ is the unperturbed elastic function from Equation 9.25.

The advantage of this method is that the potential need no longer be weak. All that is required is that the coupling between states should be small, so that while the diagonal terms in the S matrix may be large the off diagonal ones remain small, a fairly common situation. A typical application of this approximation is to vibrational transitions in the system He/H_2 (F. H. Mies, 1965).

(iv) Time dependent perturbation methods

These methods are semi-classical in nature, using classical mechanics to describe the nuclear motion and reserving quantum theory for the internal behaviour. A number of different prescriptions have been used. Their common feature is the calculation of an average classical trajectory and the conversion of the R dependent matrix elements to an equivalent time dependent form. At high velocities, for example, the trajectory might be approximated by a straight line with the appropriate impact parameter b so that:

$$t = (R^2 - b^2)^{1/2}/v. \qquad (9.27)$$

The standard results of time dependent perturbation theory then yield:

$$\dot{a}_1 = (i\hbar)^{-1} \sum_n V_{1n}(t) \, a_n \, e^{i(E_1 - E_n)t/\hbar}$$
$$\vdots$$
$$\dot{a}_m = (i\hbar)^{-1} \sum_n V_{mn}(t) \, a_n \, e^{i(E_m - E_n)t/\hbar}. \qquad (9.28)$$

The matrix elements are those defined previously but with the R dependence replaced by the approximate t dependence and the $|a_n|^2$ are the probabilities of excitation to the state n.

This approximation is useful under the usual requirements for a semi-classical theory — that the trajectory be well defined so that $\lambda \ll$ the potential range. An additional constraint is that the energy change be small with respect to the incident energy so that the trajectories associated with the inelastic process approximate to the elastic path used in calculating the time dependent perturbation.

If the internal motion of the target is also slow in comparison with the relative velocity a further simplification, the 'Sudden' approximation can be obtained and at $t = \infty$ the final amplitudes are:

$$a_n^\infty = \int \phi_n^* \, e^{i\int_{-\infty}^\infty V(\mathbf{r}_B, t) \mathrm{d}t/\hbar} \, \phi_i \, \mathrm{d}\mathbf{r}_B. \qquad (9.29)$$

For small transition probabilities a first order approximation to the solution of Equation 9.28 is useful:

$$a_n^\infty(b) = (i\hbar)^{-1} \int_{-\infty}^\infty V_{ni}(t) \, e^{i(E_n - E_i)t/\hbar} \, \mathrm{d}t \qquad (9.30)$$

and the transition probability $i \to n$ for a trajectory following the path of integration in Equation 9.30 is:

$$\mathscr{P}_{in}(b) = |\, a_n^\infty(b) \,|^2.$$

The total cross-section for the transition is:

$$\sigma_{tot}^{i \to n} = 2\pi \int_0^\infty b \mathscr{P}(b) \, \mathrm{d}b. \qquad (9.31)$$

Expression 9.30 serves to define the regions of strong $a_n^\infty \geqslant 1$, and weak $a_n \ll 1$, coupling and it may also be noted that Equation 9.29 reduces to Equation 9.30 upon expanding the exponential in Equation 9.29 and retaining only the leading term in V. Equation 9.30, if valid for all impact parameters, is essentially equivalent to Equation 9.24. Inspection of Equation 9.30 shows that the integrand is composed of a function $V_{ni}(t)$ that rises to a maximum near the turning point and decays again, while the second factor, $e^{i \Delta E t/\hbar}$, is a rapidly oscillating one. In general, therefore, appreciable transition probabilities will only be obtained in either near resonant cases (ΔE small) or when $V_{ni}(t)$ contains a Fourier component of frequency $\Delta E/\hbar$, which will lead to a region of stationary phase in the integration of Equation 9.30.

(v) Perturbed Stationary State method (PSS)

In the PSS approximation a different expansion for the total system wave function is used. The expression 9.17 in terms of the eigenfunctions of the isolated species is replaced by an expansion in the eigenstates of the *whole* system A + B (D. R. Bates, 1961). The aim of this transformation is to diagonalize the matrix $\{V_{ij}\}$ so that transitions, now due to the *dynamic* coupling of states, are minimized and attention is focused on the non-adiabatic aspects of the problem rather than coupling through the potential energy. The requirement for adiabaticity is that $\Delta Ea/\hbar v \gg 1$, where ΔE and a are, respectively, the separation between the compound states (a function of R) and a is the range over which the new states are a rapidly varying function of R. The dynamic coupling can either be due to the rotation of the AB system or to the relative radial (R) motion. In atomic collision processes in which electronic levels are excited — for which the method was originally devised — this rotational coupling is a troublesome complication. Furthermore, collisions of small impact parameters which are usually the most important in producing inelastic effects, unfortunately have the largest radial velocity so that the approximation can become least useful in the most important region. It is at its most powerful in discussing spin exchange scattering (Section 6.17 or 6.16) where the new molecular states (defined by their total electron spin) can be regarded as completely uncoupled, at least for collisions at thermal speeds and non-adiabatic effects (spin decoupling in this case) only become apparent well above these relative energies.

(vi) Classical mechanics

Treatments based purely on classical arguments will be valid under the same conditions as described for elastic scattering, well defined trajectories that result in momentum changes that are not too small, but with the added requirement that quantization of the internal motion must be reliably modelled by simple box partitioning of the classical energy and momentum transfer. Techniques based on classical trajectories, as is the Monte Carlo approach to chemical reaction, Section 8.7, are useful in dealing with rotational and vibrational excitation.

9.4   Experimental methods

(i) State change technique

This technique is reminiscent of beam resonance spectroscopy in that both selection 'A' and analysis fields 'B' are employed. The RF 'C' field which produces transitions in the spectrometer is, however, replaced by a collision region; either a cross-beam or target chamber may serve this purpose. The resulting transitions are detected by the analyzer field.

Most experiments of this type have used TlF of CsF in the primary beam, molecules with a very large dipole moment which can also be detected by surface ionization methods. As described in Chapter 4, a four pole electric field can focus such diatomic polar molecules at a point dependent upon their effective dipole moment or (jm_j) state and their velocity. The combination of such a field fitted with suitable stops and orifices to define molecular trajectories and a velocity selector can therefore be made to transmit only specified (jm_j) states.

In the experiments of Bennewitz and co-workers (H. G. Bennewitz; K. H. Kramer; W. Paul and J. P. Toennies 1964) total collision cross-sections for TlF in the (1,0) and (1,1) states and CsF (2,0) and (2,2) were measured for a range of atomic and molecular targets. In this work only a single selecting field on the primary beam was used so that the observed total collision cross-sections included contributions from transitions to all the accessible states. A uniform steady electric field was applied throughout the collision zone to maintain the polarization of the beam as prepared by the selector. By applying this field either perpendicular or parallel to the relative velocity the (1,0) or (1,1) polarization of the beam with respect to the collision could be achieved. It was thus possible to make accurate comparisons of the ratio $\sigma_{tot}(1,0)/\sigma_{tot}(1,1)$ over a range of velocities and by a classical impact approximation of the type discussed in Section 9.3 (iv) to obtain estimates for the long and short range potential anisotropies q_6 and q_{12} in a potential of the form:

$$V = \epsilon \left\{ \left(\frac{R_m}{R}\right)^{12} (1 + q_{12} P_2 (\cos \beta)) - 2 \left(\frac{R_m}{R}\right)^6 (1 + q_6 P_2 (\cos \theta)) \right\} .$$

$$(9.32)$$

Both selection and analyzing fields were used in the experiments of J. P. Toennies (1965; 1966), shown schematically in Fig. 9.1. The second, analyzer, field had an acceptance angle of $\sim\frac{1}{2}°$ so that either partial elastic or inelastic cross-sections, $\sigma_{jm ji' m j'}(\theta \sim 0)$ for forward scattering into the acceptance cone could be measured.

The rotation period of the TlF molecule is long compared to the interaction time of the collision, while the energy change (and change in k) associated with a rotational transition is only a small fraction of the translational energy. This situation is a favourable one for the application of time dependent perturbations methods. We may also regard the polar molecule as stationary in orientation during the interaction so that the anistropy in the potential can be treated by post-averaging the results of these computations over all orientations. In this 'sudden' approximation the rotor experiences a brief time dependent electric field in which the appropriate

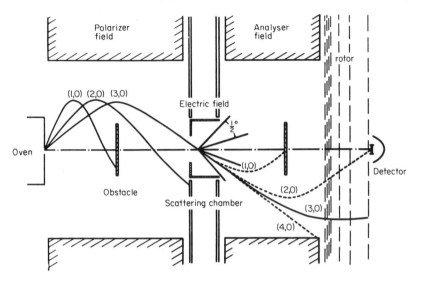

Fig. 9.1 Apparatus used by Toennies to study rotational transitions in TIF produced by collisions. The TIF rotational states are selected in the four pole electric field on the left and are analysed after collision by an identical analyser field. The velocity selector is required to define the velocities through the electric fields and thus to ensure that only the specified states are transmitted. (H. Pauly et al., 1964).

Fourier components can induce transitions $\Delta j = \pm 1$ for dipole interactions, ± 2 for quadrupole ones etc.

Experiments of this type in which interference effects e.g. glories, may in principle be observed make it possible to determine phase relations as well as amplitudes (probabilities) in the exit channels. In comparison most bulk experiments yield only the rate constants for processes and hence no phase information.

(ii) Velocity change method

Measurement of the pre- and post- collisions velocities is frequently sufficient to identify the scattering into specific quantum states if these are well spaced in energy. The ratio of incident and final relative velocities is given by:

$$v_{final}/v_{initial} = \left(\frac{E \mp \Delta E}{E} \right)^{\frac{1}{2}} \tag{9.33}$$

where $E = \frac{1}{2}\mu v^2{}_{initial}$ and ΔE is the exoergicity. The technique becomes less useful at high collision energies or as ΔE decreases since the resolution in E is limited by the spread of incident relative velocities present in the apparatus. In the most favourable case a light test particle in the primary beam interacts with a heavy slow target molecule. An additional reduction in the contribution of the target velocity can be made by moving the detector in a plane perpendicular to the main and cross-beams since in this configuration the target velocity contributes only in the second order.

The velocity change technique was first used by A. R. Blythe (1964) to study the de-excitation process:

$$K + o - D_2 \ (j = 2) \ \longrightarrow \ K + o - D_2 \ (j = 0)$$

Velocity selectors with a resolution (half intensity full width) of 4.7 per cent were used on both the primary and scattered K beams and the ortho D_2 source was operated at 200K so to obtain the optimum concentration of the $j = 2$ state (55 per cent). Observations were made at a laboratory angle of 3° at which two centre of mass angles can contribute, as shown in Fig. 9.2. The narrow CM angle one at 29° associated with a fast velocity in the laboratory

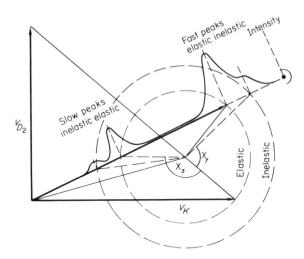

Fig. 9.2. Newton diagram for velocity change experiment used to study the process:

$$K + D_2 \ (j = 2) \rightarrow K + D_2 \ (j = 0)$$

A monenergetic K beam is prepared by the first velocity selector and the change in velocity after collision with the cross-beam of D_2 is measured by a second selector. (A. R. Blythe et al, 1964).

and the wide angle scattering at $108°$ with a slow laboratory velocity. Since $\sigma(29°) \gg \sigma(108°)$ for atomic and molecular potentials, the fast component is the dominant contribution to the total signal observed. This narrow angle scattering arises from large impact parameters collisions which are unlikely to produce inelastic effects so that the more favourable final velocity range for observing these effects is that of the slow component corresponding to wide angle (CM), small impact parameter scattering. The D_2 excitation process $j = 0 \rightarrow j = 2$ is unlikely to be seen, since a velocity decrease in the backward (CM) direction results in an increase in laboratory velocity, and consequently to overlap with the spread of velocities in the particles in the fast elastic peak (Fig. 9.3). On the other hand the D_2 de-excitation process, rotational $\rightarrow$ translational energy transfer, moves the elastic peak into a velocity region where there is only a small elastic contribution so that this is a favourable situation for measurement. These experiments nevertheless were still very limited in signal/noise and the cross-section for $\sigma_{j=2}^{j=0}(108°)$ was estimated as $0.05 \ A^{°2}$. As a relatively early experiment (published 1964) it would seem worth repeating these measurements with the more intense beams now available.

The velocity change method has also been applied (J. P. Toennies and J. Schottler, 1968; W. D. Held et al, 1970; R. David et al, 1971; P. K. Dittner and S. Datz, 1971.) to systems such as:

$$Li^+ + H_2 \ (v = 0) \longrightarrow Li^+ + H_2 \ (v = 1, 2, 3 \ldots)$$
$$\longrightarrow Li^+ + H + H \tag{9.34}$$
$$K^+ + H_2 \ (v = 0) \longrightarrow K^+ + H_2 \ (v = 1, 2 \ldots)$$

where the light mass of the Li^+ ion and the wide spacing of the H_2 vibrational levels assist the resolution of the individual state transitions. The apparatus used by Toennies in these investigations is shown in Fig. 9.4. The Li^+ beam is formed by surface ionization, energy analyzed electrostatically to a spread $\Delta E/E \sim 0.4$ per cent and pulse modulated with a 50 ns width at a 10 kHz repetition rate. The beam then intersected the H_2 target formed by expansion to high Mach number through a nozzle, fluxes of the order 5×10^{20} molecules steradian^{-1} s^{-1} being achieved in the target. The ion arrivals at the electron multiplier detector were recorded in a 400 channel multi scaler synchronized to the beam pulse rate. A flight time spectrum recorded in this fashion is shown in Fig. 9.5. The peak labelled $0 \rightarrow 0$ is the elastic backward scattered contribution, the forward elastic peak is off the figure to the right at zero time. These experiments are capable of considerable development and

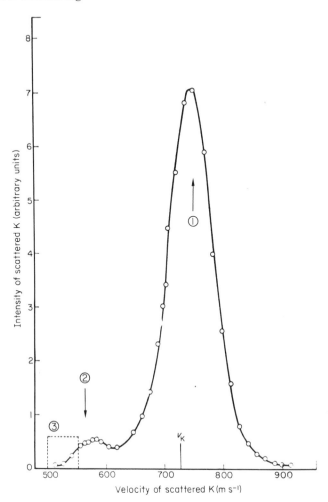

Fig. 9.3 Plot of the K intensity transmitted through the second selector as a function of velocity. The fast (1) and slow (2) elastic peaks together with the inelastic de-excitation contribution (3) are shown. (A. R. Blythe et al, 1964).

are likely to be an important source of information on translational energy transfer processes.

(iii) Techniques involving ion or photon emission

In some collisions the transitions may be either directiy to ions or to short lived electronically excited states. In either case the process can be studied since the product ions or photons (formed by decay of the excited species)

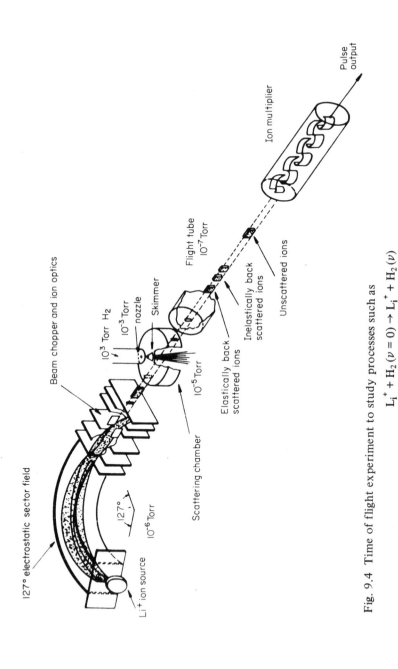

Fig. 9.4 Time of flight experiment to study processes such as

$$L_i^+ + H_2(\nu = 0) \rightarrow L_i^+ + H_2(\nu)$$

The almost monoenergetic Li$^+$ ion beam is pulse modulated and the scattered ion arrivals at the detector are recorded in a multichannel scaler as a function of their flight time. (R. David et al, 1971).

Labels in figure: Pulse output; Ion multiplier; Flight tube 10^{-7}Torr; Inelastically back scattered ions; Unscattered ions; Elastically back scattered ions; Skimmer; nozzle; 10^{-3}Torr; 10^3 Torr H$_2$; Beam chopper and ion optics; 10^{-5}Torr; Scattering chamber; 127° electrostatic sector field; 127°; 10^{-6}Torr; Li$^+$ ion source

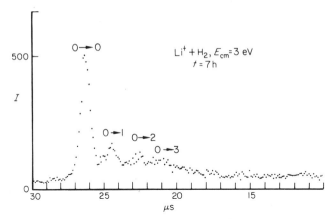

Fig. 9.5 Time of arrival spectrum for Li^+ ions inelastically scattered from H_2. Only ions backward scattered in the CM are observed, those forward scattered arriving before the time covered by this trace begins. The peaks are labelled with the relevant vibrational transition. (R. David et al, 1971).

are both fairly readily detectable and also serve to identify the inelastic transition.

This class of experiment is usually directed at measurement of a total cross-section for some process, but the work of G. A. L. Delvigne and J. Los (1971) on chemi-ionization yielded relative differential cross-sections for processes of the type:

$$K + Br_2 \longrightarrow \begin{cases} K^+ + Br_2^- \\ K^+ + Br^- + Br. \end{cases} \qquad (9.35)$$

In these experiments a fast neutral beam of potassium was produced by a sputtering technique and after velocity selection collided with Br_2 molecules in a target chamber. The product ions were scattered through a field free region into a detector for K^+ ions. The results of some of this work shown in Fig. 9.6, are interesting both in their apparent scaling by $E\theta$ (which would be expected only for elastic collisions) and in the considerable structure observed. Similar experiments in which total cross-sections for ion production from a range of target molecules are measured have been reported by other workers (R. K. B. Helbing and E. W. Rothe, 1969; A. P. M. Baede et al, 1969; K. Lacmann and D. R. Herschbach, 1970; R. H. Hammond et al, 1971).

In an alternative technique an aerodynamically accelerated beam of Xe in a He carrier has been used to study the dissociative ionization processes (F. P.

Tully et al., 1971; E. K. Parks and S. Wexler, 1971)

$$Xe + KBr \longrightarrow K^+ + Br^- + Xe$$
$$Xe + TlBr \longrightarrow Tl^+ + Br^- + Xe \tag{9.36}$$

at translational energies between 8 and 15 eV.

Experiments in which excitation to levels below the ionization limit was observed have been made by using a photomultiplier and interference filter to view the collision zone where beams of translationally (R. W. Anderson et al, 1969; V. Kempter et al, 1970; K. Lacmann and D. R. Herschbach, 1970) vibrationally (J. E. Mentall et al, 1967; M. C. Moulton and D. R. Herschbach, 1966) or electronically (L. J. Doemeny et al, 1969) hot species intersected. The theoretical interpretation of collisions producing electronic excitation is not too well developed. In general the results of these experiments have supported the importance of curve crossing situations in producing electronic

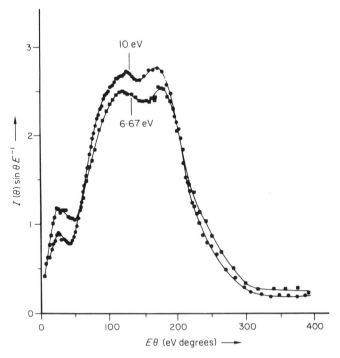

Fig. 9.6 Differential cross-sections for ionization in collisions of K and Br_2. The fast K beam was formed by a sputtering technique (G. A. L. Delvigne and J. Los, 1971).

excitation and in particular the importance of the ionic surface in alkali/halogen systems in coupling the various excited states.

This 'curve crossing' situation is usually treated by the Landau-Zener approximation (D. R. Bates, 1961) in which the transitions between states occur exclusively at their crossing points and motion outside this region is treated as purely elastic on the appropriate potential surface. In this approximation the crossing probability at each intersection is given by:

$$P_{12}(b) = 2\pi\, V_{12}(R_c)^2 / [\hbar v_r(b)\, |(S_1 - S_2)|] \qquad (9.37)$$

where V_{12} is the matrix element connecting the two electronic states evaluated at the crossing point, S_1 and S_2 are the gradients of the two surfaces at this point and v_r is the radial velocity at the crossing. Since collisions must traverse the crossing region twice, the total probability of transition is:

(i) Probability of remaining in state 1,

$$\mathscr{P}_{11} = P_{12}^2 + (1 - P_{12})^2$$

$$(9.38)$$

(ii) Probability of emerging in state 2,

$$\mathscr{P}_{12} = 2P_{12}(1 - P_{12})$$

The P_{12} in Equations 9.37 and 9.38 are impact parameter dependent through $v_r(b)$. Substituting Equation 9.38ii into Equation 9.31 we obtain the total cross-section for ion production or electronic excitation as a function of V_{12} and R_c (there is a weaker dependence on the intermolecular force operating at R_c). If R_c can be located on spectroscopic or other grounds, the energy dependence of $\sigma_{tot}^{12}(E)$ gives V_{12} directly. It must be remembered, though, that Equation 9.37 is only an approximate solution of the Equations 9.28 for two states and one that becomes less valid the higher v_r. Its validity in any particular situation must be checked. Experiments in this area are particularly interesting since electronic rearrangement is the immediate precursor of most chemical reaction and some vibrational energy transfer.

Much remains to be done in the field of collisions in which the electronic motion is non-adiabatic and their elucidation will remain a challenge to the theorist and experimentalist for a considerable time to come.

References

Abauf, N. (1966), Ph.D. Thesis, Princeton University.

Ackerman, M., Greene, E. F., Moursund, A. L. and Ross, J. (1964), *J. Chem. Phys.*, **41**, 1183.

Airey, J. R., Greene, E. F., Reck, G. P., and Ross, J. (1967), *J. Chem. Phys.*, **46**, 3295.

Airey, J. R., Greene, E. F., Kodera, G. P., Reck, G. P., Ross, J. (1967), *J. Chem. Phys.*, **46**, 3287.

Amdur, I., (1968), *Methods of Experimental Physics*, **7A**, 341. Academic Press, New York.

Amend, W. E. (1968), U. California, Berkeley, Rept. No AS-68-4.

Anderson, J. B., (1968), *Intermediate Energy Molecular Beams from Free Jets of Mixed Gases*, Project Squid O.N.R. Tech. Rept. PR166P.

Anderson, J. B., Andres, R. P., and Fenn, J. B. (1965), *Adv. Mol. Phys.*, **1**, 345.

Anderson, J. B., Andres, R. P. and Fenn, J. B. (1966), *Adv. Chem. Phys.*, **10**, 275.

Anderson, R. W., Aquilanti, V. and Herschbach, D. R. (1969), *Chem. Phys. Lett.*, **4**, 5.

Anlauf, K. G., Bickes, R. W. and Bernstein, R. B. (1971), *J. Chem. Phys.*, **54**, 3647.

Anlauf, K. G., Kuntz, P. J., Maybotte, D. H., Pacey, P. D. and Polanyi, D. C. (1967), *Disc. Faraday Soc.*, **44**, 183.

Aquilanti, V., Luiti, G., Vecchio-Cattive, F. and Volpi, G. G. (1971), *Mol. Phys.*, **21**, 1149.

Baede, A. P. M., Moutinho, A. M. C., de Vries, A. E. and Los, J. (1969), *Chem. Phys. Lett.*, **3**, 530.

Barwig, P., Buck, U., Hundhausen, E. and Pauly, H. (1966), *Z. Physik*, **196**, 343.

Bates, D. R., Ed. (1961), *Quantum Theory, I, Elements,* Academic Press, London.

Beck, D. *Proc. Int. Sch. Phys. "Enrico Fermi." Course XLIV (Varenna)* (Ed. Ch. Schlier) (1970) Academic Press, New York.

380

Beck, D., Dummel, H. and Henkel, U. (1965), *Z. Physik,* **185,** 19.

Beck, D., Engelke, F. and Loesch, H. J. (1968), *Ber. Bunsen. Physik. Chem.,* **72,** 1105.

Beckey, H. D. (1961), *Advances in Mass Spectrometry,* **2,** 1.

Beckey, H. D., Knöppel, H., Metzinger, G. and Schulze, P. (1963), *Advances in Mass Spectrometry,* **3,** 35.

Bennewitz, H. G., Busse, H. and Dohman, H. D. (1971), *Chem. Phys. Lett.,* **8,** 253.

Bennewitz, H. G., Gegenbach, R., Haerten, R. and Müller, G. (1969), *Z. Physik,* **226,** 279.

Bennewitz, H. G. and Haerten, R. (1969), *Z. Physik,* **227,** 399.

Bennewitz, H. G., Haerten, R. and Müller, G. (1969), *Z. Physik.,* **266,** 139.

Bennewitz, H. G., Haerten, R and Müller, G. (1971), *Chem. Phys. Lett.,* **12,** 335.

Berkling, K. Helbing, R. Kramer, K. H., Pauly, H., Schlier, C. and Toschek, P. (1962), *Z. Physik,* **166,** 405.

Berkling, K., Helbing, R., Kramer, K. H., Pauly, H., Schlier, C. and Toschek, P. (1962), *Z. Physik,* **166,** 406.

Berkling, K., Schlier, C. and Toschek, P. (1962), *Z. Physik,* **168,** 81.

Bernstein, R. B. (1963), *J. Chem. Phys.,* **38,** 2599.

Bernstein, R. B. (Ed. J. Ross) (1966), *Adv. Chem. Phys.,* **10,** 75.

Bernstein, R. B. and Kramer, K. H. (1964), *J. Chem. Phys.,* **40,** 200.

Bernstein, R. B. and O'Brien, T. J. P. (1965), *Disc. Faraday Soc.,* **40,** 35.

Bernstein, R. B. and O'Brien, T. J. P. (1967), *J. Chem. Phys.,* **46,** 1208.

Berry, M. V. (1966), *Proc. Phys. Soc.,* **88,** 285.

Beuhler, R. J. and Bernstein, R. B. (1968), *Chem. Phys. Lett.,* **2,** 166.

Beuhler, R. J. and Bernstein, R. B. (1969), *J. Chem. Phys.,* **51,** 5305.

Bickes, R. W. and Bernstein, R. B. (1970), *Chem. Phys. Lett.,* **4,** 111.

Bier, K. and Hagena, O. (1963), *Rarefied Gas Dynamics,* **1,** 478, Academic Press, New York.

Birely, J. H. and Herschbach, D. R. (1965), *Bull. Ames. Phys. Soc.,* **10,** 634.

Birely, J. H. and Herschbach, D. R. (1966), *J. Chem. Phys.,* **44,** 1690.

Birely, J. H., Herm, R. R., Wilson, K. R., and Herschbach, D. R. (1967), *J. Chem. Phys.,* **51,** 5461.

Birely, J. H., Entemann, E. A., Herm, R. R., and Wilson, K. R. (1969), *J. Chem. Phys.,* **51,** 5461.

Blais, N. C., (1968), *J. Chem. Phys.,* **49,** 9.

Blais, N. C. and Bunker, D. L. (1962), *J. Chem. Phys.,* **37,** 2713.

Blais, N. C. and Cross, J. B. (1970), *J. Chem. Phys.,* **52,** 3580.

Blythe, A. R., Grosser, A. E. and Bernstein, R. B. (1964), *J. Chem. Phys.,* **41,** 1917.

Brash, H. M., Campbell, D. M., Farago, P. S., Rae, A. G. A., Siegmann, H. C. and Wykes, J. S. (1969), *Proc. Roy. Soc. Edin.,* **A68,** 158.

Bredewout, J. W., Bosman, N. J., Vissen, A. G., Kerving, J. and van den Meijdenberg, C. J. N. (1971), *Chem. Phys. Lett.,* **11,** 127.

Brink, G. O. (1966), *Rev. Sci. Instn.,* **37,** 857.

Brodhead, C. C., Davidovits, P. and Edelstein, S. A. (1969), *J. Chem. Phys.,* **51,** 3601.

Brooks, P. R. (1969), *J. Chem. Phys.,* **50,** 5031.

Brooks, P. R. and Jones, E. M. (1966), *J. Chem. Phys.,* **45,** 3449.

Brooks, P. R., Jones, E. M. and Smith, K. (1969), *J. Chem. Phys.,* **51,** 3073.

Buck, U. (1971), *J. Chem. Phys.,* **54,** 1923, and 1929.

Buck, U. and Pauly, H. (1968), *Z. Physik,* **208**, 390.
Buck, U. and Pauly, H. (1969), *J. Chem. Phys.,* **51**, 1663.
Bunker, D. L., *Proc. Int. Sch. Phys., 'Enrico Fermi', Course XLIV (Varenna)* (Editor, Ch. Schlier) (1970), Academic Press, New York.
Bunker, D. L. and Blais, N. C. (1964), *J. Chem. Phys.,* **41**, 2377.
von Busch, F. (1966), *Z. Physik,* **193**, 412.

Cantini, P., Dondi, M. G., Scoles, G. and Torello, F. (1972), *J. Chem. Phys.,* **56**, 1946.
Cardillo, M. J., Chou, M. S., Greene, E. F. and Sheen, D. R. (1971), *J. Chem. Phys.,* **54**, 3054.
Cavallini, M., Dondi, M. G., Scoles, G. and Valbusa, U. (1972), *Chem. Phys. Lett.,* **10**, 22.
Cavallini, M., Gallinaro, G. and Scoles, G. (1967), *Z. Naturforsch,* **22**, 415.
Cavallini, M., Gallinaro, G. and Scoles, G. (1967), *Z. Naturforsch,* **22a**, 413.
Cavallini, M., Gallinaro, G., Manghetti, L., Scoles, G. and Valbusa, U. (1970), *Chem. Phys. Lett.,* **7**, 303.
Cavallini, M., Meneghetti, L., Scoles, G. and Yealland, M. (1970), *Phys. Rev. Letters,* **29**, 1469.
Clampitt, R. and Newton, A. S. (1969), *J. Chem. Phys.,* **50**, 1997.
Clough, P. N. and Thrush, B. A. (1967), *Disc. Faraday Soc.,* **44**, 205.
Colgate, S. O. and Imeson, T. C. (1965), *Rev. Sci. Instr.,* **36**, 932.
Collins, F. G. and Hurlburt, F. C. (1972), *J. Chem. Phys.,* **56**, 2609.
Connor, J. N. L. (1968), *Mol. Phys.,* **15**, 621.
Cowley, L. T., Fluendy, M. A. D., Horne, D. S. and Lawley, K. P. (1969), *J. Sci. Instr.,* **2**, 1021.
Cowley, L. T., Fluendy, M. A. D. and Lawley, K. P. (1970), *Rev. Sci. Instr.,* **41**, 666.
Cross, J. B. and Blais, N. C. (1971), *J. Chem. Phys.,* **55**, 3970.
Cross, R. J., Gislason, E. A. and Herschbach, D. R. (1966), *J. Chem. Phys.,* **45**, 3582.
Cross, R. J. and Malerich, C. J. (1968), *Chem. Phys. Lett.,* **2**, 481.
Cross, R. J. and Malerich, C. J. (1970), *J. Chem. Phys.,* **52**, 386.

Daley, H. L., Yahiku, A. Y. and Perel, J. (1970), *J. Chem. Phys.,* **52**, 3577.
Daley, N. R. (1960), *Rev. Sci. Inst.,* **31**, 264.
Darwall, E. C. (1972), Ph.D. Thesis, University of Edinburgh.
Datz, S. and Taylor, E. H. (1956), *J. Chem. Phys.,* **25**, 389, 395.
Datz, S. and Taylor, E. H. (1963), *J. Chem. Phys.,* **39**, 1896.
David, R., Faubel, M., Marchand, P. and Toennies, J. P. (1971), *Proceedings VII ICPEAC,* **252**, Amsterdam, North-Holland.
Davis, L., Field, B. T., Zabel, C. W. and Zacharias, J. R. (1949), *Phys. Rev.,* **76**, 1076.
Delvigne, G. A. L. and Los, J., *Proc. VII ICPEAC,* **277**, Amsterdam, North Holland.
Delvigne, P. F., and Datz, S. (1971), *J. Chem. Phys.,* **54**, 4228.
Dittner, P. F. and Datz, S. (1971), *J. Chem. Phys.,* **54**, 4228.
Doemeny, L. J., van Itallie, F. J. and Martin, R. M. (1969), *Chem. Phys. Letts,* **4**, 302.
Dondi, M. G., Scoles, G., Torello, F. and Pauly, H. (1969), *J. Chem. Phys.,* **51**, 392.
Doverspike, L. D., Champion, R. L. and Bailey, T. L. (1966), *J. Chem. Phys.,* **45**, 4385.

Drullinger, R. E. and Zare, R. N. (1969), *J. Chem. Phys.*, **51**, 5532.

Duchart, B. S. (1971), Ph.D. Thesis, University of Edinburgh.

Duchart, B., Fluendy, M. A. D. and Lawley, K. P. (1971), *Chem. Phys. Letts.*, **14**, 129.

Dunoyer, L. (1911), *Computes Rend,* **152**, 594.

Eldridge, J. A. (1927), *Phys. Rev.*, **30**, 931.

Entemann, E. A. and Kwei, G. H. (1971), *J. Chem. Phys.*, **55**, 4879.

Fenn, J. B. (1968), *Molecular Beam Engineering at Intermediate Energies*, Project Squid, O.N.R. Tech. Rept. 115P.

Fenn, J. B. and Deckers, J. (1963), *Rarefied Gas Dynamics,* **1**, 516, Academic Press, New York.

Feynmann, R. P. and Hibbs, A. R. (1965), *Quantum Mechanics and Path Integrals,* McGraw-Hill, New York.

Firsov, V. G. (1953), *Zh. Eksp. Teor. Fiz.*, **24**, 279.

Fisk, G. A., McDonald, J. D. and Herschbach, D. R. (1967), *Disc. Faraday Soc.,* **44**, 228.

Fite, W. L., Brackmann, D. S., Hummer, D. G. and Stebbings, R. F. (1959), *Phys. Rev.,* **116**, 363.

Fluendy, M. A. D. (1964), *Rev. Sci. Inst.,* **35**, 1606.

Fluendy, M. A. D. (1965), *J. Sci. Instr.,* **42**, 489.

Fluendy, M. A. D., Horne, D. S., Lawley, K. P. and Morris, A. W. (1970), *Mol. Phys,* **19**, 659.

Fluendy, M. A. D., Martin, R. M., Muschlitz, E. E. Jun. and Herschbach, D. R. (1967), *J. Chem. Phys.,* **46**, 2172.

Foner, S. N. (1966), *Adv. At. Mol. Phys.,* **2**, 385, Academic Press, New York.

Ford, K. W. and Wheeler, J. A. (1959), *Ann. Phys.,* **7**, 259.

Foreman, P. B., Kendall, G. M. and Grice, R. (1972), *Mol. Phys.,* **23**, 127.

Fox L. (1962), *Numerical Solution of Ordinary and Partial Differential Equations*, Pergamon Press, Oxford.

Freund, R. and Klemperer, W. (1967), *J. Chem. Phys.,* **47**, 2897.

Freund, S. M., Fisk, G. A., Herschbach, D. R. and Klemperer, W. (1971), *J. Chem. Phys.,* **54**, 2510.

Geddes, J., Krause, H. F. and Fite, W. L. (1970), *J. Chem. Phys.,* **52**, 3296.

Gentry, W. R., Gislason, E. A., Mahan, B. H. and Tsao, C-W. (1968), *J. Chem. Phys.,* **49**, 3058.

Gersh, M. E. and Bernstein, R. B. (1971), *J. Chem. Phys.,* **55**, 4661.

Gersh, M. E. and Bernstein, R. B. (1972), *J. Chem. Phys.,* **56**, 6131.

Gillen, K. T. and Bernstein, R. B. (1970), *Rept. Theoretical Chemistry*, Institute Wisconsin, WIS-TCI-377X.

Gillen, K. T., Riley, C. and Bernstein, R. B. (1969), *J. Chem. Phys.,* **50**, 4019.

Gillen, K. T., Rulis, A. M. and Bernstein, R. B. (1971), *J. Chem. Phys.,* **54**, 2831.

Giordmaine, J. A. and Wang, T. C. (1960), *J. Appl. Phys.,* **31**, 463.

Gislason, E. A. and Kwei, G. H. (1967), *J. Chem. Phys.,* **46**, 2838.

Gislason, E. A., Mahan, B. H., Tsao, C-W and Werner, A. S. (1969), *J. Chem. Phys.,* **50**, 142.

Goldberger, M. L. and Watson, K. M. (1964), *Collision Theory*, Wiley, New York.

Goldstein, H. (1964), *Classical Mechanics*, Addison-Wesley, Reading, Mass.

Gomer, R. (1961), *Field Emission and Field Ionization*, Harvard University Press, Cambridge, Mass.

Gomer, R. and Inghram, M. G. (1955), *J. Chem. Phys.*, **22**, 1279; (1955), *J.A.C.S.*, **77**, 500.

Gordon, R. G. (1969), *J. Chem. Phys.*, **51**, 14.

Gordon, R. J., Herm, R. R. and Herschbach, D. R. (1968), *J. Chem. Phys.*, **49**, 2684.

Gordon, R. G., Klemperer, W. and Steinfeld, J. I. (1968), *Ann. Rev. Phys. Chem.*, **19**, 215.

Gordon, R. J., Lee, Y. T. and Herschbach, D. R. (1970), *J. Chem. Phys.*, **54**, 2393.

Greene, E. F., Hoffman, L. F., Lee, M. W., Ross, J. and Young, C. E. (1969), *J. Chem. Phys.*, **50**, 3450.

Greene, E. F., Lau, M. H. and Ross, J. (1969), *J. Chem. Phys.*, **50**, 3122.

Greene, E. F., Persky, A. and Kupperman, A. (1968), *J. Chem. Phys.*, **49**, 2347.

Grice, R. and Empedocles, P. B. (1968), *J. Chem. Phys.*, **48**, 5352.

Grice, R., Mosch, J. E., Safron, S. A. and Toennies, J. P. (1970), *J. Chem. Phys.*, **53**, 3376.

Grosser, A. E. and Bernstein, R. B. (1965), *J. Chem. Phys.*, **43**, 1140.

Grosser, A. E., Blythe, A. R. and Bernstein, R. B. (1965), *J. Chem. Phys.*, **42**, 1268.

Grosser, J. and Haberland, H. (1968), *Phys. Rev. Letts.*, **27A**, 634.

Grosser, A. E., Iczkowski, R. P. and Margrave, J. L. (1963), *Rev. Sci. Instr.*, **34**, 116.

Ham, D. O. and Kinsey, J. L. (1970), *J. Chem. Phys.*, **53**, 285.

Hammond, R. H., Henis, J. M. S., Greene, E. F. and Ross, J. (1971), *J. Chem. Phys.*, **55**, 3506.

Halpern, I. and Strutunskii, V. M., *'Proceedings of the Second International Conference on the Peaceful Uses of Atomic Energy'*, Geneva (1958), United Nations, New York, 1958 paper P/1513.

Harris, R. M. and Wilson, J. F. (1971), *J. Chem. Phys.*, **54**, 2088.

Hasted, J. B. (1964), *Physics of Atomic Collisions*, Butterworths, London.

Helbing, R. K. B. (1966) Thesis, University of Bonne.

Helbing, R. K. B. (1969), *J. Chem. Phys.*, **51**, 3628.

Helbing, R. K. B. and Rothe, E. W. (1968), *J. Chem. Phys.*, **48**, 3945.

Helbing, R. K. B. and Rothe, E. W. (1968), *Rev. Sc. Instr.*, **39**, 1948.

Helbing, R. K. B. and Rothe, E. W. (1969), *J. Chem. Phys.*, **51**, 1607.

Held, W. D., Schottler, J. and Toennies, J. P. (1970), *Chem. Phys. Letts.*, **4**, 304.

Herm, R. R. and Herschbach, D. R. (1965), *J. Chem. Phys.*, **43**, 2139.

Herm, R. R. and Herschbach, D. R. (1970), *J. Chem. Phys.*, **53**, 285.

Herman, Z., Kerstetter, J., Rose, T. and Wolfgang, R. (1967), *Disc. Faraday Soc.*, **44**, 123.

Herman, Z., Lee, A. and Wolfgang, R. (1969), *J. Chem. Phys.*, **51**, 452, 454.

Herschbach, D. R., Kwei, G. H. and Norris, J. A. (1961), *J. Chem. Phys.*, **34**, 1842.

Hirschfelder, J. O. (ed) (1967), *Adv. in Chem. Phys.*, **12**, Wiley, New York.

Hirschfelder, J. O., Curtiss, C. F. and Bird, R. B. (1964), *Molecular Theory of Gases and Liquids* (2nd edition), Wiley, New York.

Hollstein, M. and Pauly, H. (1967), *Z. Physik*, **201**, 10.

Hollstein, M. and Pauly, H. (1966), *Z. Physik*, **196**, 353.

Horne, D. S. (1969), Ph.D. Thesis, University of Edinburgh.

Hostettler, H. U. and Bernstein, R. B. (1960), *Rev. Sci. Instr.,* **31**, 872.

Hotop, H., Lampe, F. W. and Niehaus, A. (1969), *J. Chem. Phys.,* **51**, 593.

Hulpke, E. and Schlier, C. (1967), *Z. Physik,* **207**, 294.

Hundhausen, E. and Pauly, H. (1965), *z.f. Naturforschung,* **20a**, 625.

Ioup, G. E. and Thomas, B. S. (1966), *J. Chem. Phys.,* **50**, 5009.

Johnson, J. C., Stair, A. T. and Pritchard, J. L. (1966), *J. Appl. Phys.,* **37**, 155.

Johnson, R. L., Perona, M. J. and Setser, D. W. (1970), *J. Chem. Phys.,* **52**, 6372.

Johnston, W. D. and King, J. G. (1966), *Rev. Sci. Inst.,* **37**, 375.

Jonah, C. D., Zare, R. N. and Ottinger, Ch. (1972), *J. Chem. Phys.,* **56**, 263.

Kalos, F. and Grosser, A. E. (1970), *Chem. Phys. Letts.,* **6**, 537.

Kanes, H., Pauly, H. and Vietzke, E. (1971), Max-Planck-Inst. f. Stromungs-forschung, Ber. 102.

Kantrowitz, A. and Grey, J. (1951), *Rev. Sci. Instr.,* **22**, 328.

Kempter, V., Kneser Th. and Schlier, Ch. (1970), *J. Chem. Phys.,* **52**, 5851.

Kempter, V., Mecklenbrauck, W., Menzinger, M., Schuler, G., Herschbach, D. R. and Schlier, Ch. (1970), *Chem. Phys. Letts.,* **6**, 97.

Kessler, R. W. and Koglin, B. (1966), *Rev. Sci. Instr.,* **37**, 682.

Kinsey, J. L. (1966), *Rev. Sci. Instr.,* **37**, 61.

Kinsey, J. L. (1972), *M.T.P. Int. Rev. Sci,* London, Vol 9. (Ed. J. C. Polanyi)

Knauer, F. (1949), *Z. Physik,* **125**, 279.

Knuth, E. L. (1964), *Appl. Mech. Rev.,* **17**, 751.

Kramer, H. L. and Herschbach, D. R. (1970), *J. Chem. Phys.,* **53**, 2792.

Kramer, H. L. and Le Breton, P. R. (1967), *J. Chem. Phys.,* **47**, 3367.

Kuntz, P. J., Mok, M. H. and Polanyi, J. C. (1969), *J. Chem. Phys.,* **50**, 4607, 4623.

Kwei, G. H. and Herschbach, D. R. (1969), *J. Chem. Phys.,* **51**, 1742.

Kwei, G. H., Norris, J. A. and Herschbach, D. R. (1970), *J. Chem. Phys.,* **52**, 1317.

Lacmann, K. and Henglein, A. (1965), *Ber. d. Bunsens*δ, **69**, 292.

Lacmann, K. and Herschbach, D. R. (1970), *Chem. Phys. Letts.,* **6**, 106.

Landau, L. D. and Lifshitz, E. M. (1960), *Mechanics,* Addison-Wesley, Reading, Mass.

Landau, L. D. and Lifshitz, E. M. (1958), *Quantum Mechanics,* Pergamon Press, Oxford.

Le Breton, P. R. and Kramer, H. L. (1969), *J. Chem. Phys.,* **51**, 3627.

Le Breton, P. R., Mecklenbrauck, W., Schultz, A. and Schlier, Ch. (1971), *J. Chem. Phys.,* **55**, 2940.

Lee, Y. T., Le Breton, P. R., McDonald, J. D. and Herschbach, D. R. (1969), *J. Chem. Phys.,* **51**, 455.

Lee, Y. T., McDonald, J. D., Le Breton, P. R. and Herschbach, D. R. (1968), *J. Chem. Phys.,* **49**, 2447.

Lee, Y. T., McDonald, J. D., Le Breton, P. R. and Herschbach, D. R. (1969), *Rev. Sci. Instr.,* **40**, 1402.

Lee, Y. T., Gordon, R. J. and Herschbach, D. R. (1971), *J. Chem. Phys.,* **54**, 2410.

Lempert, G. D., Corrigan, S. J. B. and Wilson, J. F. (1971), *Chem. Phys. Letts.*, **8**, 67.

Lester, W. A. and Bernstein, R. B. (1968), *J. Chem. Phys.*, **48**, 4896.

Levine, R. D. (1969), *Quantum Mechanics of Molecular Rate Processes*, Clarendon Press, Oxford.

Lew, H. (1949), *Phys. Rev.*, **76**, 1086.

Lew, H. (1953), *Phys. Rev.*, **91**, 619.

Lin, S. H. and Eyring, H. (1971), *Proc. Natl. Acad. Sci.*, **68**, 402.

Lorents, D. C. and Aberth, W. (1965), *Phys. Rev.*, **139**A, 1017.

Magee, J. L. (1940), *J. Chem. Phys.*, **8**, 687.

Maltz, C. and Herschbach, D. R. (1967), *Disc. Faraday Soc.*, **44**, 176.

Marchi, R. P. and Smith, F. T. (1965), *Phys. Rev.*, **139**A, 1025.

Margenau, H. and Kestner, N. R. (1969), *Theory of Intermolecular Forces*, Pergamon Press, Oxford.

Martin, L. R. and Kinsey, J. L. (1967), *J. Chem. Phys.*, **46**, 4834.

Mason, E. A. (1952), *J. Chem. Phys.*, **26**, 667.

Massey, H. S. W. (1971), *Electronic and Ionic Impact Phenomena, Vol. III – Slow Collisions of Heavy Particles* (2nd edition), Clarendon Press, Oxford.

Massey, H. S. W. and Mohr, C. B. O. (1933), *Proc. Roy. Soc.*, **A141**, 434.

Mason, E. A., Vanderslice, J. T. and Raw, C. J. G. (1964), *J. Chem. Phys.*, **40**, 2153.

McDermott, M. N. and Lichten, W. C. (1960), *Phys. Rev.*, **119**, 134.

McDonald, J. D., Le Breton, P. R., Lee, Y. T. and Herschbach, D. R. (1972), *J. Chem. Phys.*, **56**, 769.

Mentall, J. E., Krause, H. F. and Fite, W. L. (1967), *Disc. Faraday Soc.*, **44**, 157.

Merzbacher, E. (1961), *Quantum Mechanics*, Wiley, New York.

Mies, F. H. (1970), *J. Chem. Phys.*, **42**, 2709.

Miller, D. R. and Patch, D. F. (1969), *Rev. Sci. Instr.*, **40**, 1566.

Miller, R. C. and Kusch, P. (1955), *Phys. Rev.*, **99**, 1314.

Miller, W. B., Safron, B. A. and Herschbach, D. R. (1967), *Disc. Faraday Soc.*, **44**, 108, 292.

Miller, W. H. (1970), *J. Chem. Phys.*, **52**, 543.

Miller, W. H. (1970), *J. Chem. Phys.*, **53**, 1949.

Minturn, R. E., Datz, S. and Taylor, E. H. (1960), *J. Appl. Phys.*, **31**, 876.

Mok, M. H. and Polanyi, J. C. (1969), *J. Chem. Phys.*, **51**, 1451.

Morgenstern, D. and Beck, D. See reference to Pauly H. and Toennies, J. P. (1968).

Morse, F. A. and Bernstein, R. B. (1962), *J. Chem. Phys.*, **37**, 2019.

Mott, N. F. and Massey, H. S. W. (1965), *Theory of Atomic Collisions*, (3rd edition) Oxford University Press, London.

Moulton, M. C. and Herschbach, D. R. (1966), *J. Chem. Phys.*, **44**, 3010.

Munn, R. J., Mason, E. A. and Smith, F. J. (1964), *J. Chem. Phys.*, **41**, 3978.

Munn, R. J. and Smith, F. J. (1966), *Mol. Phys.*, **10**, 163.

Muller, E. W. (1960), *Adv. Electronics and Electron Physics*, **13**, 87.

Muschlitz, E. E. Jun. (1966), *Adv. Chem. Phys.*, **10**, 174.

Newton, R. (1966), *Scattering Theory of Waves and Particles*, McGraw-Hill.

Neumann, W. and Pauly, H. (1970), *J. Chem. Phys.*, **52**, 2548.

Neynaber, R. H., Myers, B. F. and Trujillo, S. M. (1969), *Phys. Rev.*, **180**, 139.

Norcliffe, A. and Percival, I. C. (1968), *J. Phys. B.*, **1**, 784.

Odirone, T. J., Brooks, P. R. and Kasper, J. V. V. (1971), *J. Chem. Phys.*, **55**, 1980.

Ogryzlo, E. A. (1961), *Can. J. Chem.*, **39**, 2556.

Olson, R. E. and Bernstein, R. B. (1968), *J. Chem. Phys.*, **49**, 162 and 4499.

Olson, R. E. (1968), Theoretical Chemistry Institute, U. Wisconsin, Report WISTC 1, 310.

Olson, R. E. and Bernstein, R. B. (1968), *J. Chem. Phys.*, **49**, 162 and 4499.

Owen, P. L. and Thornhill, C. K. (1948), Aeronautical Research Council (U.K.)., R & M No. 2616.

Parks, E. K. and Wexler, S. (1971), *Chem. Phys. Letts.*, **10**, 245.

Parrish, D. D. and Herm, R. R. (1969), *J. Chem. Phys.*, **51**, 5467.

Parrish, D. D. and Herm, R. R. (1971), *J. Chem. Phys.*, **54**, 2518.

Parson, J. M., Schafer, T. P., Tully, F. P., Siska, P. E., Wong, Y. C. and Lee, Y. T. (1970), *J. Chem. Phys.*, **53**, 2123.

Parson, J. M., Siska, P. E. and Lee, Y. T. (1972), *J. Chem. Phys.*, **56**, 1511.

Pauly, H. and Toennies, J. P. (1965), *Adv. At. Mol. Phys.*, **1**, 195.

Pauly, H. and Toennies, J. P. (1965), *Adv. At. Mol. Phys.*, **1**, 201.

Pauly, H. and Toennies, J. P. (1968), *Methods of Experimental Physics*, **7A**, 227, Academic Press, New York (Ed. Bederson, B. and Fife, W.).

Persky, A., Greene, E. F. and Kuppermann, A. (1968), *J. Chem. Phys.*, **49**, 2347.

Petty, F. and Moran, T. F. (1972), *Phys. Rev. A.*, **5**, 266.

Pierce, J. R. (1954), *Theory and Design of Electron Beams*, Van Nostrand, New York.

Polanyi, M. (1932), *Atomic Reactions,* Williams and Norgate, London.

Politiek, J., Kol, P. K., Los, J. and Ikelaar, P. G. (1968), *Rev. Sci. Instr.*, **39**, 1147.

Politiek, J. and Los, J. (1969), *Rev. Sci. Instr.*, **40**, 1576.

Present, R. D. (1958), *Kinetic Theory of Gases,* McGraw-Hill, New York.

Pritchard, D. E., Carter, G. M., Chu, F. Y. and Kleppner, D. (1970), *Phys. Rev. A.*, **2**, 1922.

Pritchard, D. E. and Chu, F. Y. (1970), *Phys. Rev. A.*, **2**, 1932.

Rabi, I. I., Kellog, J. M. B. and Zacharias, J. R. (1934), *Phys. Rev.*, **46**, 157.

Raff, L. M. and Karplus, M. (1966), *J. Chem. Phys.*, **44**, 1212.

Ramsey, N. F. (1956), *Molecular Beams,* Oxford University Press, London.

Roberts, R. E. and Ross, J. (1970), *J. Chem. Phys.*, **52**, 1464.

Robinson, C. A. (1967), *Statistical Communication and Detection.*

Rodberg, L. S. and Thaler, R. M. (1967), *Introduction to the Quantum Theory of Scattering*, Academic Press, New York.

Ross, J. (Ed.) (1966), *Adv. Chem. Phys.*, **10**, article by R. B. Bernstein.

Ross, J. and Greene, E. F. in *Proc. Int. Sch. Phys. 'Enrico Fermi' Course XLIV (Varenna)* (Editor, Ch. Schlier) (1970), Academic Press, New York.

Rothe, E. W. (1964), *J. Vac. Sci. Tech.*, **1**, 66.

Rothe, E. W., Neynaber, R. H. and Trujillo, S. M. (1965), *J. Chem. Phys.*, **42**, 3310.

Rothe, E. W. and Neynaber, R. H. (1965), *J. Chem. Phys.*, **42**, 3306 and **43**, 4177.

Rothe, E. W. and Helbing, R. K. B. (1968), *J. Chem. Phys.*, **49**, 4750.

Rothe, E. W. Reinhard, K. and Helbing, B. (1970), *J. Chem. Phys.*, **53**, 1555, 2501.

Schafer, T. P., Siska, P. E., Parson, J. M., Tully, F. P., Wong, F. C. and Lee, Y. T. (1970), *J. Chem. Phys.*, **53**, 3376.

Schlier, C. (1969), *Ann. Rev. Phys. Chem.*, **20**, 191.

Schlier, C., Duren, R. and Raabe, C. P. (1968), *Z. Physik*, **214**, 410.

Schottler, J. and Toennies, J. P. (1968), *Ber. Bunsengesellschaft*, **72**, 979.

Scoles, G. and Torello, F., 'Production of Molecular Beams from Free Expanding Jets, part 1', Report of the Gruppo di Strutture Della Materia del C.N.R., August 1967.

Scott, P. B. (1965), M.I.T. Fluid Dynamics Lab. Rept. No. 65 − 1.

Secrest, D. and Johnson, B. R. (1966), *J. Chem. Phys.*, **45**, 4556.

Siska, P. E., Parson, J. M., Schafer, T. P., Wong, Y. C. and Lee, Y. T., *Phys. Rev. Letts.*, **25**, 271.

Siska, P. E., Parson, J. M., Schafer, T. P. and Lee, Y. T. (1971), *J. Chem. Phys.*, **55**, 5762.

Skinner, G. T. (1966), *Proc. 7th Agard Colloquium on Advances in Aerothermochemistry*, Oslo.

Skofronik, J. G. (1967), *Rev. Sci. Instr.*, **38**, 1628.

Smith, F. J. and Munn, R. J. (1964), *J. Chem. Phys.*, **41**, 3560.

Smith, F. T., Marchi, R. P. and Dedrick, K. G. (1966), *Phys. Rev.*, **150**, 79.

Smith, I. W. M. (1967), *Disc. Faraday Soc.*, **44**, 194.

Smith, K. F. (1955), *Molecular Beams*, Methuen, London.

Struve, W. S., Kitagawa, T. and Herschbach, D. R. (1971), *J. Chem. Phys.*, **54**, 2759.

Taylor, E. H. and Datz, S. (1955), *J. Chem. Phys.*, **23**, 1711.

Toennies, J. P. (1965), *Z. Physik*, **182**, 257.

Toennies, J. P. (1965), *Z. Physik*, **193**, 76.

Treanor, C. E. (1965), *J. Chem. Phys.*, **43**, 532.

Trouw, T. R. and Trischka, J. W. (1963), *J. Appl. Phys.*, **34**, 3635.

Tully, F. P., Lee, Y. T. and Berry, R. S. (1971), *Chem. Phys. Letts.*, **9**, 80.

Vanderslice, J. T., Mason, E. A., Maisch, W. G. and Lippincott, E. R. (1959), *J. Mol. Spectr.*, **3**, 17 and **5**, 83.

Visser, C. A., Wolleswinkel, J. and Los, J. (1970), *J. Sci. Instr.*, **3**, 483.

Waech, T. G. and Bernstein, R. B. (1968), *Chem. Phys. Letts.*, **2**, 477.

Warnock, T. T., Bernstein, R. B. and Grosser, A. E. (1967), *J. Chem. Phys.*, **46**, 1685.

Weiss, R. (1961), *Rev. Sci. Instr.*, **32**, 397.

Wellner, M. (1964), *Amer. J. Phys.*, **32**, 787.

Wharton, L., Berg, R. A. and Klemperer, W. (1963), *J. Chem. Phys.*, **39**, 2033.

Wharton, L., Klemperer, W., Gold, L. P., Strauch, R., Gallagher, J. J. and Derr, V. E. (1963), *J. Chem. Phys.*, **38**, 1203.

Whitehead, J. C., Hardin, D. R. and Grice, R. (1972), *Chem. Phys. Letts.*, **13**, 319.

Wiener, N. (1949), *Extrapolation, Interpolation and Smoothing of Stationary Time Series*, John Wiley, New York.

Wilets, L. (1964), *Theories of Nuclear Fission*, Clarendon Press, Oxford.

Williams, W., Mueller, C. R., McGuire, P. and Smith, B. (1969), *Phys. Rev. Letts.*, **22**, 121.

Willner, M. (1964), *Amer. J. Phys.*, **32**, 787.

Wilson, J. F. and Lempert, G. D., Private Communication (1970).

Wilson, K. (1964), Ph.D. Thesis, Harvard University.

Wilson, K. R. and Herschbach, D. R. (1968), *J. Chem. Phys.*, **49**, 2676.

Winicur, D. H., Moursund, A. L., Devereaux, W. R., Martin, L. R. and Kuppermann, A. (1970), *J. Chem. Phys.*, **52**, 3299.

Wu, T. Y. and Ohmura, T. (1962), *Quantum Theory of Scattering*, Prentice Hall, New York.

Wykes, J. (1960), *J. Sci., Instr.* (J. Physics E), **2**, 899.

Zandberg, E. Ya and Ianov, N. I. (1959), *Usp. Fig. Nauk.*, **67**, 581.

Author Index

Subject Index